123

Hope in the Valleys

Hope in the Valleys

Francesca Capaldi

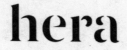

First published in the United Kingdom in 2022 by

Hera Books
Unit 9 (Canelo), 5th Floor
Cargo Works, 1-2 Hatfields
London, SE1 9PG
United Kingdom

A CIP catalogue record for this book is available from the British Library.

Print ISBN 978 1 80032 783 2
Ebook ISBN 978 1 912973 85 9

Look for more great books at www.herabooks.com

Printed and bound in Great Britain by Clays Ltd, Elcograf S.p.A.

1

Chapter One

Elizabeth Meredith spied Sergeant Harries through the motorcar window, leaving his house at the beginning of Gabriel Street, as she drove slowly into the centre of the village of Dorcalon. He looked harassed as always. A large group of miners came into view, standing in and around the public gardens of Jubilee Green. There must have been about thirty of them. She heard a few indistinct shouts through her open windows. Some men were also hanging around outside the McKenzie Arms on the opposite side of the gardens' gate.

How curious. She was sure that the coal company hadn't granted the bank holiday Wednesday to them that other workers had been given. It was late for them to be leaving the early shift at the mine, but in any case, these men bore no signs of blackened clothes or grubby faces. It was drizzling out there, causing some to turn up the inadequate collars of their jackets.

Was it possible they were on strike? No doubt her father, the colliery manager, would be able to enlighten her when he returned home.

With a little gasp, she applied a sudden pressure to the brakes of the Morris Oxford, just outside the bookshop. Two men had jumped into the road and a fight had broken out. She pulled up on the side of the road, not wanting to knock anyone over, and peered out at the spectacle. One of the men was David Keir, the union representative, though she didn't recognise the other. A few men spilled onto the road to surround them.

I

On the pavement, calling to the men to stop fighting, she spotted Gwilym Owen. His clothes were neat and clean, if not fashionable. His reddish curls poked out from his cap, needing a cut as they often did. He was a sensible soul, someone she worked on the community allotments with. If anyone could get them to calm down, he could.

A voice suddenly boomed out, making her jump. She looked around to see Sergeant Harries rushing down the road with a megaphone. She'd never seen him use one of those before.

'Stop that at once, you're causing an obstruction.'

Old Constable Probert, out of retirement for the duration of the war, was close behind, and soon they'd separated the men. They stood between them as Harries remonstrated with them.

Curiosity getting the better of her, she cut the engine of the motorcar and got out, making her way over to Mr Schenck, who owned the bookshop. It was still being rebuilt after a recent fire. Mr Schenck himself was there, in overalls, mucking in with the men of the village who were taking turns to help with work.

It was then she saw the two large pieces of cardboard, being held up by two of the younger miners. On one, in household paint, was written: *PAY US THE MINIMUM WAGE.* On the other was: *GIVE US THE BANK HOLIDAYS WE'RE PROMISED.*

Ah, that's what all this was about.

'Hello Miss Meredith,' said Mr Schenck, bowing slightly. 'Are you sure you want to leave your motorcar there with all this hullabaloo?'

'How long has this been going – ooof!' She was unable to finish her sentence as someone shoved her back.

She turned to see Gwilym there, looking as surprised as she felt. 'Oh, I'm sorry, Miss Elizabeth. I was walking backwards and didn't realise you were there.'

'That's all right. You're on strike, then?'

He fiddled with his cap and lowered his head, looking embarrassed. 'Not exactly, was just meant to be a small protest, like. Got out of hand. Regrettably.' He looked towards David Keir and his opponent.

'Wanted it to get a bit more forceful like, did Keir,' said Gwilym's friend, Idris Hughes, coming up behind. 'Always been a loose cannon, that one. Not sure he makes the best union rep.'

'So, you're still not being paid the minimum wage?' said Elizabeth, pointing to the makeshift sign. 'I must talk to my father about that.'

'Aye, for all the good that'll do,' said Keir, as he was being hauled away by Sergeant Harries.

'No need to be rude to Miss Meredith,' said the sergeant.

'Of course, perish the thought,' said Keir, in a put-on posh accent.

Mr Schenck tutted.

Gwilym walked off, calling to people that it would be a good idea to bring the protest to an end. Idris stayed behind a few seconds. 'I'm sure it couldn't hurt to talk to your father, Elizabeth, though I've a feeling this is more to do with the coal company.'

Elizabeth nodded. 'You're probably right. Say hello to Anwen from me.'

'Aye, will do.' He ran to join Gwilym as the crowd started to disperse.

She turned her attention to the bookshop owner. 'You seem to be getting on well with the building work, Mr Schenck.'

'I have the volunteers to thank for that. I hope you will pop by once I get the shop up and running again.'

'Of course I will. You know how much I love reading.' The road had now cleared of men, who were heading off home in various directions. 'I'd better get back to the motorcar and get home. Mama will wonder where I've got to. Cheerio, Mr Schenck.'

'Good day to you, Miss Meredith.'

Drawing up outside McKenzie House, on the other side of the village, Elizabeth breathed out a long, noisy sigh. What mood would her mother be in today, she wondered. She knew things had not been going well between her parents, and, with her brother Tom at the Front now, her mother, Margaret, was constantly worried.

No sooner had Elizabeth called, 'Hello!' on coming through the front door, than her mother rushed into the hallway from the drawing room, holding an envelope aloft.

'At last, a letter from your brother. I was so worried. You'd think he'd have had the sense to write sooner.' She came to an abrupt halt beside Elizabeth, who was in front of the mirror removing her straw hat.

Placing the hat along with the hatpin on the occasional table, Elizabeth said, 'That's good to hear. I don't suppose Tom's had the time before, what with—'

But her mother had already executed an abrupt turn and was heading back to the drawing room. Elizabeth followed, undoing her new checked jacket with its pinch tucks, and slipping it off. She'd rather have headed to the kitchen for a cup of tea but knew that would not go down well.

As she shut the door, she tried again with, 'I don't suppose Tom has had the time, what with this "battle which all the world has expected" having begun.' She was quoting the *Cambria Daily Leader*, from which her father had read extracts each evening.

Margaret swirled round, her full serge skirt swishing as she did so. 'Exactly! Aren't you at all concerned about your brother's safety?'

'Well of course I am, Mama! Which is why I think it's better for him to concentrate on the job in hand rather than be worrying about writing letters home.'

'I was so afraid...' Margaret lowered her head. She composed herself and looked up once more. 'The newspapers writing of

4

intense bombardment and the desperate fighting of the enemy, and the, the, what was it? The great weight of artillery, that was it, and big counter-attacks and guns going on for weeks and—'

'Yes, yes, I know all that, but our aeroplanes have complete control of the sky and we've gained ground everywhere. That is cause indeed to be optimistic.'

'Is it? The newspaper said that men are fighting and dying in Flanders. And I don't suppose they're allowed to report how bad it really is.'

There was likely a good deal of truth in that, but she couldn't let her mother fall into this despondency. 'We have a letter from Tom, so we know he's all right.'

'At least when he sent it.'

'Why don't you read it and see what he has to say?'

Her mother opened it. Her eyes darted across the single page. 'Here, it's short and sweet, and basically says he's fine.'

Elizabeth took the brief missive and read it. 'Probably too busy for his usual chatty letters.'

'I suppose.'

Not knowing how else to lift her mother's mood, she said, 'Would you like me to make us some tea, Mama?'

'Not for me.' There was a pause, where she seemed to pull herself together. 'So how did your lunch with Julia Fitzgerald go?'

'It was most enjoyable, thank you. She had much to tell me about being a nurse with the Voluntary Aid Detachment. She's going out to France next week.'

Margaret gave a small humph, seating herself on one of the cream velvet Chesterfields. 'It's not like she's a *professionally* trained nurse though, is it? They only do menial tasks, not like the real nurses.'

Oh, here we go. 'It's still a worthy job, and they can do the less specialist tasks, allowing the nurses to get on with saving the men.'

'Yes but – oh, was that the front door?' Margaret stood abruptly. 'I hope that wasn't Mrs Rhys slamming it like that.'

She was interrupted by the drawing room door being flung open, only to be caught by Herbert Meredith, before it hit the wall.

'Papa, what on earth is wrong?'

Herbert stayed by the door, closing it carefully behind him. 'I'm sorry, I shouldn't let my temper get the better of me. The telephone in my office is not working and I need to ring people. Of all the days for this to happen. Quite a few of the men didn't turn up for work this morning, claiming they were entitled to the full three days off for the bank holiday, like other mines. Some are protesting around the gardens on Jubilee Green and some at the colliery gates. Or they were. They seem to have dispersed now. They were also complaining about not being paid in accordance with the recent Minimum Wage Act.'

'Yes, I stopped to talk to a couple.' She didn't want to admit there'd been a fight and start her mother off. But it didn't make any difference.

'Atrocious!' announced Margaret. 'Who do they think they are? They're lucky to get two days off, what with a war raging. You won't find our brave boys on the Front having bank holidays off.'

'The miners have a point though, Mama. If other collieries are giving three days and paying the minimum wage—'

'Of course they don't have a point, you silly girl! And what are you doing, stopping to talk to the hoi polloi? You're the *manager's* daughter!'

'I'm afraid I agree with Lizzie,' said Herbert. 'In their position, I'd feel the same way.'

'Then why don't you do something about it?' said Elizabeth.

'Because I'm only the manager of this mine and it's not my decision. That's up to the company bosses. And what's worse, they're finally going to have the inquest into the accident from last year. Thirteen months, it's taken them. Leaving it this long has made the men even more frustrated.'

'That's not your concern,' said Margaret.

6

'I believe it is. Would you have said the same when I was a hewer, or an overseer?'

Margaret didn't reply.

'I'm going to the study to make those calls now. I'd appreciate it if I wasn't disturbed.' He opened the door and left, closing it quietly behind him.

'Well! As if there isn't enough to fret about.' Margaret straightened her skirt as she sat back down. This, and the blouse she was wearing, were new. Mrs Bowen, the seamstress on Jubilee Green, had run them up for her recently, along with a jacket. She'd come right up to date with a skirt a little shorter than her ankles, as fashion now dictated. Her hair, which had been greying at the temples, had gained its former colour, a dark honey, similar to Elizabeth's.

To try and cheer her mother up, she said, 'You look very fetching today, Mama.'

'I do my best. If one can't keep up appearances, even in wartime, what is to become of us?'

Elizabeth wondered if the appearance she was trying to keep up went deeper than the clothes.

'Anyway, at least there is some good news to impart,' said Margaret. 'I hear that Julia's brothers, Sidney and Horace Fitzgerald, will be home on leave soon. They are officers – a captain and a lieutenant.' Margaret pronounced their ranks with much emphasis. 'I've asked their mother to call in with them when they return, for afternoon tea. I trust you will *not* be looking like a tramp.'

'Do I look like a tramp now?'

'No, you look – acceptable. But I don't want you coming in muddy from the allotments in trousers and a shirt. It's just the kind of thing you'd do to spite me.'

'I would not, Mama! As long as you tell me when they're coming, I'm sure I can look *acceptable*.'

Sidney and Horace were nice enough boys – and Elizabeth did think of them as boys even though they must be twenty-seven and thirty by now. How they'd ever been considered

7

officer material was beyond her. The pair of them had entered their father's business from university into executive positions from the off. Their interests lay in cricket, the arts and gentlemen's clubs. The only skill she imagined they could lend to army life was that of marksmanship, since their other passion was shooting.

'Did you hear what I said, Elizabeth?'

'Sorry, Mama. I was miles away.'

'I said, you are to do your utmost to be polite and feminine with Sidney and Horace. They are quite likely the best prospect you'll have for a good match.'

'A match? Oh Mama, you're surely not trying to pair me off with one of them?' Yet why else would she invite eligible bachelors to the house?

'Since you don't seem to be making any effort in that direction yourself, despite your determination to find your own husband and not have me interfere, you have plainly got nowhere. We shan't mention the mess you made of your relationship with Ralph Tallis.'

'You have just mentioned it. And you know jolly well he turned out to be a scoundrel, leading both me and Gwen Austin on.'

'If you'd made yourself attractive and interesting enough, he wouldn't have found the need to walk out with another woman at the same time.'

There was much Elizabeth could have said on the subject, but the quicker this conversation was over the better.

'So, as I said, make sure you make the best of yourself when Sidney and Horace come, and practice charming them.'

Elizabeth raised her eyes heavenward and was tempted to yawn.

'Don't raise your eyes like that, madam! Twenty-seven you are now. Soon no man will look twice at you.'

Elizabeth's mood dipped a little further. She was probably right. And independent as she was, she did rather like the idea of a husband and little family of her own. But who with? Not the likes of socialite-seeking men like Sidney and Horace, she was sure. She'd prefer somebody more – ordinary. But her mother wouldn't stand for that, thinking their family of higher status than they really were.

'By the way, I'm interviewing Brenda Prothero for the maid's position.'

'Why, is Mrs Rhys leaving?'

'No, but the odd bit of cooking she has done for us has made it clear how good she is. I've asked her to take that job over instead. And thank goodness, Brenda is willing to do five and a half days. I suppose she needs the money, with her husband deceased.' Margaret shook her head. 'I shall be glad when this war is over for all sorts of reasons. At least women will be able to return to their traditional jobs and there won't be all these servant shortages, with girls going off to the munitions and places they have no business.'

'I wouldn't be so sure, Mama. I think the war might be the catalyst by which things change forever for women. From next year, some of us will be able to vote.'

She tutted several times. 'Right, that tea you offered earlier, I'm ready for it now.'

Elizabeth rose swiftly, shaking off the weariness always provoked by her mother's old-fashioned views. 'Of course, Mama.'

–

Two days later, Elizabeth was delighted to spot Gwilym on the allotment in front of Edward Street, where he lived. He was bending to dig up some potatoes. She hadn't seen him here for a few days. He was a fellow organiser of the allotments, and she was keen to discuss what needed doing on the three fields they worked.

She couldn't believe they'd been growing the vegetables as a cooperative for nearly a year and a half now. They'd been so

9

lucky when the coal company had agreed to let them work the fields for nothing, to provide more food for the working men and their families here. Farmer Lloyd had been wonderful at helping them get started, and they, in turn, had provided him with some helpers on his farm. Then there was Mr James, the greengrocer, who'd agreed to buy the veg off them to sell in his shop.

'*Prywnhawn Da*, Gwilym.'

He straightened himself swiftly and slammed the point of his spade into the ground. 'Good afternoon, Miss Elizabeth.' He went to lift his cap, but realising he didn't have it on, stuck his arm awkwardly by his side.

Oh goodness, he was back to the *Miss* business, was he? 'Just Elizabeth will do. You know that.'

Gwilym said nothing. Elizabeth felt uncomfortable, which wasn't like her, who could usually find plenty to say to people. She considered him a handsome man, with his dancing green eyes and ready smile, at least, when not covered in a coat of soot. He rarely smiled at her though, even now, after working closely on the allotment project.

'Well, how's it been going? We've been working in different places, so I haven't managed to catch up with you, or Mary Jones,' she said.

'The field behind the allotments is going to plan. I've got a good lot of men working over there, so I left Idris in charge and came over to see if they needed any help this side. Mary seems to be doing all right on the Alexandra Street field. Don't seem to be so many in this field today, though.'

'A few more women will be out after they've seen to their husband's baths and food, I dare say. You're out early today,' she said.

'Got home prompt like, so I could get out before it rained.' He pointed up to the sky. 'Not been good for August.'

'No, I was thinking that about Violet and Hywel and their honeymoon to Barry Island. I haven't seen them since they got back. I hope they had a good time.'

'Aye, they did.'

'I'm so glad. Now, I'd like to discuss the next round of planting, and what we're going to put where. I've got a few ideas.' She pulled a small notebook and pencil from her trouser pocket.

'Aye. Give me a minute to finish digging up this row of potatoes and I'll be with you.'

'I'll have a word with some of the others while you're doing that. You can catch me up when you're done.'

'Right you are.'

Elizabeth headed off towards Molly Prior, who'd started helping on the allotments that summer.

'Good afternoon, Mrs Prior, how are the beetroots doing?'

'Very well, Miss Elizabeth.'

'Just Elizabeth, please.'

'I hear my Brenda's going to be working up at the Big House.' She seemed delighted with the arrangement.

'Why yes. My mother is immensely pleased to be able to engage someone else in the house.'

'My Brenda's that happy to get a job that doesn't involve sorting coal. And she needs the money since losing Harold. Not been well for a while, she hadn't. Took it out of her, losing her husband like that. But she's more than fit enough to work now.'

'I have no doubt about that.'

'Only twenty-four she is, so I've told her she's bound to meet someone else, especially with no children in tow. Never happened for them, see, though they'd been married three year. Probably just as well now.'

Elizabeth noticed Gwilym sauntering across the field towards her.

'I'm sure things can only get better for Brenda. I've got to have a chat with Gwilym about plans for the allotments, so I'll speak to you later.'

She walked a few steps to meet him. They took the pavement down Edward Street, past the Workmen's Institute at the top of Jubilee Green and onto Alexandra Street, where the next allotment took up the patch opposite the last half of the houses. Most of the talking was done by her as they walked, with him nodding and agreeing with most of her suggestions. He normally had more of his own opinions to offer than this but seemed preoccupied.

Mary Jones came to meet them, her young daughter trailing behind her, holding the end of her long skirt. She picked the girl up and they took a turn around the perimeter of the field, discussing Elizabeth's proposals. Mary was more forthcoming with suggestions than Gwilym had been.

'Well, I'd better get back to work,' Mary said when they got close to the houses again. 'Those carrots won't pick themselves.'

'I do appreciate all the hours you put in,' said Elizabeth. 'I hear your oldest girl has been getting involved too.'

'Aye, there she is.' She pointed to a girl who looked around ten, her fine, light brown hair loose and tipped over her head from where she was bending over.

'Reckon it's good for the older children to learn about growing veggies. Trying to get my two sons involved as well, with the digging and the like.'

'What a good idea, Mary. Perhaps we could start to encourage all the children more, especially while they're on their summer holidays.'

As Gwilym and Elizabeth took the route back to the other field, she said, 'So did anything else happen after the protest on Wednesday?'

'No. We all just went home.'

'My father mentioned it when he returned.'

'I'm sure he would have done.' Gwilym kept looking ahead as he spoke, a note of weariness in his voice.

'He agrees with you, you know.'

Gwilym did now turn his head, his eyes scrunched up. 'Really?'

'Of course. Not that he can be seen to be siding with anyone. Please keep that to yourself. It is unacceptable, not being paid the minimum wage, or being allowed the bank holiday most other people are getting.'

'Aye, well.' He was back to looking ahead.

'You know, we were once, that is...' She wasn't sure if she should be telling him that her father started as a hewer, like him. Anwen knew, but she could trust her to keep that to herself. She didn't have Gwilym down as a tattle-tale, and he might be friendlier towards her if he knew. 'You see—'

But she didn't get a chance to tell him anything before a group of four women appeared at the end of Bryn Road, laughing. One called over, 'Miss Elizabeth, where do you want us working today?'

'I'll leave you to it then and head back over to the far field,' said Gwilym. '*Hwyl fawr.*' With that he bounded off down Bryn Road, nodding to the group of women as he passed.

That must be fate telling her not to divulge her humble beginnings, thought Elizabeth. She didn't care for herself, but if Mama found out she'd told anyone, she would not be amused.

'Why is he in such a hurry?' said one of the women. 'Was it something we said?'

'He needs to get back to work on the far field, that's all. Come on, I've got a few jobs for you.'

She couldn't help thinking similar, though. What was wrong with him that he still couldn't relax in their company? She tutted to herself and led the way.

Chapter Two

Gwilym was ready for his supper by the time he headed home that evening. After four hours digging on the Edward Street allotment, he'd gone back briefly to see how the men were getting on at the field behind McKenzie Cottages.

Taking the small bridge that spanned Nàntygalon, the tiny stream that trickled down to the valley bottom, he continued around the sweeping corner that led onto James Street and back into the main village. He surveyed the tall brick buildings of the colliery and the pit wheels on his left, glad he was outside, free, in the fresh air. He put his hand out to feel the sprinkle of light rain. At least it had held off until supper time. He thought about what he needed to do next behind the cottages, but soon the conversation with Elizabeth was invading his thoughts.

What was she up to, agreeing about the strike, claiming her father felt the same? Was she trying to trick him into revealing some information? Not that he had any to give. It wasn't like the men were planning anything underhand. Unless their union representative, David Keir, had something up his sleeve. You couldn't always tell with him.

In his heart, he couldn't really see Elizabeth as a spy for her father. More likely she was one of those middle-class socialists. He seemed to recall there'd been a bit of argy-bargy with Mrs Meredith when she found out Elizabeth had been on a suffragette march before the war. Jenny Richards, who'd been their maid then, had heard the argument and it had gone around the village.

He looked up to see that the sky was getting darker. He'd better get a move on, before the proper rain arrived.

Gwilym stepped into the scullery of his house at the end of Edward Street, leaning his arms out of the back door to shake the wet off his cap and jacket. He placed them on the edge of the wash tub to dry, then plodded over to the kitchen door and went in.

'Ah, here you are now,' said his mother, Rachael, at the range, sounding as cross as she had two days ago when she'd found out he'd been on the protest march.

His nose caught an aroma that suggested she might have got hold of a little meat to put with the vegetables of the cawl. He nodded over at his grandfather, Abraham, before taking a seat at the table opposite him. 'Hello Grancher.'

'Hello, *bach*. How're the allotments going? I'd have been over there myself today, but my knee's playing up.' He tapped the offending body part.

'Aye, it's all going fine.'

'So you were on the allotments then, not on another demonstration,' Rachael muttered under her breath.

'Oh, don't keep on, woman,' said Abraham. 'If I'd been a bit younger, and still working, like, I'd have been standing there with him.'

Gwilym glanced at his mother, who glared at her father-in-law.

'That's all very well and good,' she said, 'But we're short of money for the coming week now.'

'We've got to try, Mam, otherwise the bosses'll always be keeping us short and depriving us of holidays.'

'As for taking your brother with you... Where is he now? Still out with his mates, no doubt. Did you see him?'

The back door opened then banged shut. Evan never had been the quietest of boys. The door from the scullery was flung open and his brother marched in, shaking the drips of his jacket everywhere.

'Stop that now!' Rachael grabbed the offending bit of clothing and stomped out to the scullery with it.

Evan pulled his mouth into a grimace and went to look at what was cooking.

Rachael was soon back. 'You know not to bring wet jackets in here, you daft boy!'

'I'm not a boy, Mam, I'm sixteen, seventeen in a coupla months.'

'Then it's about time you grew up and got a bit responsible, like. Short of money we'll be, with you and your strikes.'

'Not again! What's in here?' He pointed to the pan.

'Some cawl. Managed to get some scraps of lamb. Dunno what I'll be buying food with next week.'

'Some lamb! Thank the Lord,' said Evan, planting himself on a chair at the table, next to Abraham.

Rachael tutted. 'Don't you be taking the Lord's name in vain, my boy.'

'I wasn't, I was thanking him, wasn't I?'

'But in a way that sounded resentful.'

Gwilym picked up the abandoned newspaper on the table, staring unseeing at it. His family had changed since his father had died in the mine explosion last year. Abraham was quieter when once he'd been a chatty soul. Evan was getting cheekier by the week, not restrained by their mam's discipline in the way he had been by their father's. Mam seemed either cross or upset about something most of the time. And him? He felt an increasing sense of hopelessness, especially with the war still raging. At least when working on the allotments he could concentrate on life and growth, and put death to one side, if just for a while.

'As for being short of money,' Evan said, 'what'll we do if Gwilym gets married? It's about time.'

'Then I'll have to work, won't I?' Rachael stood up straight and crossed her arms tightly around her middle. 'And why not? It's only fifty-one, I am. Your grancher there worked 'til he were near seventy.'

'Hah!' said Abraham. 'And I wouldn't recommend it, though I did love looking after them ponies.' He turned towards Gwilym. 'You gotta girl, *bach*? You've been quiet about that.'

Gwilym laughed drily. 'No Grancher, I haven't.'

'You'll find somebody soon, a handsome, well-read boy like you.' Rachael seemed to cheer up at this thought.

'I really am *not* a boy, Mam.'

'Exactly. You'll see, there'll be a girl for you out there. Probably right under your nose, like with your da and me.' She looked thoughtful.

'If you say so.' Gwilym shrugged his shoulders and glanced over the headlines of the newspaper.

Chapter Three

'It sounds like you had a lovely time in Barry, despite the weather,' said Gwen Austin, having listened to Violet's animated account.

The change in her friend over the last couple of months had been remarkable, since her previous mother-in-law had been made to leave the house for harassing her. Olwen Jones had made her life a misery, moving herself into her home after Violet's first husband Charlie, had been killed. She'd almost starved her and had bullied the spirit out of her. But the change was not only down to getting rid of Olwen Jones, but down to Hywel Llewellyn, her new husband. Gwen hoped that getting the special licence to get married quickly wasn't going to prove a mistake though. But who was she to judge, who couldn't entice one man to marry her, let alone two? This disheartening thought she pushed to one side.

'Oh we did, Gwen. I haven't been on any kind of holiday for such a long time.'

'I'm sure Uncle Hywel will take you on as many holidays as you want now,' said Anwen.

'Or as many as we can afford,' laughed Violet.

'It was good of Hywel to take the kiddies out for a walk, to give us some time to catch up,' said Gwen leaning back, 'especially Sara Fach in her pushchair. Don't see many men with pushchairs.'

Violet stood to fetch the kettle from the range to top up the teapot. 'Don't see many pushchairs at all here. You were so lucky Mary Jones had one to give you, Anwen. Bet that's seen lots of children from different families.'

'And it'll be passed onto you when you have your next.' Anwen gave her a wink.

'Oh no, you're bound to have one before me, being married longer.'

'It hasn't happened so far. Anyway, I've enough on my hands with my little sister at the moment.'

Anwen said this cheerily, but Gwen knew she was hurting inside. She so longed for a babby of her own, even if she did adore looking after her half-sister. What a situation: little Sara, being brought up by her sister, with a grandmother who was no relation to her, and a great-grandmother who was actually her grandma! All because her vicious father had got a mouthy trollop pregnant, when neither were fit to be parents.

'I don't suppose anything's been heard of Sara's *mother*?' said Gwen.

Anwen shook her head. 'No, not hide nor hair has been heard of Delyth Bryce. And I hope it never will since we've applied to adopt Sara Fach.'

'I still can't believe a mother would abandon a baby like that, at a lodging house,' said Violet. 'Anything could have happened to her.'

'Mam has had several letters from my father saying we're to get rid of the *brat*, as he put it, so I suspect Delyth has been to see him in prison, or at least contacted him.'

'He's still got a good long time in gaol left yet, over eleven years,' said Gwen. 'Surely he'll have more sense than to come back here when he leaves. And Sara Fach'll be a twelve-year-old by then.'

'How would Delyth Bryce know she's with you?' said Violet.

'Dunno. Perhaps she's guessing,' said Anwen. 'Anyway, Hywel indicated there was some news you wanted to tell us?'

Violet took a deep breath before standing to walk over to the dresser. She opened one of the cupboards below and pulled

19

out a small case and a letter, placing it on the table when she sat back down.

'This arrived yesterday.' She opened the box to reveal a silver medal hanging from a short navy and red striped ribbon. 'They apologised for its lateness and said it was an oversight. It's for Charlie's bravery at Mametz Wood.' Violet's face was solemn.

'That's wonderful,' said Gwen, taking the medal from Violet for a closer look. On one side was written: *For Distinguished Conduct in the Field*. 'That is something Clarice and Benjy will be proud of when they're old enough to understand its significance.'

'Yes, it—' But Violet didn't finish before she had to tug her handkerchief from her pocket to wipe the tears away. 'I'm sorry. I shouldn't feel like this now, and I am so happy with Hywel, but it was a life wasted.'

'Of course it was,' said Gwen, leaning over to give her arm a rub. 'He didn't deserve that. So many young men have been lost in the village. What is it now? Fifteen?' And who knew if there'd be more, including her dear brother, Henry?

'At least there's been no news of any casualties with the latest battles,' said Anwen. 'Elizabeth told me in chapel this morning that Tom had written to say they'd been at Pilckem Ridge. He's in the 114th Brigade, the same as our boys, but in the 10th Battalion rather than the 13th.'

'Perhaps we should do something to celebrate Charlie's bravery,' Gwen suggested.

Violet clapped the box shut. 'No, I don't think so.' She took it and the letter back to the dresser and put them away, before returning to the table, saying as she sat, 'There's something I've been meaning to say to you, Gwen.' She looked at Anwen.

'We both have,' said Anwen. 'And I know we've said it before, but, well, you do seem to be more yellow than normal. And your lovely blonde curls are sort of – greeny.'

Gwen slammed her back against the chair. 'Ooh, not this again. I've already told you, I'm perfectly all right.' It wasn't true though. She'd felt more tired, while her appetite wasn't as good as it had been.

'We're only concerned for your health, Gwen,' said Anwen. 'I've read of what's happened to some munitionettes and, well, it's not—'

'I'm well aware that some have died. But only a few. A much smaller proportion than the soldiers. And they may well have had other health problems.'

'And there's the danger from explosions, like that one in Silvertown near London, back in January. Over a hundred were killed.' There was a plea in Anwen's voice.

Just then they heard a knock at the open back door, and a voice calling, 'Hello.'

Gwen thanked whoever it was in her head, hoping that would be the end of the subject.

'In the kitchen,' Violet called.

Gwilym soon poked his head round the door, cap in hand, looking sheepish. 'Sorry, ladies, I didn't mean to disturb your tea. I was wondering if Hywel was around.'

'He's taken the kiddies for a walk round to the woods,' said Violet. 'You'll probably catch him on the path, as he won't be able to go too far with the pushchair.'

'Thank you.'

He went to move away, but when Violet called, 'Just a minute, Gwilym,' he poked his head back round.

'We could do with your opinion. Come in the room.'

He did as he was told.

'Don't you think Gwen here is looking a little too yellow now?'

Gwilym's eyes widened as he considered her. 'Um, well, I suppose she is a little. I, well, assumed it was the sun and a bit of a tan, with working on the allotments of a Sunday, like.'

'Tans aren't yellow, they're brown,' said Violet, holding out her own bronzed hand to illustrate. She'd always been pretty dark-skinned.

'Look!' said Gwen, scraping her chair along the floor and standing. 'I don't want to give up this job. What else would I do? I don't want to be sorting coal. I've done that and it's dirty and, in the winter, cold.'

'The munitions factory's not exactly the cleanest place, judging by the state of you, Mabel Coombes and Farmer Lloyd's Nora, when you return from work,' said Anwen. 'And there are still families looking for servants, which seem to be thin on the ground now.'

'I don't want to be a servant! I get jolly good money and I love the freedom, travelling to Ebbw Vale. I came round here for a nice cuppa tea, and I end up being set upon by you all.'

'I'd better get going if I'm going to catch Hywel,' said Gwilym, disappearing quickly.

'And I'll be going too!' said Gwen, picking up her shawl from the back of the chair and storming out after him.

She'd got out of the back gate and around to the front, on Bryn Road, before she stopped, watching Gwilym disappear around the corner onto James Street. Why had she been so hasty? She could have thanked them for their concern but said it was her business and left it at that. She probably would have done, if they hadn't got Gwilym involved. What must he be thinking?

She'd been looking forward to this tea and chat at Violet's. She wasn't going to lose face though.

Coming to a standstill, she pondered her yellow skin. In a shop in Ebbw Vale she'd recently seen two items, a satin skin cream and a powder to go along with it. It was a little expensive, but now might be the time to purchase some.

The houses beside her and the tall colliery buildings ahead hid the sun, which had been flitting in and out of the clouds all day. She longed to get into the sunshine, where it was warmer. She might as well go home and get changed to work on the allotments. That would be a better use of her angry energy. Mary Jones would be glad of some help at the Alexandra Street field.

She turned back up Bryn Road and hurried down a path on the right, that took her to the back of her terrace of houses.

In the scullery, her mother was washing up the tea things.

'You're back early, *fach*. I thought you'd have a good long chat with Violet and Anwen.'

'I would have done if they hadn't—' She stopped, not wanting to get into this conversation with her mother but was mortified to find herself sobbing.

Ruth left the washing up, drying her hands on a tea towel. 'What on earth is it, *cariad*?' She put the cloth down and placed an arm around her daughter's shoulders. She was slightly shorter than Gwen, but tall all the same for a woman. Her pinny was a little wet and was making Gwen damp, but she let it pass.

'Oh Mam, I had an argument with them, because they kept on about my yellow skin.'

'Well, it's no more than I've said. You know your father and I hate you working at the munitions. It's not just the skin, but you're not your old, lively self. Used to have loads of energy, you did. But you're an adult now and we can't force you not to work there. It just scares me though, see, with all the stories you hear of munitionettes.'

Ruth pulled away slightly to consider her daughter. 'I've been praying it'll be over soon, the war, and that will solve the problem. With this "big push" they've been talking about in the papers, it's looking that way. And that will also bring Henry home and I'll have my family back together again, and healthy.'

Gwen nodded. She longed for the war to be over, to have her brother home, but equally she dreaded it, as it would also mean the loss of her well-paid job and the liberty she had. The men who'd previously worked making shells would need their jobs back. What would she do instead?

'And with men returning from war, the single ones will be thinking of settling down, I've no doubt.'

'Mam, there aren't many from here who enlisted or were called up who aren't married.'

'There are other villages around and about. You love going to the theatre and picture houses, so I'm sure you'll meet someone there. You're a pretty girl, and I'm sure your skin will be its lovely self again once you stop working at the factory.'

Her thoughts led her to Councillor Ralph Tallis, with whom she'd walked out until a couple of months back. 'Ralph said I was attractive, even with my yellow skin. But it didn't stop him walking out with Elizabeth Meredith at the same time.'

'I wish you'd told me about that when it happened. I'd have given him what for! I'm proud of you and Miss Elizabeth for confronting him together, though. The cheek of the man, thinking it was all right to walk out with the two of you because he was unable to choose between you.'

Gwen had never told her mam about his assertion that she was not a *lady*. The taunt still stung.

'That aside, if he thought you attractive even with your yellow skin, think how much *more* attractive the young men will think you once it's back to normal.'

Gwen nodded, not really convinced her complexion would ever recover. And was attractiveness all a man wanted in a relationship?

'I'm going to get changed and go and help on the allotments.'

'That's a good idea. I might join you. Your father's settled in with his pipe and the newspaper and quite happy on his own.'

'I'll see you back here in a coupla minutes then, and we'll walk over together.'

—

'So what do you think this meeting might be about?' said Gwilym, as he and Idris ambled along Edward Street towards the Workmen's Institute.

'Your guess is as good as mine,' said Idris. 'All David Keir would say was that he had news from Pilckem Ridge. Not sure what that's got to do with us specifically. Gwen told Anwen they'd had a letter from Henry, and that all our lads from the village in the 13th Battalion were safe.'

'Keir's as bad as Philip Hubbard used to be, God rest his soul, with calling these meetings for the least little thing. And I'd rather be getting on with the allotments.' Gwilym pointed to the field on the left as they passed by. Elizabeth spotted him as she forked the ground, giving him a wave. He simply nodded in response, leaving Idris to wave back.

Reaching the Institute at the top of Jubilee Green, they climbed the steep steps on the right, greeting fellow workers as they went. In the large room they used for meetings, the men took their seats, Gwilym and Idris sitting six rows back. There must have been a couple of hundred men there. David Keir came storming onto the space at the front, with two friends.

'Oh Lord,' said Idris. 'He's got a face on him. I wonder if this is about the protest on bank holiday.'

Others must have been thinking the same, as someone called out, 'Have they decided to give us the minimum wage, then?'

David Keir looked grim, despite the smart trousers and waistcoat he was sporting, standing tall with his legs akimbo and arms crossed in front of him. He was flanked by his friends in a way that made them look like his henchmen.

'I've no idea,' said Keir. 'And it's not why I've called everyone here.'

'Then why on earth have you called us here?'

Gwilym and Idris turned, recognising the irritated voice of Gwen's father, Albert Austin, several rows back.

'You look fit to burst,' said Albert.

'Aye, so would you, if your cousin had just been killed by the bloody Hun. A sergeant in the 10th Battalion he was, a fellow battalion to the 13th, where our lads from here are.'

'Well, I'm sorry to the heart of me,' said Albert, standing now. 'But I'm still not sure why you needed to call a meeting about this. You could've told us on the way back from work.'

'Because it's time we took action!' Keir thumped his right fist into his left palm. 'Are we going to let the Hun take over the world?'

Gwilym stood up. 'The newspapers are saying that we're getting the better of them now, so it could soon all be over.'

'Like it was the first year, over by Christmas, eh? I don't trust them newspapers to report what's really going on. Top secret, it is. No, it's about time we all went out there to fight.'

Albert, still standing, shook his head slowly. 'And who's going to dig out the coal if you youngsters enlist? The navy's relying on us, and we need them to protect our shores, so *we* don't get overrun here.' Hoots of agreement followed.

'They'll have to get some of the older miners out of retirement. But we younger ones are fit and raring to go. What do you say, comrades?'

'I'm not going nowhere, apart from back home,' said a voice from the front. He rose, with several other men, and left the room.

'You bloody cowards!' Keir shouted after them.

'I thought you communists didn't agree with fighting wars,' shouted a voice from the back.

'No, they just like locking up their royal family,' called another. 'Like them Russians.'

'I'm not a communist, I'm a socialist,' Keir bellowed. 'And I believe in fighting for what's right!'

'You're not alone in that lad,' said Albert. 'But we've all got our place in this conflict, and ours is here, in the mine.'

'Who else is with us?' the union rep persisted, ignoring him.

There was mumbling from those gathered, but nobody volunteered to join them.

'You can't sign up, mun,' said Gwilym. 'Reserved occupation, isn't it?'

'If we leave and are unemployed, we can.' David Keir lifted a hand and pointed his forefinger. 'You are just a coward, Gwilym Owen.'

Gwilym lost patience with him. 'Do you think I care about your opinion? And I've been called a coward before, by better than you.'

Beside him, Idris stood up. 'Aye, and I was fool enough to be the caller, but I know better now. You think men who risk being buried underground are cowards, do you? We all have our place in this war: I found that out the hard way.'

'I'm off, whatever you lot have to say, so you'll have to get yourselves a new union rep.' Keir pointed at Gwilym. 'Perhaps this mouth almighty here, since he's so much to say for hisself.' With that, he and his friends marched off as if they were already in the army.

There was a general hum of voices for a few moments, before Albert, still standing, spoke to the crowd. 'One thing Keir was right about was having to choose a new union rep.'

Noah Schenck, the nephew of the bookshop owner, stood. 'I reckon Keir was right about Gwilym being a good representative for us to the management. He speaks clearly and puts his points over well.'

'Aye, that he does,' Albert agreed, as several nods and voices of assent were heard.

Gwilym felt the panic rising. 'No, I'd be no good at that. Not forward enough, I'm not.'

'You seemed pretty forward to me, mun,' said Noah. 'Not the first time you've stepped up to speak or sort a situation out, neither. And it looks to me like I've already proposed it and Mr Austin here has seconded it. All in favour?'

There was a chorus of 'aye' from the men.

'Looks like that's carried, mun,' said Noah, looking satisfied.

'Well, Gwilym *bach*, your father would have been that proud,' said Albert, patting him on the back.

'Hear, hear!' called some of the men, as they started to shift from their seats.

'Hold on a moment,' said Noah. 'When's the next meeting?'

Gwilym's panic robbed him of the power of speech for a moment. 'Um, well, I'll have to let you know that. It's all a bit sudden, like.'

The men made their way to the doors. Gwilym remained where he was, mouth slightly open.

'That was over soon enough,' said Idris, nudging his arm. 'Reckon we could get a bit of work on the allotments in, after all. What d'you say?'

'You'll get no argument from me, mun.' He followed Idris out, happy to lose himself in digging and forget the responsibility that lay ahead.

Chapter Four

Anwen tore off the calendar sheet to reveal the page headed *September 1917*. Nearly the end of summer. She went to the kitchen window and peered into the yard and beyond the slight incline of the garden, to the mountain. The rainy mist bathed the room in gloom, even though the sun should have risen by now.

Idris had just left for work, clutching his tin box and bottle, kissing her cheek as he always did before he left. She touched the skin that had been caressed by his lips.

They were still waiting to officially adopt Sara Fach. It was the 'red tape' delaying it, as Dr Roberts put it. Thoughts of her own childless state filtered into her mind, but she shook her head to dispel them. There wasn't any point going over it again. She told herself what she told others who couldn't keep their noses out of her business, that the good Lord was giving her time to look after her little sister first.

She tossed the old calendar sheet on the table and went to the range, intent on getting herself a cup of tea. When her mam and mamgu appeared, she'd cook and share out the two slices of bacon she'd managed to get from the grocer, and the tough slice of bread left from the loaf. There were also some large horse mushrooms she'd found on the patch of grass beyond Gwilym's house at the end of their terrace. The egg that Gwilym had given her from his chickens she was saving for Sara Fach, along with the bit of porridge she had left. She picked up the kettle and went to refill it from the tap in the scullery, before placing it on the already hot range.

Her mamgu, Cadi, was the first to come through the door from the hall.

'*Bore da, cariad*. And how are you this morning?'

'I was just wishing we were allowed to buy fresh bread, as this slice I have left is even staler than it would normally be the day after I've purchased it.'

'Aye, I still don't understand that Bread Order from the government.'

'It's to stop us eating so much. They reckon if it's not as appealing, we won't want to.'

'Oh, I know that. But it's not like there's enough of it in the shops to buy it whenever we please. Least the government could do is let us have it fresh.' She dropped her round body onto a chair. 'You want some 'elp with breakfast? Your mam's just getting dressed so she'll be down soon.'

'No, I can manage. It's not like there's much to cook.'

'More's the pity. I swear I've lost weight. See.' She pulled out the waistband of her old blue serge skirt to demonstrate.

'Perhaps you've just done up your laces a bit tighter.'

Cadi laughed. 'It's been a while since I've worn a corset. Don't see the point no more. It's not like I'm trying to show the young men how shapely I am – or am not, in my case.'

'Lucky you!' said Anwen, as she lifted the kettle to fill the teapot.

'Why don't you buy one of those new liberty bodices? They're meant to be more comfortable.'

'I'm not sure I've got the money for one of those.'

Enid entered the room. 'Sara Fach's still fast asleep. Ah good, you're making some tea. Parched, I am.' She sat at the end of the table.

When Anwen had finished pouring them each a cup, she said, 'I'll get on with the breakfast.'

'In a moment. Sit down, would you, *fach*?'

Anwen took a seat next to Cadi. 'What's up, Mam? You look worried.'

'I think you should know about this letter I got yesterday.' She fished in her skirt pocket and pulled out an envelope. 'It's from your father.' She plonked it on the table.

'What's he said now?'

'I finally replied to those awful letters of his that insisted we get rid of *the brat*, as he puts it. I told him straight that Sara Fach is part of our family, and that you've adopted her.'

'It's not official yet.'

'He doesn't have to know that. But he's admitted that Delyth Bryce has been visiting him in gaol and heard it from her that we have the baby.'

'So she is still in the area? How does she know?'

'I've no idea.' Enid pointed to the envelope. 'But there it is, if you want to read it. Making all sorts of veiled threats of course, about coming here and sorting us out when he leaves gaol.'

'Surely they wouldn't allow a letter like that to go out,' said Anwen.

'No, but he makes it sound reasonable, like he wants to make amends, but I know what he really means.'

Anwen nodded towards Cadi. 'Shall I read it to you?'

'No, your mam read it to me yesterday.'

Anwen pulled the letter out of the envelope and started at the front page of scruffy writing.

'I didn't want to worry you with it, but your mamgu said I should tell you.'

'Aye, it's only right she should know, and Idris, and Hywel too,' said Cadi.

'I'll make sure they see it,' said Anwen.

—

Elizabeth exited the main doors of the Imperial Cinema in Rhymney, relieved to see it was still dry outside. She'd been right to wear her wool jacket instead of a coat, since the air was still mild.

As the rest of the audience filed past her, she considered which way to go. Left to the motorcar, or right to Perilli's for a cup of tea. *A Child of the Wild* had been a charming little film, if a tad predictable. The other two shorter films hadn't engaged her attention as much, but she had passed the evening pleasantly enough. How she wished she'd had someone to accompany her. Anwen was too busy now – and married. Violet and she had never been close. Gwen, with whom she'd gone to see *The Battle of the Somme* last year, probably would not have appreciated being asked again, especially as the outing had resulted in meeting Ralph Tallis. That had been the start of his duplicity.

She saw so many people in the course of a week, either at one of the events her mother managed to drag her along to, or at the allotments. There were often women her own age at these events, but they were all acquaintances, not friends. Many were a higher status than a colliery manager's daughter. As for the folk in the village, all but Anwen's family seemed wary of her. Any friends she'd had were now busy with the war effort. There was no one to sit and have a chat and a joke with.

She watched as other people left the picture house, all in pairs or groups, nattering and laughing. A swell of solitude threatened to swamp her.

Going to Perilli's on her own no longer appealed to her, especially at this time of the evening. She was about to turn towards her motorcar, when she almost bumped into a man exiting the cinema.

'Ooh, I am *so* sor – oh, hello Gwilym. Fancy bumping into you – again!'

His eyes were wide with surprise. 'Um, Miss, I mean, Elizabeth. What are you doing here?'

'The same as you, I imagine.'

'You've been in the cinema watching the films?'

By the incredulous look on his face, anyone would have thought she'd been out causing mischief. 'It is allowed you know, ladies at the cinema,' she chuckled.

He fiddled with the side of his cap. The red curls weren't as apparent as usual, suggesting he'd had his hair cut recently. 'Oh, yes, I'm sure it is. I just meant…' He looked around. 'Who did you come with?'

'Just myself, I'm afraid. All my friends seem to be occupied with families or away doing their bit in the VAD or similar.'

The crowds leaving the picture house had dwindled now, the last of the clientele dawdling onto the pavement.

'You're not chaperoned?'

'I'm twenty-seven, Gwilym, not eighteen.'

'Aye, I suppose. Still, I thought… that is, you know, being the manager's daughter and all…'

'You don't seem to be with anyone either.'

'No, well, my friends are married too, isn't it?'

Conversation stalled. Gwilym rubbed his face, then clutched his hands together.

She could offer him a lift home, save him the walk. Instead, her mouth bypassed this sensible thought and said, 'I'm feeling parched after several hours in there and could do with a cup of tea.'

'There's Perilli's café across the road and a few doors down, which is normally still open this time of the evening.' He seemed relieved to have offered the information.

'Yes, I know it. Could you do with a drink too?'

Once again, his face registered surprise. Her stomach squirmed. What had she expected? For him to say, *Well of course, Elizabeth*, then take her arm, in the way Ralph Tallis might have done? No, maybe not that, but perhaps just a pleasant acceptance. She should learn to assume nothing.

'Am I dressed well enough though?' He looked down at his brown trousers and jacket, not matching but both neat and clean.

'Of course you are. You don't have to dress up for Perilli's.'

He shrugged. 'I suppose there'd be no harm in a cup of something.'

She was about to exclaim, *Splendid*, but realising it would make her sound like her mother, said instead, 'Let's go, then.'

They crossed the road and soon reached Perilli Bros Refreshment House. Its usual, splendid window display had dwindled slowly in the last couple of years, so that now there was a view straight through to the counter selling a shrinking selection of sweets and chocolates. The range of cigars, tobacco and pipes had not diminished as much, but was nonetheless smaller. As they entered, she breathed in the mingling sweetness of the varied products.

A few other cinema patrons had clearly had the same idea, as a small queue formed by the entrance of the café area, in which they were second.

Several tables were already occupied. They, at least, had not changed much during the war, with their stiff white cloths, red napkins and dainty pots of blossoms. Elizabeth had always admired the large, square floor tiles, in white and shades of green, laid out in a mosaic pattern that looked almost like flowers.

It wasn't long before Elizabeth and Gwilym were seated. He let her go ahead, looking around awkwardly as he sat. She picked up the menu and surveyed it quickly before handing it to Gwilym.

'There's only a fraction of what was on offer last time I came in, but I suppose that's to be expected. I'll have a cup of tea, and maybe a small packet of biscuits. I rushed out after only having a snack for dinner – supper,' she amended.

Gwilym didn't comment but stared at the menu a few moments. 'Think I'll try the coffee. It's not something Mam keeps in the house and I like the odd cup.'

The waitress, who looked around eighteen, was all smiles when she approached, though the dark patches under her eyes suggested she was tired and would have preferred to be tucked up at home. She sported a spotless black dress with a white collar and cuffs and a short, crisp white apron with a small bib.

Her hair was neatly pinned up and on top sat a frilly white cap. Her badge said 'Loretta'. She had a Latin colouring and was undoubtedly of Italian origin, despite her broad Welsh accent. Probably another relative of the proprietors, Mr Giuseppe and Mr Antonio, as they liked to be called.

The girl took the order. Gwilym also ordered the biscuits.

'Can't resist a biscuit if it's there one to be had,' he said when the waitress had gone, 'especially as there are a lot fewer about nowadays.'

The ensuing silence was interrupted by the waitress bringing over the drinks and a plate of wrapped biscuits, offering them a choice. Gwilym and Elizabeth both picked out a packet of ginger nuts at the same time.

'Snap!' she exclaimed.

'I'm the only one in my family who likes these,' said Gwilym, 'so they're a bit of a treat, like.'

'Rose used to make good ones, for all her faults,' she said, regretting it immediately. Talking of one's cook was not the way to break down barriers, and she did feel she was constantly doing that when talking to people in the village.

'A right one she turned out to be,' said Gwilym, 'the way she stole food from your home, then went to the police to tell tales about hoarding. Not to mention all the trouble she's caused since.'

'Indeed, like stealing books from Mr Schenck. At least it didn't turn out to be her who had set the bookshop on fire, though I think she would have been convicted of it if it hadn't been for Anwen sharing her doubts with my mother, who then spoke to the chief constable's wife.'

There she went again, emphasising her family's connections in society.

He had a sip of his coffee, his eyes crinkling as if he wasn't sure about the taste. When he put the cup back on the saucer, he gave a little nod. 'That's all right.'

There was another gap in the conversation. Elizabeth was wondering whether to talk about the allotments when another subject came to mind.

'Did you see *The Battle of the Somme* last year?'

'I did. Took Evan and Jenkin so's they could see how it was no place for young boys, after them and the other lads running off and trying to enlist last summer. It shocked them. Shocked me too, and I was expecting it.'

She noticed he was less hesitant now, warming to the subject.

'I went with Gwen, and we both found it quite disturbing. It gave me a better idea of what is happening, though. I think it upset Gwen, what with Henry being part of it already.'

'It wasn't a pretty picture, that's for certain. My mam wasn't happy I'd put Evan through that, but I think it did him some good, seeing how it isn't all glory and victory.'

'No. Even now the images keep coming back to me: the dead men lying in ditches, the poor deceased horses and the little dog.' She looked up. 'I know the latter sounds insignificant next to the men, but they were innocents. It just, just shows... Oh, I don't know.'

She poured the tea, impatient with herself for her lack of fluency.

'I can't abide the glorification of it all,' he said. 'They referred to the German prisoners as the *less fortunate* who were departing for England. Less fortunate? I can only imagine what most of the British soldiers would rather be doing. The little that our lads in the Pals have told us on leave confirms that for me.' This was said with a quiet passion, his frown something between worry and irritation.

She was about to comment but was stalled by him saying, 'And that part where they showed the British dead lying there after a "glorious" and "successful" charge, as they put it, on a ridge near Mametz... Glorious? And not very successful for them lying there, shot to pieces.' His jaw stiffened, almost as if he were trying not to cry. And who knew, maybe he was.

'You remember it very vividly, Gwilym.'

'Aye, I wrote about it in a notebook when I got home. Thought it'd be worth quoting to any fool who thought signing up was simply a trip abroad and a bit of a lark.'

'I agree with all you're saying, Gwilym, every word. And I can't help thinking that a lot of our so-called enemies must feel the same. All those young Germans shown in the film were simply doing what our young men are doing: fighting for their country. No doubt they've been persuaded with words of glorious victories and evil enemies too, but they're not ultimately to blame. That honour goes to the leaders who started it, the ones who believe someone else's land should be theirs. And let's face it, Gwilym, the British, French, Italians, and more, are all guilty of empire-building and being conceited enough to believe it's their God-given right.'

Gwilym considered her carefully as she spoke.

'And I'll tell you something else,' she continued, hoping she wasn't going too far. 'It's just a more international version of what happens in our own country, every day, never mind in war time, with very few rich men owning the businesses and paying very little to those who do the work. They've all got their own little industrial empires.' She stopped there, despite having much more to say on the matter.

Gwilym blinked rapidly and leant back. 'Well, you are full of surprises.'

'Please, don't tell anyone what I said. If my mother got wind of it...'

'Of course, I'm likely to tell all and sundry I went for refreshments with the manager's daughter. You can imagine what some would make of that.'

Elizabeth's cheeks burned. 'I'm sorry, Gwilym, I did rather give you no choice. You must think me overbearing in the extreme.'

He lifted his eyebrows, though there was the hint of a smile there too. 'It's been enlightening to hear the opinion of the manager's daughter.'

'Manager now, yes, but before I was born, he was a hewer.'

Gwilym, lifting the cup to his lips, stopped midway. 'A hewer?'

'Yes. A terrace in Georgetown is where we lived. He did correspondence courses and took exams, slowly working his way up the ladder. Pushed by my mother, of course, who was a bank clerk's daughter, but at least she was there to support him.'

'I thought I'd heard it all tonight.'

'It's not a crime you know, trying to do better for yourself. It depends what you do with it. I'd say, by all accounts, my father's been a good manager, fair to the miners.'

Gwilym nodded. 'Yes he has that. Very fair indeed. Better than Edgar Williams was as undermanager and better than the manager before, who was a hard taskmaster and inclined to deprive men of money any way he could. Thick as thieves he was, with the mine bosses.' He turned his head to look at the long wooden wall clock. It was twenty-five past ten.

'Past your bedtime?' she joked.

'Some of us have to be up at five.'

'Fair enough. I've got lots to do on the allotments tomorrow, so I dare say I could do with a good night's sleep, too. I'll give you a lift home, that way you'll get to your bed quicker.' She lifted her hand to call the waitress over.

'Let me pay for this.'

She opened her mouth to protest, but he ploughed on with, 'as a way of paying my share of the petrol.'

'Oh, that's kind. Thank you.'

'Never been in a motorcar before. Might be interesting. Best drop me off at the end of the village, though.'

She huffed a small laugh to herself. There was a kind of snobbery that went the other way too.

'I hear some of the soldiers are home tomorrow,' he said. 'Will your brother be among them?'

'No, sadly not; he's in a different battalion.'

38

'Sorry about that. Esther Williams was telling me today that her Daniel'll be back. Which reminds me – she waylaid me when I was on my way to do a coupla hours on the allotment, asking me if they needed any more help.'

'Mrs Williams? Offering to help on the allotments? The woman who tried to argue that the women shouldn't waste time on them because they should be looking after their men?'

'Reckon she's a bit lonely, like. Anyway, I said I'd have a word with you.'

It would have been easy to be petty and say she didn't want her anywhere near the allotments, but there was maybe the opportunity here to build some bridges. 'On the contrary, Gwilym, I think it's a good idea. You know what they say about keeping your friends close and your enemies closer. And maybe we could even make a friend of her yet?'

Gwilym narrowed his eyes. 'Seems unlikely, but if you want to give her a try.'

'Yes. She can come and work on the Edward Street field with me.'

'I'll pop round and tell her tomorrow.'

The waitress brought over the bill, which Gwilym promptly paid.

'By the way,' said Elizabeth, 'have you been called to the inquest being held at the McKenzie Arms, into the accident last year?'

He looked down at the table, raising only his eyes. 'I've to appear tomorrow afternoon, as the only one who survived in that end of the mine.'

'I'm sorry, Gwilym, you probably don't want to talk about it.'

'Not really, no. It's enough to have to relive it tomorrow for a committee.'

'Of course. Sorry.' She seemed to be spending a lot of her time apologising. Outside once more, walking towards her motorcar, she said, 'I'm going to a lecture in Tredegar on the twenty-seventh, by Dr John Clifford. "Is the World Growing Better?" it's called.'

'Oh?' he said, as if questioning her decision.

She stopped and turned to him, and he did likewise. 'What's wrong with that? Do you know something about it?'

'No, it's not that, it's just, I was going to go too.'

'Then I might as well give you a lift, rather than you take – the motorbus, I presume? Oh, unless you're going with friends of course.'

'No, as I said, they're all married. Or in France.'

Oh dear, she'd done it again. In her effort to be generous, all she'd done was make him feel awkward.

'I'm sorry, of course I'm not insisting I give you a lift. I just thought, since I'm going anyway...'

'No, that's fine. All right. It might be better than the bumpy motorbus going up and down the hills.'

'You haven't experienced my driving yet,' she said, following it with a chuckle.

'I've seen you driving though, and you look competent enough.'

'Yes, I believe I am. All right, I will meet you at the end of Gabriel Street on the twenty-seventh, at a quarter past six, though I dare say I'll see you on the allotments before then.'

He pulled his cap from his pocket and threw it onto his head. 'I'll make a note of it.'

With that they walked back to the motorcar together, in silence.

–

There they were, poor sods, trooping up from the railway station. Gwilym was stepping out of the grocer's door when he noticed them, the surviving remnant of the Dorcalon men who'd enlisted in the Rhondda Pals, dragging their bodies and their knapsacks up the hill. The khaki uniforms had seen better days, worn as they were. At least they looked clean. People stopped along the way to welcome the fifteen of them back.

Gwilym exchanged a mumbled greeting with a couple of them, until Gwen's brother reached him.

'Hello, Henry. You'll be glad of the rest, by the looks of you.'

'Never a truer word, Gwilym, mun. I'm tired to the very bones of me. We all feel the same.'

'Had just about enough of it, we have,' said Maurice Coombes, catching up.

'At least it seems to be drawing to a close.'

'Dunno where you heard that, but we've not seen no signs of it.'

'Just seems to get worse,' Henry agreed.

'I'm just repeating what I've read in the newspapers. They reckon it's the last big push before the Germans are beaten.'

'News to me,' said Maurice. 'Better get home to my Mabel and Lily. I hear that my sister has got rid of that thug, Gus Smith, and his family, at last.'

'Yes, Gus is in gaol, along with his brother-in-law. His mother and sister have gone back to London.'

'Good bloody riddance. Didn't take to him when I met him.'

'None of us did,' said Gwilym.

Maurice moved on.

Gwilym looked up and down the street. 'Are you all here? I mean—'

'You mean, have any more of us been lost? Not since Mametz, so yes, we are,' said Henry. 'I'd better be getting back to Mam and Da's.'

They walked a short way together, parting at the crossroads. Gwilym carried on to Jubilee Green. He had a mission there this afternoon.

At number seventeen, on the other side of the triangular gardens, Gwilym knocked on the door. It was a while before it was answered. Esther peered round the door cautiously. When she saw it was him, she opened it a little more.

'Hello, Mrs Williams. I've come to tell you that Miss Elizabeth is willing to have you do some work on the Edward Street allotment, if you're still interested. How many hours you put in is up to you, but even if you can only spare a coupla hours a week, it would help.'

'Yes, I'd like to spend an hour or so a day in the fresh air, after I've done the sewing I need to do for Mrs Bowen, that's why I asked.'

'If you take a trip to the field whenever you're ready, Miss Elizabeth, or whoever's in charge in her place, will show you what to do.'

'Thank you, Mr Owen, it was kind of you to ask, and then to come so quickly to tell me.'

Gwilym was unnerved by her politeness, given how sharp her tongue used to be. 'Right you are, well I'll be—'

'Who's that?' came another voice. The door opened wide, and Daniel Williams stood there, still in uniform but with his jacket undone.

'It's just Mr Owen here, offering me some hours on the allotment.' She patted her son's shoulder affectionately.

He shrugged the hand away. 'Hello Gwilym, mun. How are you?'

'I'll leave you to it.' Esther trudged away down the hall.

Daniel seemed taller than he had been, standing straight and proud, with a slightly arrogant air about him. His mid-brown hair was slicked back and parted on the right, emphasising the high forehead that was so like his mother's. He bore little resemblance to the shy young man who'd been conscripted not eighteen months back. Gwilym spotted, with some surprise, the addition of a single chevron on the arm of his jacket.

'Hello, mun, not so bad. How long are you all home for?'

'Five days. Back on Wednesday the twelfth. To be honest…' He stepped out, pulling the door towards him, then looked around as if checking for prying neighbours. 'I'd not have come home at all, but would have taken leave in France, if it hadn't

42

been for Christopher. My mother can go to hell after the way she tried to protect my father.'

'Maybe he threatened her and she was afraid,' said Gwilym, giving her the benefit of the doubt. 'He could be a real—'

'Bully?' Daniel interrupted. 'Yes, I know. But it's not like she was a browbeaten wife, is it? What's all this then, on a Friday, your Sunday best?' He tugged gently at one of Gwilym's lapels.

'I'm due at the enquiry at three o'clock, into the accident last year.'

Daniel's face became grim. 'It's taken them long enough.'

'Aye, well. I see you've had a promotion.' He indicated the single chevron.

Looking at his sleeve, Daniel sniffed. 'There were a couple of corporals killed, one after another, so I guess they ran out of candidates. "You're an educated lad, aren't you?", the sergeant asked me. "Worked in a bank, isn't it?" And that was that.' He seemed unimpressed with his own achievement. 'Anyway, I'd better not keep you.'

Gwilym pulled his great-grandfather's fob watch from his waistcoat pocket. 'Aye, it's quarter to. Better go.'

'Good luck, and I hope the coal company will be held to account for shoddy practices.'

Gwilym waved goodbye. He was sure that the inquest would do no such thing, that they were simply going through the motions. He'd liked to have been proved wrong, but he had no expectation of it.

–

Gwen was a little late getting out to chapel on Sunday morning, fussing about her appearance. Her parents, Henry and her mamgu had gone on ahead.

It was yet another dull day as she hurried along past the parish church and the school on Gabriel Street. Gwen was sick of the gloom, with not seeing much light during the week at the munitions, especially now the nights were starting to draw in quite noticeably. Opposite the far end of the school was the Ainon Baptist Chapel with its pointed roof and five first-floor arched windows. She scooted up the stairs and opened one of the wooden double doors to let herself in.

Her family didn't appear to be nearby, and being late, she didn't want to disturb anyone. Relieved to spy Anwen and her family near the door, she headed for their row. Anwen treated her to a smile, shuffling up a little to give her more room. In her arms, Sara Fach was lying half-asleep, her eyelids fluttering. She was so adorable. For a brief moment, Gwen pictured herself with her own babby. That wasn't likely to happen in the near future.

'I hate being tardy,' she said, out of breath from hurrying. 'My own fault, though.'

'Pastor Thomas is a bit late starting, so you're all right,' said Anwen.

After the minister had welcomed the soldiers home on leave, much of the rest of the service passed Gwen by, dwelling on her own thoughts as she was. She spoke the words and sang the hymns by rote, so well did she know them. By the end of the minister's sermon, she could barely remember a word.

It wasn't until Anwen patted her arm that she realised the service was over.

'Oh, that went quickly.'

'Did it?' said Anwen, looking puzzled. 'Maybe because you're not worried about a baby fussing,' she laughed.

Gwen was certain Anwen didn't say it to hurt her, but it emphasised once more how alone she felt.

'It's a bit busier here than it has been of late,' said Gwen. 'I wonder whether the people who've fallen away have returned to see the lads on leave.'

'I expect so.'

The rest of Anwen's family stood up and filed out of the pew.

'Shall I get you ladies some tea?' Idris offered.

'We'll be along in a minute,' said Anwen, rocking the baby. 'I'm just going to tell Gwen something.'

Violet appeared through the crowd, squeezing herself between the backs of two women chatting to different groups.

'There you are,' said Anwen. 'I was about to tell Gwen about Rose.'

'What's she done now?' said Gwen, expecting the worst.

'Mrs Brace told me in the grocer's yesterday that Rose's court case for the thefts of books from Mr Schenck's shop, and the attempted theft of Gwilym's chickens back in the summer, is taking place in Merthyr tomorrow.'

'I wonder how it'll go,' said Gwen. 'Everything seems to be happening at once, what with the boys home on leave and the inquiry into the accident too.'

'Hywel reckons she'll get a fine and a caution, since it's her first time in court,' said Violet. 'He says that's what always seems to happen in cases he reads in the newspaper.'

Gwen caught sight of a khaki uniform out of the corner of her eye. 'Look, it's Daniel Williams. He used to have a soft spot for you, Anwen.' She nudged her arm.

'Don't remind me. He was a little tetchy with Idris about it last time he was home. 'Wonder what he's doing here, since Esther took herself and the family off to the Anglican church.'

Gwen, speaking in a whisper, said, 'He's rather fetching in his uniform.'

The old-timer he'd been talking to patted him on the back and limped off. Daniel looked up, and spotting them staring at him, strode over.

'Hello ladies,' he said coming to a halt beside them.

'We haven't seen you here in a long time,' said Violet.

'No. My mother prefers the parish church, but I never did. Old enough to make up my own mind now. How's married life, Anwen? I hear you've adopted this little one.' He was smiling, not sounding resentful.

'We're about to,' said Anwen. 'Just waiting for it to go through.'

Sara Fach started to grizzle, her face looking a picture of misery.

'What's wrong with her?' said Daniel.

'Wants me to be on the move. I'll take her for a walk and get a drink.'

'I'd better find Hywel,' said Violet. 'He went to fetch the children from Sunday School.'

Gwen, about to say she'd join them, realised it would sound rude. She felt awkward, being alone with him, but hopefully he'd move on to talk to others soon.

When the other two women had gone, Daniel said, 'So, you've not married or become betrothed while I've been away?'

Gwen felt he was pointing out some inadequacy in her. The other two were married, so what was wrong with her?

'My goodness, I put in long hours at the munitions, six days a week. There's no time for walking out with a man. There's a war on and I'm doing my bit. I'll worry about marriage and all that lark when it's over. What about you? I don't see you arm-in-arm with anyone.'

He nodded. 'Same reason: no time. I know a few who've married in haste, worried about the war.' He pulled a face. '*Marry in haste, repent at leisure*, that's what they say, isn't it?'

'I heard about you becoming a lance corporal.' She nodded towards his chevron. 'Well done.'

'Thanks. So much has changed in the village while I've been away. I wonder how much more will change before we get back for good.'

'I dare say it'll go back to the way it was eventually. Well, for some.'

'Aye, for some. Perhaps I won't even come back here. I should get my position back at the bank in Tredegar. I could lodge there instead.'

'Lots of people do. And you could go for promotion in a bank, maybe be bank manager one day. You could buy your own place.'

He let out a wry huff of a laugh. 'Maybe. Suppose I should go and talk to a few more people. A couple of my old mates are here somewhere. I'll see you around.'

'Bye Daniel. Good luck when you return to the Front.'

He took two steps away, before whirling back on the balls of his feet.

'I hear there's an operetta on at the Institute tomorrow evening, *A Holiday on the Sands*. Would you like to go with me? Unless you're already going with other people, of course.' He looked less sure of himself.

She'd thought of going, but neither of her friends had been able to make the time, and her parents and Henry hadn't wanted to go. Was it wise to go with Daniel? 'Trouble is, I don't normally get back on the motorbus from Ebbw Vale before about seven.'

'It doesn't start 'til eight. That gives you an hour. It would be nice if you could. I'm going back Wednesday, see.'

Poor lad. He looked at her with his appealing, dark eyes with their long lashes. She could cheer him up a bit, before he had to go back to the hellhole, as Henry had called it, couldn't she? But what about Henry? He was going back Wednesday, too. She still had the rest of today and Tuesday evening to see him. And it would be nice to have a man's attention for a bit.

'Well, why not then,' she said with a cheery grin. 'I'll meet you outside the Institute at a quarter to.'

He gave her a wide smile. 'Thank you. Now I really must go and mingle.' He clapped his heels together and saluted her, making her laugh. 'Until tomorrow.' With that, he wove his way through the throng.

She waited until he was out of sight before going to find her friends. She located them in the side room, at one end of the long trestle tables, where the teacups and saucers were stacked.

'You'll never guess what I've just done.'

'What's that?' said Violet, looking alarmed.

'I've agreed to see *A Holiday on the Sands* with Daniel tomorrow night.'

47

'I didn't know you liked him,' said Anwen.

'It's only for the one time, before he goes back to the Front, just to keep him company. Thought he deserved a bit of fun.'

'You won't do anything silly,' said Anwen, her brow furrowed.

'You sound like my mother! Of course I won't. But I reckon it can't be nice, having to come back to his house, with Esther there.'

'You'll give him the wrong idea,' said Violet.

'Of course I won't. He'll be gone on Wednesday. And you know, if anything happens to him, at least he'll have a jolly memory to, to… you know…'

'Be careful, that's all,' said Anwen. 'He used to be a very nice boy, but he seems a bit full of hisself now.'

'Don't worry, I can handle myself. Right. Tea.'

—

Gwen could spy a vague orange sunset over the mountains, in a mostly cloudy sky, as she reached the top point of the triangle of Jubilee Gardens the next evening. She spotted Daniel in the queue outside the Workmen's Institute, only a dozen or so people from the front. He was sporting his uniform once more. She did her coat up, not feeling chilly, but apprehensive.

It had been a rush having some supper then getting dressed and applying the satin skin cream and powder she'd finally got around to buying, in the lightest shade they had. Then there'd been the rouge, geranium lip stain and eyebrow pencil to put on, before she'd had to re-pin her hair. She wasn't doing it for him, more for herself, trying to draw attention away from the deepening yellow of her skin. It seemed to do the job, to a certain extent.

'Hello Daniel,' she said, joining him.

He turned, smiling, about to say something, when a voice behind complained, 'Hey, you can't just push in! Came early, we did, to get a good seat.' It was Matilda Bowen, the under-manager's wife, with a friend, the two of them glaring at her.

'It's all right, Mrs Bowen, she's accompanying me for the evening,' Daniel said sweetly.

'Well, all right, since you're home on leave, I'll let you off,' she said, but gave Gwen a sidelong glance of disapproval, her eyes travelling up and down her outfit.

'You look very nice, Gwen,' he said, when Mrs Bowen started chatting to her friend again.

'Thank you.' Gwen looked down at the suit she'd purchased from the other Mrs Bowen, Matilda's sister-in-law, the dress-maker. It was a blue, striped gabardine two-piece, with a large navy collar. It was second-hand and had been altered to fit her slimmer waist and shoulders.

'I've no idea how good this operetta is going to be,' said Daniel. 'I heard about it from Maurice, who's taking his Mabel tonight.'

'It's a group of local people,' she said. 'Good, they are. A couple are in the choir at the parish church. I saw them do *The Bohemian Girl* here a coupla years back.'

'I saw that too. That's promising, then. Here we go.' He pointed to where the queue was starting to mount the left-hand steps.

Despite her reservations, Gwen was looking forward to the show. She had to admit to herself that having someone's atten-tion for an evening was also appealing.

–

By the time the applause for *A Holiday on the Sands* was over, Gwen felt thoroughly cheered up. The final song, 'Shout, Shout, Shout', had been jolly, with the audience joining in the final chorus. What fun it had been.

'That wasn't so bad, was it?' said Daniel as they inched their way towards the outside door, following the departing audience.

She was pleased now she'd accompanied him here; it had perked him up no end – and her.

'It was excellent.'

They dawdled to the exit and the top of the double-sided steps, chatting about their favourite songs, before taking the right-hand side down.

At the bottom, Gwen said, 'I need to go left, and you need to go right to get home, so I'll wish you good—'

'No, that's not right, letting you walk home on your own.'

'There'll be plenty of others taking the same route. I need to get off, to see Henry before bedtime.'

'That still wouldn't be gentlemanly,' he insisted. 'It's James Street you live on, isn't it?'

'That's right. Number forty.'

'Why, that's right near the end of the village, with not so many streetlamps. I'll walk you round. It'll only take five minutes.'

He'd made his mind up, and what did it matter? 'Come on, then.'

They headed off, down the side of the gardens.

'A day and a bit until you and the others are off again,' she said. 'How long will it take you to get back to wherever you're going to in France?' She already knew this from Henry, but it was conversation.

'About seven or eight hours. Maybe nine. Depends. There'll be a few stations to change at: Newport, Paddington and Victoria. And then the ship back over the Channel. And more trains.'

'At least the train journeys should be interesting.'

Daniel stuffed his hands into his trouser pockets. 'If you can get a seat, that is. Oh no, what's *she* doing here?'

Coming around the corner from James Street, was his mother, Esther. As they approached each other, the three of them came to a halt.

'Why Daniel, I wondered where you'd gone. And you're with Miss Austin?'

'What are you doing here?' he said, accusingly.

'Only been round to Mrs White's to collect some items what need mending. Couldn't go 'til late 'cos she was out.' She lifted up a sack bag.

'I'll be home soon,' he said, walking past her.

Esther stayed where she was, causing Gwen to falter momentarily before she said, 'Goodnight, Mrs Williams,' and hurried to catch Daniel up. He slowed down and turned, waiting for her to reach him.

'Sorry about that, but I didn't want her poking her nose in, wondering where we'd been.'

'She might draw her own conclusions, and wrong ones at that.'

'When doesn't she?'

Gwen didn't want to agree, even though she did. What he thought of his mother was his business.

He kept his head forward, not looking at her as he said, 'I was wondering, Gwen… I don't really get to write to anybody anymore, only Christopher, and he's not good at answering much.'

She felt trepidation as she anticipated what was coming next.

'Would you write to me, Gwen? Not as my sweetheart, of course, just as a friend. I could do with one. I'm not as pally with the other men from the village, with them all coming from the mine and me from the bank. And they signed up together, they have a bond. I'm an outsider really. 'Specially now I've got the promotion.' He looked down at his sleeve with what seemed regret.

What harm would it do, just to write to him, in the way she wrote to Henry? It would take up some of her time, but it wasn't like she had so much to do in the evenings anymore. And she could do with another friend.

'All right, if you want. I suppose I'd address the envelopes to the same place I address Henry's?'

'That's right. Thank you, Gwen. You don't know how much I appreciate it.'

'Only a few more houses and we'll be at mine.' She crossed her gloved fingers against her jacket, hoping that he wouldn't try to kiss her, before holding out her other hand in front of her. 'Just as well, as it's starting to spit.'

As they approached her door it opened. Henry stepped out. 'There you are. I was just going to walk up to make sure you were all right.'

'Of course I'm all right,' said Gwen. 'Goodnight, Daniel. Thank you for buying my ticket tonight.'

'You're welcome. Goodnight, Gwen.'

With this, he turned and ran back up the road. When he was halfway along, she stepped inside and Henry moved back. Despite it being an enjoyable evening, she was relieved to be home.

'Did you have to be so embarrassing, Henry?' she admonished him.

'No need to thank me. Reckon I might have saved you from his advances.'

'I told you, I was only going to keep him company. If you lot were a bit friendlier to him, and invited him out, perhaps he wouldn't have asked me.'

'He's all right, but he's never been one of the gang.' He headed off to the kitchen.

Gwen removed her jacket, placing it on a peg. Though she was acting cross with Henry, she was relieved he'd been standing guard, just in case. She wasn't going to let him off the hook that easily, though. She followed him to the kitchen, determined to make another small protest, before she let it drop.

Chapter Five

A couple of days later, on her way home from Ebbw Vale on the motorbus, Gwen thought about Henry and Daniel and how they'd be back in the war now, maybe not at the Front, but near enough to be in danger.

'You all right, Gwen?' asked Mabel Coombes, sitting next to her. 'You look miles away.'

Gwen sat up from her slouching position, gazing out of the window. She always felt a little nauseous on these journeys along the hilly roads. 'I was thinking about our boys being back in France.'

'Including the handsome Daniel?' Nora Lloyd teased, leaning over the seats behind.

'I told you this morning, I only went to the operetta with him to keep him company. Anyway, they'll all be back there: Daniel, Henry, your brother Alun, Mabel's husband Maurice.'

The smiles of the other two women faded.

'I don't relish losing Alun, like we did Bryn,' said Nora.

'Nor me, Maurice,' said Mabel. 'Little Lily's loved having her da home the last few days. I can't imagine what it must be like for the little children in the village what's lost their das. Don't suppose they'll even remember them as they get older.'

'I'm sorry, I shouldn't have said anything.'

'It's what we're all thinking, a lot of the time,' said Nora.

They went silent, looking out as the motorbus trudged round the sharp bend, then travelled past the two rows of cottages and McKenzie House. In the distance, Gwen spied a few people working on the allotment, taking advantage of the fading light.

'Shan't be sorry to get home tonight,' said Nora. 'That tired, I am.' She rested her cheek against the seat. Its yellow hue was not unlike Gwen's, or Mabel's, though, both being darker, it wasn't quite as obvious as it was with her.

'Me too,' said Mabel. 'And I want to see Lily before I have to put her to bed. My mother's so good, looking after her. Don't know what I'd do without her. It's useful being able to save up a sum of money for when Maurice returns. Got plans to rent a better place, we have, maybe one on Jubilee Green, or one of those on Mafeking Terrace.' Her eyes sparkled with hope. 'And he's wanting to do a bit of training, get some mining exams, when he gets back. Get a promotion or two.'

That's at least something she'd been able to do, thought Gwen, save a bit of her money from the munitions. How much more could she have saved if she hadn't squandered it on clothes and the like? Oh, but she did enjoy being able to afford the latest fashion.

'What's going on there, then?' Nora leaned closer to her window, causing Gwen to do the same. Mabel stood, to look above her.

Motoring towards the beginning of James Street, Gwen saw a gathering outside the gardens. There were often people around there, helping with the rebuilding of the Schenck's shop, but this was different. The men here weren't dressed for labouring. Sergeant Harries was there, with Constable Probert, trying to shuffle them along.

The bus came to a standstill, its engine whirring. Gwen and the other two women alighted, standing on the pavement in front of the bookshop. The motorbus trundled on, towards Rhymney.

'What's up now?' said Nora. 'They were only protesting here a month or so back. Oh Lord, and there's Gertie Pritchard, looking as miserable as ever.'

Gwen peered a couple of buildings up, where Gertie was standing, arms crossed, in the butcher's shop doorway. She was looking over towards the gardens at the men.

'At least it's them getting the brunt of police harassment this time,' Gertie called down to them. 'Not my poor Rose. Not that she could, locked up as she is.'

The women looked at each other in surprise.

'Court case not go well, Mrs Pritchard?' said Nora.

The butcher's wife stepped out onto the pavement. 'Found guilty, she were. Police have to get a result, and they blamed my poor Rose. She were offered thirty-one days gaol or five pounds fine.' She clucked her tongue, glancing back into the closed shop. 'Could easily afford it, Stanley could, but he refused to pay. Said it would teach her a lesson. Hm! Won't forgive him easily, I can tell you.'

Of that, Gwen had no doubt.

Nora said, 'Oh dear. Well, it could've been worse. A month'll pass quickly and she'll soon be out.'

Gertie humphed once more and returned to the shop, closing the door noisily.

Idris crossed the road from the gardens, lifting his cap as he passed the women. 'Evening, ladies.'

'Idris, what's going on?' Gwen called.

'Gwilym's trying to tell the men about the inquest verdict, but Harries is asking them to move along, so they're decamping to the public house.'

'So what was the verdict?'

'Your da will know about it, as he was with us when John Bowen told Gwilym after our shift. I've just got to scoot home quickly.' He carried on, breaking into a run.

'Come on, Mabel, you want to get home to your Lily, don't you?' said Nora. 'And I want to get home for my cuppa tea.' She pushed Mabel in the direction of James Street. 'Bye now.' Nora headed down Station Road, towards Dyffryn Gwyrdd Farm.

With the other two women gone, Gwen looked to where the men were moving across the road, towards the McKenzie

Arms. No doubt they'd hole up there for the evening, especially since the day was fast drawing in now. She'd get home and see what Da had to say.

–

Hywel placed a pint of GHB beer in front of Gwilym as he sat next to him in the saloon bar of the McKenzie Arms. 'They're only brewing this and the 4d at the moment, due to restrictions, Steven says. Hope that's all right.'

'Don't mind what it is, mun, as long as it quenches a thirst.' Gwilym picked it up and took a couple of swigs. 'And gives me a little courage to say my piece. Looks like word's getting round.' He nodded towards yet another group of miners coming in the door and shuffling to the bar through the throng.

By the time Idris returned, the noise had lowered to a murmur, persuading Gwilym that this was a good time to speak. He stood up, his heart thumping. He was surprised when the room went silent.

'All right, it's time to tell you the verdict of the inquest.' He'd summarise and make it quick.

'You'd have thought Mr Meredith might have found the time to come and talk to us,' called Twm Bach. 'He was there, at the inquest, after all.'

'Be that as it may, I'm the one who's been tasked with it.' *Lumbered, more like.*

He pulled the carbon copy of the typed report shown him by the undermanager, Bowen, out of his pocket, though he'd already memorised it.

'Gas caused the explosion, though they couldn't tell whether it was a broken lamp what caused it, or a gas shot at an intact lamp. They reckon the ventilation was satisfactory.'

'We know that's not true!' called Noah Schenck.

'Anyway,' said Gwilym. 'The jury declared that the colliers should be aware of putting their lamps in careful positions in future.'

'In other words, they're blaming us!' bellowed Twm Bach. 'And there's nothing about Meredith having any responsibility?'

'I believe he has been trying to get more money from the coal company for safety measures,' said Gwilym. 'That's what he said at the inquest the day I was there.'

'What can we do about it?' said one of the overmen. 'Can we appeal, or something?'

'No, the matter is now closed.'

Gwilym would have liked to have sat down now, but this was an opportunity to tackle another problem that would soon be looming.

'What we will need to think about next, is the court case in Tredegar some of us have been called to in November, for breach of contract on the August Bank Holiday Wednesday protest.'

Noah Schenck stood up. 'I've been having a think about that, how we could make an impression. I'm the bass trombonist in the Silver Band, as some of you know, and there are a coupla other members here. I'm sure we can persuade the rest to join the march to Tredegar. What a sight that would be!'

There were many voices of agreement.

A march? Gwilym hadn't even considered this. He didn't want to antagonise the authorities even more. But they could show them how passionately they felt about the situation, how committed many of the men were to the cause.

'All right. It needs to be a peaceful one, though. Let's have some ideas then and we'll see what we come up with.'

Chapter Six

Gwen sat in chapel in a world of her own after Sunday service. Anwen and Violet prattled on about their children, while enjoying a rest from them.

She wasn't resentful; she just felt left out. What could she contribute to the conversation? Her mind wandered to the letter she'd received yesterday, from Daniel. It had been cheerful, all about how they were passing their time on the back lines at that moment.

'What do you think, Gwen?' said Anwen.

'About what? Sorry, I was distracted.'

'You seem to be distracted a lot recently,' said Violet, frowning. 'I'm sorry if what we're saying's not entertaining enough for you.'

'Oh, I didn't mean—' Gwen started, knowing full well it was the case.

'You know what she's distracted with,' said Anwen, smirking. 'How many letters have you had from Daniel now?'

'Three.'

'Three in under two weeks. How many have you sent?'

'Two,' she admitted. 'But only because it seems rude not to reply.' Wanting to get away from the subject of Daniel, Gwen said, 'I was actually thinking how the congregation don't seem as large as it used to be.'

'I've noticed that,' said Violet. 'I wonder if people aren't so fond of the current minister. I think they've got him down as a bit of a conscientious objector. It doesn't go down well when half the men from here who went off to fight have – have died.'

Enid, talking to Gwen's mother close by, who'd obviously been listening to two conversations at once, turned towards them. 'Ruth and I were saying the same. But I don't think it's Pastor Thomas; it's the war, robbing people of their faith.' Enid's attention was taken elsewhere before she said, 'But then, we've got them what have come back, albeit from another church.'

They all looked to where she indicated with her head, to see Esther Williams standing alone in the middle of the room, cup and saucer in hand, smiling at people as they went by, though they largely ignored her.

'Daniel came here when he was home,' said Gwen. 'Said he could make his own mind up now. Maybe that persuaded her.'

'They've probably all snubbed her at the Anglican church, realising what a trouble-maker she is,' said Ruth. 'Dunno why she thinks she'll get a better welcome here.'

'Perhaps she's realised the error of her ways?' Gwen offered.

'Ha! Highly unlikely with that one. Oh heavens, she's not coming this way, is she?'

'Come on,' said Enid. 'Let's move; I've no desire to talk to her.' The two older women walked off.

Esther stopped a couple of yards away from her. 'Hello Gwen, dear, could I have a word?'

Dear? What would her friends think; that she'd made friends with her, or that there was indeed something more between her and Daniel? If she ever had any temptation in that direction, the thought of Esther Williams as a mother-in-law would scupper it. A shame, really, as Daniel was a presentable young man.

'Well, I suppose so.'

'I'm going to find the kiddies,' said Violet. 'Give Hywel a rest.'

'And I'd better find Idris and Sara Fach,' Anwen added.

Gwen had a moment's panic, where she tried to think of an excuse, but just like when Daniel had approached her here, she didn't want to seem rude.

'I'm sorry, I didn't want to take you away from your friends, but I was wondering if you'd heard from Daniel at all. I thought maybe you were writing to each other, after walking out.'

'I wouldn't call it walking out, Mrs Williams, just being friendly, like.'

Esther gave her an indulgent smile. 'Whatever you want to call it. I do worry about my poor Daniel and was wondering if you'd had news. Not good at writing to his old mam, he isn't.'

She could just say she hadn't heard a word but found herself putting her own mother in that position. What if Henry had fallen out with her? She'd still want to know how her son was.

'As it is, I had a letter from him yesterday. He was in the back lines.'

'So, they're not fighting at all?'

She could have told her they alternated days in the front line and days in the back but didn't want to alarm her. 'Not at the moment.'

Esther's face drooped. 'Doesn't seem any point in them being there, then. Why did they have such a short leave if they're doing nothing?'

'They're not doing nothing. They repair defences, put up barbed wire, dig out new trenches. And fill sandbags.'

'So where do they live and sleep? In the trenches they dig, I suppose.'

'He said something about living in barns. I suppose there are a lot, being in the countryside.'

'Thank you for sharing that, my dear.' Esther squeezed her hand.

Gwen felt her cheeks heat up as she glanced round to make sure no one was looking at them. But several people were, including Elizabeth who was chatting with Mary Jones.

'It's not easy, being a mother.' Esther lowered her head. When she looked up again, she said, 'You don't look so well, my dear, a little more yellow than you have been. I know you munitionettes do suffer for the war. Such a pity with your light skin. You need to get yourself well and pretty again for when your sweetheart comes home.'

'I – that is, I mean…'

'Ah, Gwen, here you are. I need an urgent word please, when you have a moment.'

It was Elizabeth. Gwen was torn between being thankful she'd interrupted this challenging conversation and irritated to be approached by yet someone else she didn't want to talk to.

'I'll leave you to it, Miss Meredith,' Esther said, walking backwards whilst slightly bowed.

With the older woman out of earshot, Elizabeth said, 'Don't look so worried, I don't really have anything urgent to say. You looked uncomfortable, with Esther fawning all over you, so I came to rescue you.'

'Thank you for that.' Gwen felt awash with guilt about her previous thoughts concerning Elizabeth.

'She seems to have taken a shine to you.'

'Only because she's got the wrong idea about my trip to the operetta with Daniel. We went as friends, and I agreed to write to him, just to keep his spirits up.'

'That is very commendable, Gwen. It's not like Daniel's responsible for what his father and mother did.'

'And I thought, what if Henry were in that position, having parents like Daniel's and not having anyone nice to write to? I'd like to think someone would be kind to him.' She pushed back the swell of emotion that this possibility produced.

'I'd feel the same about Tom, so I do understand. I don't suppose Christopher's good at writing regularly, if at all.'

'No, Daniel gets the odd letter from him, but not many.'

'Anyway, I need a word with Gwilym about the allotments. See you soon.'

There was no point in Gwen going to find Violet and Anwen again as they'd be with their families. She'd go and find her parents and mamgu instead, to persuade them it was time to get home for some dinner.

Gwilym was half-listening to Noah Schenck telling a few of them about the Silver Band's upcoming performance at the Workmen's Institute. Out of the corner of his eye he was aware of Elizabeth, talking to Gwen by the front pews, looking for signs of them parting company.

This talk they were meant to be going to together next week had never seemed like a good idea. Since the inquest verdict, and the plans they'd formulated to march to Tredegar in November, it was now a particularly bad one. He'd have to tell her he couldn't make it, come up with some excuse. But what? He'd thought about this for days, but he'd never been good at fibbing. *Just tell her the truth then, mun.* She'd surely see that it was a conflict of interests; him, the union rep, hobnobbing with the manager's daughter. But he'd really wanted to go to the talk. He could hardly turn up separately.

His moment came when he noticed Elizabeth move away from Gwen.

'Excuse me,' he told the group.

He was surprised when she headed straight for him too.

'Just the person I want to see,' she said.

'I wanted to speak to you too.' With any luck, they'd come to the same conclusion.

'I need to discuss some allotment matters for next week, but first, I want to say how sorry I am to hear about the inquest verdict. A terrible injustice. You must be particularly disappointed, given your father was a victim.'

'You could say that.'

'I can't believe they're passing the blame onto the men. My father is very disappointed with the outcome, as he thought the coal company might be persuaded that their lack of investment was a contributing factor.'

'And when do they ever take responsibility for that?'

'Indeed. I pointed out to my father that if justice didn't happen at a major disaster like Senghenydd, it wasn't going to happen at a smaller one.'

He didn't want to dwell on the inquest. 'We need to think ahead now, see what we can do to make things better in the future.'

'That's good, a positive attitude. Which reminds me: only three days until the talk, "Is the World Growing Better?". I am looking forward to it and hoping for some positive ideas from that too. Anyway, about the allotments. I was thinking we could maybe…'

Listening as she suggested various activities on the three fields, he added his own ideas in between. The opportunity to cancel the trip had been lost. He'd just have to make sure he didn't agree to any such outings in the future.

Chapter Seven

Elizabeth considered her reflection in the long mirror in her bedroom. Yes, the teal corduroy suit was elegant enough, without looking like she was trying to make too much effort.

Why was she making an effort at all? It was only Gwilym she was going with, two people interested in a talk. Somehow it seemed second nature to want to look her best when going out for the evening. Her mother had instilled that in her. Yet Gwilym had seen her in Tom's cast-offs, covered in mud, on the allotments, so what difference did it make?

She went to the window, pulling back one of the ivory net curtains, looking down the drop to the colliery, then up towards the houses. The sun had already dipped below the hill beyond the village, creating a swirl of orange that mingled with pink-hued clouds. She ran her eyes along the houses of the village, spying Gwilym's right at the end. And Anwen's, two doors away, she added to herself. The clock on her mantelpiece chimed half past six. A little something to eat before she left would be a good idea. Her stomach fluttered. She really wasn't at all hungry. Maybe a cup of tea would suffice.

She picked up her brown, crocodile skin handbag and left the room.

In the kitchen, Margaret Meredith was already sitting at the table with a cup of tea. That was most unusual for her, who thought eating in this room 'lower class' and liked always to take her tea in the drawing room.

Elizabeth placed her handbag on the table. 'Has Mrs Rhys left already?'

64

'Yes. And I let Brenda leave at five. I wanted to talk to Mrs Rhys about what menus to prepare with the little food we've managed to purchase. Would you believe, I had to go down to the butcher with her earlier, because Mrs Pritchard wouldn't believe she was buying meat for my household. She accused her of trying to have more than her fair share. Mr Pritchard had gone out at the time, otherwise I'm sure there wouldn't have been any trouble.'

'Did you expect anything else from Gertie Pritchard, after all that's happened? Especially now Rose is locked up.'

'For not long enough, if you ask me. Anyway, I quite enjoyed Mrs Rhys's company. A practical soul, she is.'

Enjoying the company of a servant? Then it occurred to her: her mother was lonely too. Elizabeth hadn't long got in from the allotments. Goodness knows what time her father would arrive, probably in time for dinner at seven. Although Mama was still involved in her committees, and met certain women for coffee or afternoon tea, there was no one nearby, in the village, with whom she had a close friendship. They had that in common.

'Is there some tea left in that pot?' Elizabeth asked.

'It will be a little stewed now.'

'I'll add some hot water.' She made the tea and sat down.

'At least we managed to get a little lamb for dinner tonight, though we wouldn't have been allowed that if Mr Pritchard hadn't intervened when we returned. Mrs Rhys made it into a delicious casserole with some of the leeks and carrots from the allotments.'

'A cawl, then.'

Margaret sniffed. 'A casserole.'

'Anyway, I'm going out, as I told you yesterday, so I'll have a little when I return.'

'You can't go out on an empty stomach! Why not have a little now, before you go?'

'I'm really not hungry enough.' She removed a fob watch from her handbag. Ten minutes to six.

'I can't understand why Tom didn't want that watch. Especially since it belonged to Grandfather Powell.'

'He's not sentimental like me. And he prefers his wristwatch.'

'They're so vulgar.' Margaret tutted. 'Where did you say you were going this evening?'

Elizabeth stirred her tea, even though there was no sugar to put in. 'To the Siloh Chapel in Tredegar, to hear Dr John Clifford. He's a nonconformist minister and well known as a brilliant orator. He supports trade unions, believes in Irish Home Rule and in extending voting rights.'

'By which you of course mean, votes for women. One good thing about this war, at least those suffragettes have suspended their meetings and aggressive actions, and you've been able to untangle yourself from them.'

'You say that as if they forced me to join. And the suspension is only for the duration of the war. Most have gone off to war work.' She emphasised this last sentence.

'Heaven help us. So what's the lecture about tonight?'

'It's entitled "Is the World Growing Better?"'

Margaret looked heavenward. 'We already know the answer to *that* question. Look what's happening in Russia at the moment. They've declared it a republic, and heaven only knows what's happened to the royal family there.'

'The czar *has* been rather a tyrant.'

'For all the good it's done them. They're on the brink of civil war and have started surrendering their conquests to our enemies!'

'I admit it's not a perfect situation.'

'They should be concentrating on getting the war won.'

Elizabeth's mother was in an argumentative mood once again. No wonder her father went out so much in the evenings, or stayed late at work. She checked her watch again. Two minutes to six.

'I'll have to be going shortly.'

'Are you going with any of your friends?'

Elizabeth had hoped to avoid this conversation, but she didn't want to lie, even though her mother wouldn't like it. If she found out about it from someone else, there'd be even more trouble.

'Gwilym Owen mentioned he was interested in hearing Dr Clifford, so I'm giving him a lift there.'

'Gwilym Owen? What's an uneducated miner like him want with an intellectual talk like that? Who does he think he is?'

'Someone who wants to instruct himself about things. Many in the village do. The library at the Workmen's Institute is very popular. Why do you have to be so scathing? The villagers here aren't ignorant pigs, you know.' Elizabeth felt a huge amount of irritation at her mother's assumptions. She had more to say on the matter but wasn't in the mood for an argument, even if her mother was.

'And is it seemly for the manager's daughter to give one of the workers a lift?'

'It's just convenient, Mother. And, as I am going at night to Tredegar, you could say he'll be like a chaperone. I'm sure you'd approve of that, since you're always saying I should have one at night.'

After daintily sipping at the last of her tea, Margaret asked, 'How do you know he won't be the one who's indiscreet?'

'Mother! Why must you always think the worst of people? He's a *good* man, as Mamgu Powell would have said.'

'Hm! Is any man really?'

Elizabeth was saved from offering an opinion by the chimes of the grandmother clock in the hall. She rose from the seat. 'I'd better get on my way.'

Margaret sighed. 'I'll get on with this washing up and get the dining room ready for dinner. Go on then, you'd better get off, or you'll be late.'

Elizabeth saluted her and did an about turn. In the hall she took her coat down from the walnut hat stand. She'd need it this evening. Midway through putting it on, she stalled. What if Gwilym failed to turn up? A surprising degree of disappointment washed over her at the thought. Nonsense, of course he'd turn up. He'd have said if he wasn't. She did the coat up, put on her gloves and picked her bag up from the hall table before letting herself out.

—

Siloh chapel was quickly filling when Elizabeth and Gwilym arrived. He'd been almost silent in the motorcar, sitting bolt upright, staring ahead, as if embarrassed to be there.

He dragged behind now, as they walked into the building, so she geed him along. 'Let's find a seat.'

Elizabeth pointed out room for two in the third pew back. He followed without a word.

'We should be able to hear fine from here,' she said. 'I have looked forward to this so much.'

He rolled up the cap he'd removed on entering and shoved it in his jacket pocket. 'I'd certainly like to know whether Dr Clifford has an answer to his question, for it seems to me the world's growing worse.'

'That's my mother's opinion too.'

His face relaxed and he even chuckled a little.

'I guess you're laughing at the idea that you two might agree on something.'

Going pink, he cleared his throat. 'Begging your pardon, Miss Elizabeth. I meant no offence.'

It was her turn to laugh, and she did so louder than he had. 'Don't apologise. It surprises even me when she and I agree upon a matter.'

Unwrapping her scarf and removing her gloves, Elizabeth retrieved her notebook and pencil from her handbag and was surprised to see Gwilym fetch the same from his jacket pocket.

'You like taking notes too?' she asked.

'Best way to remember the salient points.'

The murmuring chatter in the room lessened, then stopped. When the applause began, Elizabeth realised someone had stepped into the pulpit. He was an old man, probably in his eighties, with a long, white beard. He was mostly bald, with tufts of snowy hair around his ears.

When the applause stopped, he cleared his throat and introduced himself. It was Dr John Clifford.

He talked of war and how it would soon pass, of supreme self-sacrifice and how it would shorten the war and secure a lasting peace. Although the war would destroy many things, he claimed, it would clear the way for human progress and a better world.

Elizabeth found his speech spellbinding. She glanced a couple of times at Gwilym, who appeared equally enchanted, busy scribbling notes, as was she.

At the end of the lecture came rapturous applause and a standing ovation.

As the applause died down, Gwilym leaned a little towards her to say, 'Why, that was a treat, that was. The man makes a lot of sense.'

Elizabeth was glad to see him so cheered after such a long time of frowning and sadness. She guessed his father's death still lay heavy on him. Such a happy soul he'd been once, trying to lift Idris from his gloom when he was medically discharged from the army. Now it appeared it was him who needed lifting.

'I like a good lecture,' said Elizabeth. 'There are plenty round and about. Perhaps we could go to another in the future.' There she went again, imposing herself on him. Would she ever learn?

His head swung in her direction and he regarded her with wide eyes.

She didn't want him getting the wrong idea so said, 'I believe Anwen and Idris enjoy talks. Perhaps if Mrs Rhys would look after Sara Fach one evening, they could come as well.'

'Aye, I guess so, though neither of them gets out much of an evening these days. Only for choir practice and Idris comes to union meetings and the odd evening at the public house.'

'That's a shame. Come, let us get back to the motorcar.' She hesitated, not ready for the evening to end. 'Unless you'd like to visit a café for refreshments first?'

'If it's all the same to you, Miss Elizabeth, I'd like to get back for some supper. It wasn't ready before I left.'

'I quite understand. I was the same. And it's just Elizabeth.' She pulled on her gloves and tucked the handle of her handbag over the crook of her arm. She was disappointed all the same.

She did most of the talking on the way home. Although Gwilym agreed with many of her points, he offered little in return. Back in Dorcalon, he asked to be dropped off near her house, at the first terrace of McKenzie cottages, on the road from Tredegar.

'I can walk easily from here,' he insisted, when she tried to protest.

'Very well.' She came to a halt outside her house and cut the engine. 'Thank you for your company tonight, Gwilym. It's nice not to have to turn up to these events by oneself.'

'Goodnight – Elizabeth.'

They got out of the motorcar the same time, and she watched as he started off down the path in front of her house, to the road below which housed the second row of cottages. She opened the gate and went inside but was called back by Gwilym's voice calling her name.

'I was wondering,' he said, back at the top of the path again, 'whether you were interested in going to a gardening talk on October nineteenth on winter planting.'

She was inordinately pleased that he'd asked and didn't have to consider her answer.

–

What on earth was he doing? Gwilym couldn't believe he'd opened his mouth to invite Elizabeth to this talk he'd seen advertised in the *Monmouth Guardian*. What of his resolve that this wouldn't happen again? Yet he'd enjoyed this evening, all the more because she'd been there. She was uncomplicated company, didn't expect anything. Yet there *were* complications, because other people wouldn't understand that they could simply have a friendship. With any luck, she'd turn the idea down and it would be a problem solved.

'That would be splendid, Gwilym. That talk must have passed me by, so I'm glad you pointed it out. I can give you a lift there.'

'It's only in Rhymney. It's not far to walk.'

'You're quite right, of course. We shouldn't be using petrol when we don't need to. We'll make arrangements nearer the time.' She wound her scarf, until now only hanging loose, around her neck.

'Right you are. You look cold. You'd better get yourself in.'

'*Nos da*, Gwilym. No doubt I'll see you on the allotments.'

'Goodnight, Elizabeth.'

He started off down the path to the houses ahead once more. Reaching the pavement, he looked up. She was still there but turned at that moment to go through her gate.

Another trip out to look forward to. Yet he shouldn't be. Maybe he could get some of the men who worked on the field with him interested in gardening talks. He knew before the thought was complete that they wouldn't be bothered about them, especially the older, retired men. There must be others who'd be interested in coming along, make it a bit of an outing. Who, though?

No point in torturing himself. He'd make this the last talk they'd attend together. Or last anything. That way there could be no misunderstandings from anyone.

Satisfied with his decision, his pace increased as he came to the little bridge that went over the Nantygalon.

–

'I really could have done without this, Mother,' said Elizabeth, pulling off the muddy boots and the old jacket in the scullery.

'The weather's reasonable out there today, and I wanted to get a bit more work on the allotments done before it got dark. It'll be October tomorrow, and there's still so much to do.'

Margaret squeezed her lips together and closed her eyes momentarily. 'You and those wretched allotments. You're not getting any younger, my girl, and need to make an effort to secure a good man.'

Elizabeth draped the jacket over her arm. 'By which, I suppose you mean, one with money and a position.'

'Nothing wrong with that.' Margaret checked the old wooden clock on the wall. It had once been proudly displayed in Mamgu Powell's kitchen, the hub of her house, but its worn face had marked it fit only for the scullery. 'The Fitzgeralds are arriving at three. Now for goodness' sake get yourself bathed and into some elegant clothes. I suggest you wear that lovely cream dress I bought you from Cardiff, with the full skirt and the sailor collar. So nice that more elegant clothing has come back into fashion.'

'You mean that "war crinoline" as they call them. Really, you'd think they'd be trying to save on fabric at the current time.'

'And those Louis heeled shoes, the green ones; they'll look lovely with it. And please do something about your hair. A nice Pompadour roll should do it.'

'I'll see what I can do.' She'd half a mind to have her hair cut into one of the new short styles that had come into fashion. What her mother would have to say about that she could only imagine.

'I wish you wouldn't trail those dirty clothes through the house.'

Elizabeth regarded her mother for a moment. 'What would you have me do, walk through the house in my undergarments?'

Margaret pinched her lips in, releasing a 'Huh!' through her nose. 'There's no need for vulgarity. But then, what would one expect when one has been cavorting with the lower classes?'

As she hurried through the kitchen, Elizabeth passed a surprised Enid who was arranging cakes on a plate. Tearing through the hall and taking the stairs two at a time, she imitated her mother's last sentence in the pseudo-English accent Mama had adopted. It would serve her mother right if she got a job sorting coal and lodged with a family in one of the terraces.

Flying into her room, she almost slammed the door, but grabbed it quickly. No point getting angry. And who was she cross with, anyway? Her mother, but also herself. She'd allowed Mama to have so much say in her life, maybe because it was easier to sit at home and be the manager's daughter than go out in the world and risk being – normal.

She removed the muddy jacket, trousers and shirt. After a wash, she put on the obligatory corsets, resenting them more each day. The next time she was out shopping, she'd have a look at the more forgiving liberty bodices. She arranged her hair as requested.

That her mother had been in her room was obvious by the dress that was hanging up over the wardrobe door. The suggested shoes were posed underneath. She put the garments on, then considered herself in the mirror, turning this way and that. It was certainly pretty, but still she wished Mama wouldn't keep buying her clothing without her say-so.

Facing the mirror once more, she imagined sitting in the café in Rhymney with Gwilym. It wouldn't be a good venue for this dress. Maybe one of the tearooms in Cardiff. Gwilym would have to be spruced up a bit. He did own a three-piece suit, for she'd seen him wear it to chapel. She gazed out of the window, remembering their conversation, his eloquence and passion. The smile on her lips soon melted when she remembered it was Sidney and Horace she'd be entertaining this afternoon, along with their mother, Lady Fitzgerald.

'How tedious in the extreme,' she said mimicking the woman's plummy English accent.

She checked the clock on her mantelpiece. Ten minutes to three. Time to arrange oneself on a chair in the drawing room and await one's guests.

–

Brenda Prothero showed the guests into the drawing room, announcing their names as Margaret had instructed her. Sidney and Horace were dressed in their uniforms, the stripes on their sleeves showing they were a captain and a lieutenant. They both bowed ever so slightly in Elizabeth's direction. Their mother, Lady Anna Fitzgerald, was resplendent in a silk barrel skirt of marine blue. Around her waist was an attractive jewelled belt. On her head sat a navy turban with plaited ribbons at the front, on which was set a jet ornament.

'Shall I bring in the tea?' Brenda asked, standing to attention, her hands folded in front of her.

'In about ten minutes,' Margaret replied.

'Very well, madam.' She left the room.

'Please, do sit here.' Margaret gestured Anna Fitzgerald to one of the two cream, velvet Chesterfields. 'I will sit here with you, and perhaps Sidney and Horace would like to join Elizabeth on the other.'

Elizabeth resisted rolling her eyes, a habit that had become ever more common when dealing with her mother these days. Could she be more obvious in her match-making? It would serve her right if both men took a shine to her and she had them duelling at dawn. The absurdity of the idea put a smile on her lips, which she used to welcome the young men to her chair. They had to sit either side of her, as she was perched in the centre.

'Hello Elizabeth, long time, no see,' said Horace, saluting her, his small, blue eyes twinkling. He had always been the chirpier of the two. Sitting upright, his legs splayed, he placed a hand on each knee. His sandy hair was oiled and combed back with a side parting. He sported a small moustache these days, pale, like his hair.

'Well, you two have been rather preoccupied,' she said, answering with all the charm and enthusiasm she could muster, knowing her mother was watching, even while having her own conversation, and would pull her up on any little impropriety afterwards.

'We have rather,' said Horace. 'Haven't we, Sidney?' He leaned forward to regard his brother.

Sidney, in contrast, was leaning back, his legs close together, his hands linked tightly on his lap. His face was neutral. Perhaps he wanted to be there as little as she did. He looked very different to Horace, having dark hair, bronze eyes and sculpted cheekbones. He sported no facial hair, unlike the last time she'd seen him. He'd likely shaved it off when the army recently abolished the compulsory wearing of moustaches for officers. It was hard to believe the two men were brothers.

'Sidney?' Horace repeated.

'What?' He looked round as if he'd just noticed them.

'Elizabeth here said we've been preoccupied, busy, you know.'

The older brother turned his head slowly and sighed. He caught Elizabeth's eye only briefly before looking slightly past her. 'Preoccupied is one way to put it, I suppose.'

'They were in the thick of it in the Somme, and now with Ypres.' Lady Fitzgerald pronounced it the French way, not 'Wipers', as the soldiers tended to call it. 'I'm so glad the 10th Battalion could spare them both on leave.'

'It looks absolutely awful out there,' said Elizabeth.

Sidney looked directly at her, his eyebrows knitted. 'How would you know what it's like?' It was a challenge.

'I saw *The Battle of the Somme* last year. You could see what terrible conditions you were all living under, and I dare say they didn't show the half of it. I doubt that it's got any better.'

'Daughter dear, do not speak of things of which you know nothing,' her mother reprimanded. 'Honestly, if it's not war, it's politics she has an opinion on.' She gave a merry little giggle.

Elizabeth was furious, being spoken to as if she were a silly little child commenting on grown-up things.

'On the contrary,' said Sidney, a little more animated, 'I'm glad that those at home can see a little of what we are going through. And I think it wholly appropriate that a woman, in this day and age, has opinions on a world in which they also have to live.'

'Steady on,' said Horace. 'You'll be saying next they should have the vote.' He leant back, laughing heartily.

'The very *thought*,' said Margaret, chuckling along.

Horace leant forward once more, eyes wide. 'I *was* jesting, Mrs Meredith. Our sisters were vehement supporters of Mrs Pankhurst before the war. And why not? It's only right that the House of Commons has passed the Representation of the People Act. Let's hope the House of Lords is sensible enough to do likewise. It's time women got the vote.'

'Along with the men who are currently disenfranchised, a lot of them soldiers,' Sidney added. 'And who knows, perhaps women will even be able to sit in Parliament one day.'

'Oh the young and their idealism,' said Margaret, shaking her head. 'What can you do with them?'

'I'm afraid I agree,' said Anna. 'At least, about women of a certain standing getting the vote, and eventually sitting in Parliament. I'm rather amazed that you feel the way you do.'

Elizabeth saw the fleeting panic in her mother's eyes, before she rallied. 'I simply think we might be getting ahead of ourselves. One step at a time.'

'There may be something in what you say,' said Anna. 'But it doesn't mean we should stop trying. I attended a few Suffragette meetings myself, before the war, as Elizabeth will know. I'm very proud of Julia and Daphne for their dedication to the cause. And now they're both in France, Julia as part of the Voluntary

Aid Detachment and Daphne in a clerical role. *They* certainly deserve the vote.'

'And don't we know it,' said Horace. 'Anyone would think they're the ones out there, fighting the Hun.'

'I had a letter from Julia recently, so have been reading of her endeavours,' said Elizabeth.

'So, what do *you* do with your time?' Anna asked, lifting her chin in a superior fashion.

'She's the manager of all the allotments in the village,' Margaret replied in her stead. 'She instigated the plan, you know, got permission from the coal company to put people to work and grow vegetables for the villagers, to make up the shortfall. She's had wonderful results. And she organised a rota of farmhands to help Farmer Lloyd out when his sons enlisted.'

Her mother made it sound like she'd achieved so much more than she felt she had. After all, Anwen had been instrumental in much of the success, particularly when it came to getting the villagers on board. And later Idris and Mary Jones, and then Gwilym, had done so much work.

'My, you have been a busy little bee,' said Horace, twisting the end of his moustache. 'I dare say the inhabitants need somebody like you to lick them into shape. A bit like having a battalion of working-class men to train up. Though at least your battalion, as it were, won't be mown down.'

'Do you have to?' said Sidney, wincing. 'It's not something to take lightly. The losses were horrendous. Our brigade was decimated at Mametz Wood, along with the 113th and 115th Brigades, as I'm sure you know.' He looked at Elizabeth.

'Yes, almost half the men who enlisted in Dorcalon were killed there,' she said, the fact heavy on her heart.

'Appalling loss of life.' Sidney closed his eyes and turned his head away for a moment. 'It was months before we could be sent to the front lines again.'

'Tom is with the 10th Battalion, like yourselves. A second lieutenant he is now, having been an undergraduate at Reading

University,' said Margaret with a satisfied grin. 'I must say, I shall be glad when it's all over and he can go back to his degree. Do you ever see him?'

'Yes, of course,' said Horace. 'Bad luck that the war started in his last year.'

'He'll be back home in a few days as well. And as I was—'

The door opened and Brenda wheeled in the oak tea trolley, resplendent with the tea set and a plate of cakes, made from what flour, sugar and margarine they could find. Elizabeth had appreciated Enid's offer to make the dainties, saving her mother from an attack of the vapours.

'Right, now,' said Lady Fitzgerald, clapping her hands. 'Let that be an end to talk of war. Let us speak of the theatre, or concerts we've attended. Or maybe, Elizabeth, you can tell us more about these allotments.'

Margaret's expression of pique was subtle but obvious to Elizabeth.

'I will tell you a little, as I don't want to bore you, then you can tell us what you've heard from Julia and Daphne.'

She was eager to learn how they were getting on.

–

Elizabeth closed the front door behind her and caught Sidney up, where he was holding open the gate for her.

'Which way?' he asked.

She pointed right. 'This way. You can see them on the hill.'

'Ah yes, of course.'

Sidney had expressed a wish to see the allotments, which Margaret had enthusiastically encouraged. Elizabeth had cringed with embarrassment. She'd no doubt though that his interest in the project was genuine, since he'd asked several questions during her brief account of it. She was relieved when Horace turned down his mother's suggestion that he accompany them. She'd wearied of his tendency to make a joke of everything. Sidney at least listened with interest to what she had to say, even if he was rather serious.

As they reached the edge of the field, Sidney said, 'They've clearly been jolly busy.'

'Oh yes. The older, retired miners put in a full day's work there sometimes, and some of those still working come and do a few hours after their hard shifts. The other two fields have mostly women working on them, fitting in as many hours as they can around families, and sometimes work as well.'

'It's impressive.'

'*Prynhawn da*, Miss Meredith,' called Abraham, the closest of the workers. 'Good afternoon to you, sir.'

'Good afternoon,' said Sidney. 'Miss Meredith has been telling me about your efforts here. It's all going very well, I see.'

'Aye, that it is, sir. We have lots of nice veggies to feed our mining lads, giving them strength to dig out the good steam coal for our navy.'

'Very commendable indeed.'

Elizabeth spotted Gwilym, a quarter the way up the field, at the same time he noticed her. He trooped down to meet her.

'Hello Elizabeth. Is everything all right?' He glanced at Sidney.

'It's fine, Gwilym. I've just brought a family friend, Captain Fitzgerald, over to have a look at our project.'

'Sidney,' he said. 'How do you do?'

Gwilym took the offered hand. 'How do you do?'

'Gwilym's one of the other allotment leaders,' said Elizabeth. 'Despite what my mother said, there are four of us running it. It's not just me being the *manager*.'

'I can see it's well organised,' said Sidney. 'And there are two other fields?'

'On the other side of the village,' said Gwilym, pointing, though you couldn't see them for the houses.

'And what are you growing on this one?'

Gwilym pointed to various parts of the field, naming the produce there. Elizabeth felt a little uneasy, with the two men standing there in conversation. She had the sensation of her two worlds colliding, though she wasn't sure why. Despite this, she was relieved to see them chatting, with Sidney treating Gwilym as an equal in the way he spoke to him, not acting the officer, as Horace might have done.

'Must get back to my planting,' said Gwilym. 'We've got the autumn veg to think about.'

'Of course,' said Sidney. 'Thank you for taking the time to speak to me.'

Gwilym nodded and headed on up to the patch he'd been working on.

As Elizabeth and Sidney strolled back to the house, he said, 'You mentioned that half the men who'd enlisted from here were killed at Mametz. I understood that mining is a reserved occupation, so they weren't allowed to be conscripted.'

'Most of those who went enlisted before the law came into being. Thirteen were killed at Mametz Woods. Two were killed previously, at Nord-Pas-de-Calais. Such a loss. At least the newspapers sound hopeful of victory soon.'

He turned his head sharply to study her. 'I don't know where they get that idea. An attempt to keep up morale, I imagine.' She was considering a reply when he continued with, 'Elizabeth, would it be too much to ask you to write to me? I'll understand if you're too busy, or simply don't wish to. It's just... it's just, I've enjoyed conversing with you, and I'm sure letters from you would cheer me up on the Front and would be a change from the serious tomes my mother sends. I do feel I need something to lift me from this gloom.'

She groaned inwardly, thinking of the time it would take out of her week, but felt immediately guilty. Didn't Anwen say Gwen was writing to Daniel Williams, for much the same reason? If Gwen could put herself out, working long hours at the munitions as she did, then it would be selfish of her to refuse to write to Sidney.

'I don't see why not,' she said brightly. 'Though I warn you, I'll have little beyond the allotments, mother's committees and the odd trip to the cinema or a talk to share.'

'And I will look forward to the normality of it all, Elizabeth.'

'All right. But don't say I didn't warn you,' she laughed.

He emitted a small chuckle too, the first expression approaching a smile she'd seen from him today. She was pleased to have cheered him up a little.

'I wonder, Elizabeth. It's just... maybe this is too much of an imposition, but I'm taking my motorcar out for a ride tomorrow. Poor old girl hasn't been out since my last leave. I was hoping to escape for a few hours to the Brecon Beacons. I find it so peaceful there. Would you be interested in accompanying me?

There was much to do still on the allotments, and her mother had mentioned a meeting about future fundraisers for the Dorcalon bed at Netley Hospital, but surely Mama would forgive her absence. Besides, she also longed to escape the valley, if only for a while.

'That sounds splendid, Sidney. The Brecon Beacons are also a favourite of mine.'

'I know a nice café where we could stop for refreshments. My treat, of course.'

'Thank you. I'll look forward to it.'

And to her surprise, she found she was.

—

Elizabeth heard the front door close as she reached the top of the stairs, having just changed out of her gardening clothes after an afternoon on the Edward Street allotment. She rushed down, looking forward to seeing her brother, relieved he was back, safe, for some days.

'Must you hurtle around the place like a herd of cattle?' her mother admonished.

Ignoring the scolding, Elizabeth flung her arms around her brother. 'It's good to see you!'

'Steady on, you'll have me over!'

She took a step back, examining her hands. 'You're all wet. Is it raining now?'

'There's quite a squall. Came on suddenly as we were coming up in the motorcar.'

'How was your journey?'

'Do let him get his overcoat off,' said Margaret, undoing her own. 'We'll talk in the drawing room.'

Tom raised his eyes and smiled, only for his sister's benefit. She grinned before making her way down the small corridor to what she preferred to call the sitting room.

Elizabeth sat in one of the padded armchairs, making herself comfortable to hear Tom's tales. He stopped short of the chairs, picking up the book she was currently reading from the side table.

'D.H. Lawrence's *The Rainbow*,' he said. 'Yours I presume, Lizzie. Any good? I haven't got round to reading it yet.'

'I'm enjoying it. I've nearly finished it so you could take it back with you.'

'I might do that. I can't guarantee you'll get it back in one piece, though. Or at all.'

'That's all right. I bought it from Mr Schenck's second-hand section. You could pass it round, if you like.'

It wasn't long before her mother came through the door, though not in her usual, elegant way, more like she was slightly annoyed about something.

She marched over to the Chesterfield on the left of the fire before saying, 'Haven't you noticed, Elizabeth?'

'Noticed what?'

Tom pointed subtly to the two stars on his epaulette before sitting in the other armchair.

'Oh my, Tom, you've been made a full lieutenant! You didn't say anything in your letters.'

'Seems to be the way of things with university boys, pushing them up through the ranks. God knows why. I doubt we're any better at leading a troop of men than anyone else.'

'Of course you are, you have *breeding*,' said Margaret.

'No, Mother, many of us have education, not the same thing at all. And what does breeding mean anyway? We're not horses or dogs.'

Margaret waved his words away and rubbed the middle of her forehead as if suffering a headache. 'I don't want a debate about it, just to welcome my son home.'

'And I'm glad to be home. Perhaps I'll get a decent meal, apart from anything else.'

'I suppose we should go and start preparing,' said Elizabeth.

'I've only just arrived back and would like some time to talk to Tom,' said Margaret, frowning.

'That's all right, I'll come to the kitchen. It's cosier in there anyway,' he said.

His mother looked round the room. 'What are you implying? I'll have you know the furnishings in here are top quality.'

Tom and Elizabeth exchanged glances. 'I wasn't implying anything, Mother. The kitchen was always the centre of our home when we were little, especially with Mamgu Powell sitting there, telling her tales of long ago. It has quite a few of her old things in it too. I suppose that's why that room always seems more – homely.' He shrugged.

Margaret's expression returned to the one she'd worn when she first entered. 'If you say so. I shall go and change first. If only we could have persuaded Enid to work Saturdays.'

'You're lucky to get domestic servants at all, Mama,' said Elizabeth.

'Hm!' said Margaret as she opened the door and left.

Tom stood up. 'Have you done something to upset her, Lizzie?'

'Seems I've been a great big disappointment all round, the way she's been going on recently, though I'd have thought I'd have been in her good books now. She invited Lady Anna Fitzgerald here and her sons when they were on leave.' Elizabeth told him about the first part of the afternoon they'd visited.

Tom threw back his head and laughed. 'You and Horace! Oh Lizzie, I can't imagine two people less alike. And Sidney is terribly serious.'

'I felt a little sorry for him. He seemed very despondent.'

'He's always been like that. I see the pair of them quite often.'

'I did manage to cheer him up a bit when I took him to see the allotments. Then he asked if I'd write to him, and I thought why not, it wouldn't do any harm.'

'If it puts a smile on his face for a change, it might be worth it.'

'He was much brighter the following day, when I took a trip out to the Brecon Beacons with him.'

'Steady on, you'll be engaged next!'

'Don't be daft, Tom. He wanted to get away, to a favourite place, and needed some company. I did see a new side of him though, a little more optimistic.'

'It was good of you to spend the time with him. We could all do with cheering up after time on the Front. As for Mother, she seems to be in a worse frame of mind than before I enlisted,' said Tom.

'She's not terribly happy, that's for certain. Come on, let's get to the kitchen. We can reminisce about living in Georgetown as children.'

He laughed and followed her through the hall to the kitchen.

When their mother joined them ten minutes later, they were both sitting at the table, drinking tea.

She smiled generously at her son, but her expression was less than happy when she considered her daughter.

'How was your luncheon with the ladies?' said Elizabeth, hoping to pull her into a better frame of mind.

'We had a sufficient meal, given the shortages. It was very *informative*.'

Both waited for her to go on, knowing how much she liked to talk about these gatherings, but she was not forthcoming.

'I hear Sidney and Horace called round,' said Tom.

'Such nice young men,' Margaret cooed. 'Both of them would be a good catch for Elizabeth.'

'Both?' said Tom, looking alarmed. 'What's this, some kind of ménage à trois?'

'Thomas! There is no need to be vulgar.'

'Sorry, Mother.' Tom made a face at his sister behind his mother's back, as Margaret went to the Welsh dresser to get a large ceramic casserole dish down.

Bringing the dish back to the table, she said, 'I meant, of course, that either would be a good catch, though Elizabeth seems to be more taken with Sidney.'

'Mother, as I've told you, the trip to the Brecon Beacons was simply a jaunt out with a friend.'

'He's clearly interested, judging by the attention he gave to you while he was here. And there you are, throwing away a perfect chance by mixing with extremely unsuitable people instead. I do believe working side-by-side with the villagers on the allotments has lowered you to their level.'

Was this what her mother was stewing over, when a few days ago she'd been boasting about her success with the allotments?

Tom shifted on his seat, putting one leg up onto the chair next to him. 'I'd say she's done a jolly good job of managing the allotments and has got the best out of those who are helping. What's so wrong about that? We've all got to do our bit.'

'Hm!' was Margaret's only reply to the comment. 'Now, you two can sit there all day and drink tea, but I've got dinner to get on with. I suppose I'd better wash and prepare the vegetables.' She marched to the scullery with the dish.

'I'm going to find out what's wrong,' said Elizabeth. 'And I'd better give her a hand.'

'I'll come along too. She might shout less now I'm the golden boy.' He raised his eyebrows twice.

'You've *always* been the golden boy!'

In the scullery, they found Margaret washing some carrots.

'Mama, what's up, for clearly something is amiss?'

Margaret waited until she'd finished and dried her hands before turning to face her children.

'We were joined at lunch by Reverend Banes' wife, Agnes.'

'Is that unusual?' asked Tom.

'Of course not. She's a stalwart on the committees.' She turned to face Elizabeth, her eyes narrowed. 'She asked me if you were courting.'

'She must have seen me with Sidney and got the wrong idea.'

'No, that wasn't it. She said she saw you at Perilli's café one evening. Noticed you through the window, what with it being dark outside and all lit up inside.'

Oh dear, she knew now where this was heading.

'Well, Lizzie, you're a dark horse,' said Tom. 'You have some other beau you're stringing along too?'

'It's not funny, Tom,' said Elizabeth.

'As Mrs Banes put it, she was with "that young man that now leads the allotments". I thought you'd only been together in Tredegar, at that talk. So what were you doing with Gwilym Owen in Rhymney, I should like to know?'

'It's quite simple, Mama. When I came out of the picture house, having seen *A Child of the Wild*, he came out behind me. I had no idea he was there until then. We got chatting and I said I was going for a cup of tea, and he came too. Quite innocent, I can assure you. If I'd told you at the time, you'd only have made a fuss. Look at the fuss you made when I mentioned I was giving him a lift to the talk.'

Margaret threw the towel onto the draining board. 'Don't give me that, like it's a coincidence him being at the film the same time. It was *so* embarrassing, with the Chief Constable's wife, Lavinia Perryman, being there too. And I'd just told them that you'd started walking out with Captain Sidney Fitzgerald and was made to look a liar! What will she think? My daughter walking out with a *miner*!'

'Then you shouldn't have told them I was walking out with Sidney when it wasn't true! And once again, Mother, you have this all wrong. Gwilym had no idea I'd be there. I had no idea he'd be there. But since we were both there, we went for a cup of tea. We see each other often at the allotments, so it's not like we're strangers. And because I had the motorcar, it seemed kind to offer him a lift home. There really is nothing else to it.'

'Make sure you keep it like that, for he is not a suitable partner for you. When Sidney comes home on his next leave, you are to show him the utmost interest.'

'Mother, Lizzie is twenty-seven. Even if there were something between them, surely she can decide for herself.'

'No, she can't, not if that is how she'd choose.'

If it hadn't been for Tom, Elizabeth may well have stormed off to her bedroom. Not wanting to spoil her brother's few days at home, however, she did nothing. She should be completely open and tell her mother about the gardening talk they were going to later that month, but it would be better to pick a different moment.

They heard a voice from the hall call, 'Hello, is anyone home?'

'There's your father, back early. Tom, go and say hello.'

'I'll go too,' said Elizabeth, relieved at the distraction.

As they left, they heard Margaret moaning about being left to do the meal on her own.

'I might as well be on the front lines as here,' Tom muttered as they walked through the kitchen.

'She's getting impossible,' said Elizabeth. 'You have no idea.'

'I'm on your side, Lizzie. You're more than old enough to decide on your own life.'

'There you are,' said their father as they entered the hall. 'Welcome home, son.'

Chapter Eight

Gwen settled down on a chair to one side of the range in Violet's kitchen, able to drop the shawl off her shoulders at last. It had been cold coming around the corner from her own house. She only hoped this little gathering would work out better than the last time, when she'd walked out because of all the talk about her yellow skin. With any luck, her friends had learned to keep quiet on the subject.

'Another Guy Fawkes night tomorrow,' said Anwen. 'Funny how I seem to mark them now, as the anniversary of when Idris came back from the war.'

'Two years ago,' said Violet, sitting at the table, pouring them all a cup of tea.

'No fireworks or bonfires allowed again this year,' said Gwen, feeling disappointed. 'I used to enjoy looking down into the valley, watching the fireworks exploding into the sky. My father hasn't bought any since Henry and I were children.'

'Clarice and Benjy don't remember them, so haven't missed them,' said Violet. 'Hywel said he'd buy a few after the war, presuming they're allowed again. The kiddies would like that. Sara Fach could come round too.'

'I can just imagine her face!' said Anwen. 'When I left, Mam and Mamgu were singing to her. A right picture she was, trying to make the sounds.'

'Another choir member in the making!' said Violet. 'It was good of your mam to say she'd have Clarice and Benjy for an hour so we could have a good gossip.'

'Where are Idris and Hywel?' asked Gwen. 'I assumed they'd taken the kiddies out.'

'In this drizzle? Mind, despite that, Idris and Hywel are doing a bit on the allotments behind the cottages this afternoon,' said Anwen. 'There's not so much to do now, but we need to keep going for the winter veg and take advantage of what light there is in the afternoons. I noticed Gwilym and Elizabeth working on the one in front of my house, as I came down here. Anyway, I meant to ask you at chapel this morning, whether Esther was still bothering you. I see she wasn't there this morning.'

Violet handed them each a cup of tea and pulled round a chair from the table to sit down. 'Probably gone back to the parish church.'

'No, she told me in the week that she wouldn't be there because she was visiting a relative,' said Gwen. 'Passing by, she was, when I got off the motorbus after work. To be honest, I think she was waiting for me, as she asked again about whether I'd had another letter from Daniel.'

'You should just tell her to go away,' said Violet. 'What right has she got to bother you?'

'She's not doing any harm. And by letting her read the letters, it shows there's nothing romantic between me and Daniel, though I think she's still convinced there is. She said I didn't have to show her any letters that were personal. But there aren't any, so it doesn't matter.'

'Or there haven't been so far,' said Anwen.

'If he starts any of that, I'll soon tell him what's what,' said Gwen. 'But as for Mrs Williams, if it keeps her content, I don't mind if she asks. I was wondering if anybody had seen anything of Rose Pritchard. Been very quiet, she has, since she finished her month in gaol.'

'I've seen her in the butcher's a couple of times, cleaning up,' said Anwen. 'But no, you're right, she's not been round the village, shooting her mouth off.'

'Probably learned her lesson,' said Violet.

Gwen tipped her head up with a, 'Hah! I can't imagine that lasting long.' She noticed a child's blanket, folded over one of the dining chairs. 'Ooh, I've just remembered. I am so sorry, Anwen, but I meant to bring those two baby blankets that my mother found in a drawer, for little Sara. I completely forgot.'

'Don't worry. I'll pop down with you and fetch them when we leave here. It'll only take me five minutes,' said Anwen. 'Violet, Uncle Hywel told me you'd been doing some painting in the children's books I bought them. Reckoned they were good.'

'They were only to occupy the children. They like making stories up about the dog and cat toys that Hywel bought them last Christmas, Woof and Meow. So I did a couple of illustrations.'

'Come on then,' said Gwen, 'Let's see them.'

'Well, if you must.' Despite her protests, Violet seemed delighted they'd asked. 'I'll fetch the books from the front room.'

–

Despite the fine mist of rain soaking her trousers and jacket, Elizabeth was content, digging and pulling up the carrots and putting them in the wooden crate. The activity was enough to keep her warm. A letter had arrived from Sidney that morning, who was currently in the back lines for a stint. She felt great relief about this and had worried when he'd been in the front lines recently. This was partly because Tom had been in the front lines too.

Gwilym, working nearby, was in shirt sleeves. He was sowing the broad beans on the Bryn Road side of the allotment. There were only two other people working out here today, which was why Gwilym had come over from the McKenzie Cottages field to help out.

Coming up closer to where Gwilym was working, she called over, 'I'm sorry I was a bit late arriving. My mother wanted me to help her with something.'

'That's fine.'

'It will get darker even earlier this evening, with the sky so gloomy. We'll be lucky to have beyond half past four.'

He stood from where he'd been hunkering down and looked up. 'Aye. I'll try and get over here sharpish after work next week, get this winter planting done. That talk we went to in October was really useful.'

'Yes, it gave us a few more ideas.'

She worked her way a little closer, dragging the crate with her, humming a chorus of 'O Sole Mio'. Her mother had bought a recording of it by Enrico Caruso and had played it several times on the gramophone.

When the crate was full, she straightened herself. 'By the way, thank you again for treating me to the picture house on Thursday. The programme was most enjoyable.'

She didn't add that it was the entertainment she'd needed after suffering another mood from her mother. When Gwilym had suggested it she'd been surprised, especially when he'd paid for the train fare as well.

'Thought it might be up your street. With the nights drawing in, and the evenings getting colder, I dare say trips outside the village will get rarer.'

Was that a way of telling her not to expect any more excursions out with him? Perhaps he was afraid she was getting the wrong idea about his intentions. Yet there had been no hint of anything of the sort between them. She could have been out with one of her friends. A surprisingly large swell of disappointment washed over her.

'Yes, I do hate winter for that reason. There are a few events at the Institute coming up to look forward to. Not as many as we used to get, before the war, but at least there are some.'

He nodded and bent back down. Oh dear, did he think she was hinting at them going together? Why did she always seem to put her foot in it? She should get on with the job in hand and keep her mouth closed.

She took the crate to the top of the field, placing it with the other one that had been filled with Brussels sprouts. They'd be dropped off at Mr James's greengrocery later on. Returning to the spot close to Gwilym to pick more carrots, her eye was caught by Violet's door on Bryn Road opening. Out of it stepped Gwen and Anwen. Violet stood in the doorway, and they laughed about something.

Anwen, noticing Elizabeth there, waved to her briefly, before Gwen and she headed down towards James Street. The other two didn't acknowledge her at all.

How lovely it must be, to have friends in the village you could visit without feeling self-conscious. She didn't call so much on Anwen now, feeling out of place, especially since she'd married. Gwen and Violet she never called on anymore, getting the distinct impression they weren't keen. This was despite Violet apologising profusely for being rude about her, back in the spring. As for Gwen, the situation with Ralph Tallis hadn't helped their relationship. The sensation of loneliness swamped her.

Gwilym straightened himself once more. 'That's the beans done. I was thinking that perhaps…' He halted. 'What's up?'

She tried to hold it back, but the fullness in her chest exploded into a strangled gasp. Barely able to get the 'I'm, I'm sorry,' out of her mouth, she spun around, looking for some haven to escape to. She started to run, having difficulty on the damp soil.

'Elizabeth?'

Reaching the road, she was able to run faster, and made for the alleyway between the two long terraces on Edward Street. At the end, she took the path on the right, which went past several back gardens. At the end, where Gwilym's house lay, she realised there was nowhere else to run, apart from up the hill of Twyn Gobaith, but she didn't want to do that. She headed down the alleyway that would take her back to the road. Halfway down, she leant against the side of Gwilym's house and sobbed.

The hurt she felt bubbled up her throat until the tears spilled over. Did she really expect she'd be invited to Violet's house, with the others, for a cup of tea and a gossip? Of course not. They didn't see her as part of their world. Yet she didn't really see herself as part of the world her mother was always trying to launch her into either.

Her chin wobbled as more tears fell. So wrapped up was she in the humiliation, she didn't hear someone approaching from the top of the alley, until Gwilym said, 'Elizabeth, oh, Elizabeth.'

She wrapped her arms around herself and twisted away.

'What's wrong?'

It was a while before she could pull herself together and turn a little towards him, her head bowed.

'It was seeing Anwen and the others there, laughing. I felt left out. It's how I always feel nowadays. I know that sounds daft, with all the things I'm involved in. I do feel like I'm, I don't know, trying to be friendly to people who don't want my friendship. I've put you on the spot several times, offering lifts, suggesting talks and tea...'

He took a step closer and dug his hands in his trouser pockets. 'It were me suggested the Hanbury Electric Theatre last week.'

'It was, but you still seem very awkward with me, like, like you don't want to be there.'

'That's just me, I guess. I'm an awkward person.'

'Not with the men, you're not.'

'That's because they're men.'

'But a lot of people still defer to me, calling me *Miss* Elizabeth, and I can tell, me being there, on the allotments, in the talks, it makes them feel – uncomfortable.'

Gwilym took a few steps forward to face her. 'Yes, I feel a little uncomfortable sometimes, but not because I dislike you.'

'You certainly did, when I first asked you to be the allotment leader.'

'No, I didn't. I was just surprised and wondered why on earth you'd pick me. And, well, maybe worried your father had sent you.'

When Elizabeth went to protest, he said quickly, 'But I don't think that now. I honestly don't.'

Elizabeth took a deep breath, holding it there to try and still the tears. In that moment, Gwilym took her in his arms, pulling her to his chest and clinging on as if he'd never let go. It wasn't right, and yet it was. She was confused, her emotions shattered, yet, mingling with the hurt was hope and joy.

Gwilym leaned slightly away from her and she was afraid his embrace was over, but instead he repositioned himself to bring his face to hers.

No, he wasn't. He couldn't be. She didn't believe he would really kiss her until his lips met hers. Her body relaxed into his as she responded eagerly.

–

Elizabeth stopped the motorcar just beyond the last house on Gabriel Street, before it became Mafeking Terrace. Gwilym was waiting as they'd planned. He ran around and got into the passenger seat. They leaned towards each other and kissed, laughing as her hat got in the way.

'What did you tell your parents?' he asked.

'My father isn't in yet, but I told my mother part of the truth, that I was keen to see *The White Raven*, as I'd heard such good things about it. However, when she made a fuss about me going on my own, I'm afraid I told her I was going with Rosemary, one of my old chums from the Suffragette meetings.' Elizabeth winced at the thought.

'What if your friend says something that makes it obvious it's not true?'

'That's the beauty of it. Rosemary's now a VAD at Netley Hospital, near Southampton, and doesn't come home often. I haven't seen her in a while. They're all doing something worthy towards the war, my old Suffragette friends.'

'You're running an allotment scheme to feed people. Sounds pretty worthy to me.'

Elizabeth considered him; the unruly curls, the warm brown eyes, a kind face. She'd always thought so.

'You're a nice man, do you know that, Gwilym Owen?'

He looked ahead, through the windscreen. 'There are worse, I guess. Come on, we'd better get going, or we'll miss the beginning of the first film.' It was clear he was embarrassed by the compliment.

She released the brake and they were off, trundling slowly along the road to Rhymney.

'Where did you tell your mother you were going?' said Elizabeth.

'I told her the truth. She's used to me going off to the picture house. She did suggest Evan might like to go, but I persuaded her the film wouldn't be of any interest to him.'

'So you didn't quite tell the whole truth either.'

'More for your sake than mine,' he replied. 'It's a bit of an awkward situation, me being the union representative and you the manager's daughter, especially with the court case in a coupla weeks. Apart from being one of the men who took the day off, I represent them.'

'It's not ideal, is it? My father has to be there too. He does agree with the minimum wage, but it's not up to him, and he has to do what he's told.'

'Aye, I guess.' After a few seconds, he said, 'Have you heard from your brother recently?'

'We had a letter yesterday, but, as usual, it was about the small, day-to-day things they get up to. They're not allowed to say too much about the situation.' She wondered if she should mention Sidney's letter.

'I read in the newspaper today that our side were attacking the enemy in Passchendaele again. I dunno if the Welsh Regiment is there, though.'

Now was her opportunity. 'I received a letter this morning from Sidney – you know, the family friend who came to see the allotment a few weeks back.'

'Aye, I remember.' He didn't seem concerned she'd had a letter from him.

'He's in the Welsh Regiment, same brigade as Tom, and he said they're on the rear lines at that moment, but I don't know if that would be the same for all of the Welsh brigades.'

'And things might have changed in the meantime.'

'There does seem to be a lot happening on all sorts of fronts. It's so hard to keep up with it all, let alone believe it's the beginning of the end, as some reports seem to suggest.' She went hot and cold at the thought of Tom, and all the other local men, involved in the madness. 'Let's talk of something other than the war.'

She recalled the conversation about universal suffrage she'd had with the Fitzgeralds and her mother and recounted it to Gwilym. She wasn't sure if she'd brought it up as an interesting subject, or a way of showing how enlightened Sidney was. All it did, however, was illustrate how unenlightened her mother was.

'I've never understood women, or anyone come to that, who don't think they should have the vote,' said Gwilym.

'Well, as Horace said, let's hope the House of Lords votes for the new law too. I understand they're not so keen. Mind you, if they stick with women being over thirty, I'll still have over two years to wait. And then there might be conditions.'

'There's unlikely to be an election until after the war anyway, whenever that ends,' said Gwilym. 'But of course, you're forgetting something.'

'What's that?'

'That I don't have the vote either.'

'Oh gosh, don't you? I knew some men didn't, but I suppose I assumed you did.'

'No. My father does, being the person what rents the house and pays the rates. So, all those miners in the village what rent rooms, they don't get a vote. So keen are the newspapers on emphasising women's rights, that they've forgotten about the forty percent of men what don't get the vote. And that'll include a lot of men fighting abroad.'

'Sidney did say something about that.' She'd been vaguely aware of the situation but hadn't considered just how many men were disenfranchised. To think she considered herself politically informed! 'I'd really never thought about it like that. I should have done.' She shook her head.

Once they reached Bargoed, she brought the motorcar to a halt outside a grand-looking terrace of houses.

'I hope some worthy policeman doesn't come along and ask me the purpose of my journey. I've already had several tellings-off from Sergeant Harries, what with the shortage of petrol.'

'We could have got the train here, like last time.'

'Yes, but it's more likely we'd be spotted and I do not relish my mother giving me another lecture about suitable men. Really, I think I would run away to the Front before plighting my troth with either of the Fitzgerald boys.' Even as she said it, she felt remorse at lumping in Sidney with Horace.

'Good job you don't have that choice as a woman then,' he said. 'Horace sounds like a right character, though Sidney seemed all right.'

'There are women at the Front, as nurses, and in other roles.'

'I suppose there are.'

They got out and walked at a fast pace down the hill, standing close but not holding hands or linking arms, as if by some unspoken agreement. They reached the Hanbury Electric Theatre in the square at the bottom, which was busy with other people arriving and joining the queue.

They found themselves in front of the poster for *The White Raven*, with a photo of the actress Ethel Barrymore in a long, fur-trimmed coat, looking a little distressed. The picture reminded Elizabeth of her own mother, suffering another of her headaches. Gwilym stood a little apart from her, pushing his hands into his jacket pockets. She took the opportunity to link her hands through his arm before she lost her nerve, her crocodile handbag hanging by its chain from her elbow. He took one of her hands in his. Soon the queue moved and they shuffled forward.

At the paying kiosk Gwilym said, 'How about we do the front circle today?'

She gave his arm a squeeze. 'That would be lovely, thank you.'

Once in the auditorium, they found seats in the middle of the front row and settled down. He took her hand where it was resting on the arm of the chair and enclosed his round it once more. Elizabeth felt a contentment she'd not experienced in a long time. It was like she was... home, like being in Mamgu Powell's kitchen.

A voice from the pit called, 'It's the newsreel,' and the noise reduced to around half the volume.

After the first break, *Pearl of the Army* began. Not finding the film particularly absorbing, she let her attention wander. What was Gwilym's aim in romancing her, if it could be called that? She should just enjoy this – diversion – while it lasted. For it surely wasn't going anywhere. And what of Sidney? Now, why had he come to mind? Undoubtedly he was who her mother would have chosen for her, and, in many ways, he would be an easy option. Everyone would be happy. Except maybe her.

The first feature finished and after a small break, *The White Raven* began, its far-fetched plot both entertaining and frustrating her. Elizabeth found herself, at times of high tension, shifting closer to Gwilym, or clutching the hand already holding hers. The audience, fully immersed in the adventure, variously gasped, called words of encouragement to the protagonists and booed the villains.

As the closing music struck up from the organ, accompanied by the applause of the audience, Elizabeth breathed out a huge sigh of satisfaction at the conclusion. The heroine, after many setbacks, had got the man she loved. If only life were so simple.

They waited until the patrons either side of them had moved to the aisles before they rose and shuffled out. They were the last out of the auditorium and a little behind those in front.

'Would – would you like to walk out with me again?' Gwilym eyed her hopefully. 'Not necessarily the pictures or a talk. Maybe the theatre. Or a concert.'

'I had assumed we would. We seem to both enjoy one another's company.'

'I'm glad we agree on that.'

They caught up with the people ahead, since the uniformed employees standing either side of the doors looked like they wanted to go home. Their progress through the entrance hall was slower as they got held up in the queues trying to get out of the main doors.

Outside, Elizabeth came to a halt as the cold air nipped at her face. 'My goodness, I wouldn't be at all surprised if it snowed.'

Gwilym took her arm and she snuggled into him.

On the way home in the motorcar they chatted about the film. It felt more natural than when they'd travelled here, and even more so than the last time they'd been out together.

When they reached Mafeking Terrace, Gwilym said, 'I can walk from here.'

Elizabeth pulled over and turned off the engine. She looked Gwilym's way but could only make him out dimly, since the streetlights had already gone out. 'It's raining again; you'll get wet.'

'I don't want to get you into trouble with your parents. But I also don't want any of the villagers' tongues wagging – you know the sort of thing, people saying I'm hobnobbing above my station. Like they did when Anwen and you started doing things together.'

She slumped back against the seat. 'I do find all this "above one's station" and "below one's station" business tiresome.'

'I'm not sure we can do much about it. But you know, what I really don't want the villagers to see is this.'

He twisted and leant over, holding Elizabeth's arms as he kissed her lips, lingering for many long seconds. She moved as close as she could, cursing the hindrance of her coat and his jacket to really getting close. She placed her hands on his waist and enjoyed the warmth of his lips, wishing the moment would never end. He was the first to pull away.

'I enjoyed this evening,' he said. 'I miss seeing you so much around the allotments now the work is dropping off for winter. I was wondering if it were possible to go into Merthyr, or Cardiff one afternoon, on the train. We'd be less likely to see anyone there, and we could have some tea somewhere.'

'I would love that, Gwilym.'

'We could meet at Rhymney Station, since that's where we'll have to change.'

'And we're less likely to be seen,' she laughed.

'I wish it wasn't so,' he sighed, 'for I would be proud to show you off to the world.'

'But the world isn't ready for us. Or at least, people like my mother.' She had no idea what her father would think of it.

'There are plenty in the village who wouldn't be ready either.'

He bent down to kiss her once more. '*Nos da, cariad.*'

'*Nos da.*'

He sprang out of the motorcar and was soon running up the street.

Now to home and sleep, perchance to dream, she thought. And what sweet dreams they would be.

Chapter Nine

The Silver Band led the way as the throng of miners travelled down James Street, the vast cathedral-like colliery looming on their right, before the structures ended and only the tramways blotted the landscape. Among the horns, cornets, trombones and tubas stood Gwen's father, Albert Austin, with the largest instrument, the one euphonium. Noah Schenck stood at the front with his bass trombone.

Today was the day Gwilym and the rest of the men who'd been summoned for breach of contract had to appear in court. What Gwilym hadn't anticipated was most of the men in the village turning up to march to Tredegar in support, not just the eighty-three summoned. Idris was by his side, as was Hywel, even though he'd been on his honeymoon on the bank holiday Wednesday.

'Oh, mun, this is going to be great fun, marching with everyone,' said Evan, on the other side of his brother. Idris's brother, Jenkin, next to him, eagerly agreed.

'It's not supposed to be fun,' said Gwilym. 'And are you sure you're all right, walking with that limp? It's over three miles to get there.'

Evan had fallen over in the mine the day before and twisted his ankle.

'Aw stop fussing, mun! We're gonna go and join our friends.' He and Jenkin went a few rows back, where some other young lads were marching.

Gwilym looked round at the scene. Several women stood at their doors, waving them off, including Gwen's mother. Soon they were falling into orderly lines, marching as if they were on their way to battle.

They rounded the corner, over the Nantygalon stream. Up ahead, Gwilym spied McKenzie House, sitting proud on a ledge, keeping watch over the village. He wondered where Elizabeth was now and whether she was thinking about him.

'I presume Meredith will take his motorcar to the court,' he said. 'Since he's got to be there.'

'Well he's not going to be marching with us, is he, mun?' said Idris, laughing.

'I believe he's quite sympathetic to our cause, though.'

'Get away with you,' said Hywel. 'Where d'you hear that?'

'Can't remember now.'

Passing the manager's house, Gwilym spotted the Morris Oxford outside. Meredith hadn't left yet, and if he was going to take the route they were taking, which would be the quickest, he was going to have to get past them. It was a country road still, narrow in some places.

When they passed in front of the house, he didn't look up. They passed the lower cottages, some voices joining in with the words of the tune playing. By the side of the road, the trees were mostly empty of their leaves, a few dried, brown ones hanging on to the branches. Winter was approaching. Gwilym always dreaded it, knowing that soon there'd be barely an hour's light after a work shift, giving him little time on the allotments.

He was nudged out of his reverie by Idris, who pointed to the sharp bend of the road leading up to McKenzie House. 'What's he come to say now? Doesn't think he'll stop us, does he?'

On the corner stood Herbert Meredith, dressed in a suit and smart, polished boots. He stepped out as the band passed, so that the men behind had to stop. The instrumentalists, realising one by one what had happened, came to a halt at slightly different parts of the tune. There were indistinct murmurings from the gathering.

'Thought I heard you coming up the road,' he said. 'Do you mind if I join you?'

Out of the two or three possibilities that had occurred to him, Gwilym hadn't considered this one.

'Got to be there as well, so might as well walk with you as take the motorcar, which my good lady wife wants to use anyway.'

Gwilym wondered what his *good lady wife* would make of him walking with the men. It didn't seem quite right, but what could he say? 'If you wish.'

'I'll go down the line, have a talk with the men while we're walking.'

Mr Meredith made his way down, passing Evan, limping badly towards them. He was being helped by Jenkin. 'You all right, lad?'

'Not really, Mr Meredith, sir. Twisted my ankle, I did. Ooh, I'm sorry, Gwilym, I'm gonna have to go home. My ankle...' he grimaced. 'Painful, it is.'

'I did tell you it was a bad idea when we set off.'

'I'll help him back,' said Jenkin, who even as he said it, looked crestfallen.

'There's good of you, *boi bach*,' said Idris. 'We'll see you later and tell you what happened.'

Mr Meredith joined the ranks further down.

When they set off again, Idris said, 'He'll be disappointed, will Jenkin, but I'm not sorry he's not coming. Time enough for marches for him and Evan when they're a bit older. Mam will be happier too.'

'And mine.'

'What do you make of Meredith tagging along?'

'I told you I'd heard he were sympathetic.'

Idris glanced back. 'Let's hope that is the case, and he's not up to something.'

'We'll find out soon enough.' He sent up a small prayer that he wasn't up to anything that would make the situation between him and Elizabeth more awkward.

Elizabeth stood in front of the hall mirror, unpinning her mush-room brimmed hat and adjusting it this way and that, until it looked straight. Pushing the pin back in, she considered herself. Was she pretty enough to make a man want to commit himself to her?

She tutted at such a consideration. Surely having something in common was more important, and simply caring for that person. Love was the crucial issue, and what fired that was often a mystery. Yet a secure future was the main consideration for many. Anwen had not only married for love but had prepared for the worst with Idris's illness. But what if your lives were poles apart?

'Stop wittering on,' she muttered to her reflection. For there was little point in debating these things with herself. Having any kind of lasting relationship with Gwilym seemed, at present, like scaling Snowdon with a pair of iron boots and a lead knapsack.

An hour or so before, she'd glanced the men passing by as she'd looked out of the landing window. What she hoped for from today was that the men who'd been called to the police court wouldn't be punished. Her father had described it as an enquiry. She wasn't entirely sure what could happen, but she suspected they could lose their jobs. She wondered how that would affect her and Gwilym's relationship.

'Wrap up warm, Elizabeth, we don't want you catching a cold now, do we?' Margaret called from the study.

She nearly called back, *I'm hardly going out in a summer frock with a straw bonnet*, but resisted the temptation. Keeping on the right side of Mama seemed the wise move to make in her current situation. She didn't want to be accused of being impertinent because of mixing with 'the wrong sort of people'. By this, her mother meant those who lacked money and status. Whether such people were always the *right* sort of people, she had grave doubts. Look at Ralph Tallis.

'Aren't you ready yet?' said Margaret, standing in the hall now.

'Yes, yes of course.'

'Then where are your boots?' Her mother pointed to her feet. 'You've been daydreaming far too much recently. It's about time you had a household and a husband to occupy you. You never did tell us what Sidney had to say in his letter yesterday.'

'There wasn't much different to the usual.'

Elizabeth fetched her boots from the under-stairs cupboard and pushed her feet into them. Sidney. Was her life or status really any closer to his than Gwilym's? But it was the status her mother wanted her to have, that was the difference. If only she could have had some kind of career, but Mama had made a huge fuss even when she'd had the temporary clerk's job last year.

While doing up the laces Elizabeth said, 'If by a household and a husband, you're referring to Sidney, then, once again, I must emphasise that we are simply friends. At least he isn't overbearing like Horace. And that's the best I can say.' Though in reality she did have a little more regard for Sidney than that.

'A sad, lonely spinster is what you'll be for the rest of your life if you keep this up.'

Her mother saying it out loud like that draped a blanket of sorrow over her. As much as she liked the idea of being independent, she also craved a special person to share her life with. Any kind of marital contentment, however, seemed a great distance away. Fate might have something else in store for her. If only she could figure out what.

'Let us venture out while it's still dry, for it's getting gloomier out there. I do hope they have a little more in the shops than on the last occasion. It's a nuisance having to go oneself, and not send a servant, but I do feel they have more respect for me and don't palm me off like they do Mrs Rhys.'

'They're not going to give you things from under the counter, if that's what you think, Mama, for there isn't enough for them to be able to do that anymore.'

Margaret picked up one of the wicker baskets by the stairs, handing it to her daughter, before she picked up one for herself. 'I'm sure there isn't, but I don't want another situation like the one Mrs Rhys had with Mrs Pritchard. Now, chop chop!' She flicked her hand, indicating to Elizabeth to leave. 'Let's go before there's nothing left at all.'

Having reached the bookshop, Margaret said, 'I just want to call in on Mrs Bowen first, as she's making me a new blouse.' She pointed towards the top of Jubilee Green.

'What on earth for? You have plenty.'

'Fashions are changing: one *must* keep up.'

'There's a war on, Mama. We should all make do.'

'Stuff and nonsense. If you'd like to start in the grocer's, I will be down shortly.'

Margaret turned right, while Elizabeth went left, across the road, to Mrs Brace's. She could hear the complaining tones of Florrie Harris before she even entered. She was almost shouting, so nobody noticed the bell as Elizabeth went in.

'...dunno what they think they're going to achieve, marching off like that, nobody in work. Be down on their pay, they will. So how're my lodgers going to be able to pay their rent, eh?'

How Mrs Harris managed to house two lodgers with her widowed daughter and seven grandchildren living with her, she couldn't imagine. Anwen had told her they had beds in the front room, but it must still have been crowded, especially at mealtimes.

'Oh, here we go,' said Winnie Price, looking heavenward, in the queue next to Florrie. 'It's only one day's wages. I do wish Mrs Brace would hurry up. How long does it take to get some potato rolls out of the oven?'

Elizabeth wandered to the various wooden crates and barrels of diminishing goods, hoping to keep out of the conversation. There was the welcome aroma of something baking, making her stomach growl.

'My Cecil wouldn't have been so stoopid,' said Florrie, before pouting.

Another woman turned round to say, 'They're entitled to protest. It were a bank holiday: they shouldn't have had to work.'

It was Gwilym's mother, Rachael Owen. Elizabeth's face heated up, wondering if she had any inkling of their relationship.

'Oh, hello Miss Elizabeth,' Rachael said, having just noticed her. The other two women twisted round to look at her.

'Hello, Mrs Owen.'

'It would be interesting to hear what you think, Miss Meredith,' said Florrie, 'being the manager's daughter and all. He won't approve and no mistake.'

This was awkward, knowing that her father had sympathy for the men's situation.

'I can't really speak for my father.'

The doorbell pinged once more, and Margaret entered.

'I'm surprised Mr Meredith even allowed the march,' said Florrie.

'I can assure you he didn't!' Margaret was most strident in the statement, made before she'd even closed the door. 'It's nothing to do with my husband. It's that wretched union representative, Gwilym Owen, who organised it.'

'I'm sorry, Mrs Meredith, but that's my son you're talking about,' said Rachael. 'And he is not *wretched*, as you put it, but a most upstanding man, who feels obligated to do what is right for the men he represents.' It was said with respect, but firmly.

'Marching off to Tredegar like a rabble's no way to deal with it. I saw them out the front bedroom window, as they walked past, with what passes for a Silver Band. And all for a bank holiday. They should know better in wartime.'

How Elizabeth wished she had a magic wand, to whisk herself and her mother away. She'd step in, try to calm things down.

'The whole situation occurred not only because of the bank holiday, but because of not being paid the minimum wage. It isn't fair, and I think my father would agree with that.'

'It's nothing to do with your father, Elizabeth, so do keep quiet.'

'If it's nothing to do with Mr Meredith,' said Rachael, 'then why did he join the men on their march earlier?'

Margaret looked confused at first, before tilting her head to one side and tipping her mouth up into a patronising smile. 'I can assure you he didn't. He's at the colliery. *He* still has work to do.'

'That's not what my son Evan said, for he were on the march first off, until he was limping so bad he had to come home. He said Mr Meredith joined them at the bottom of the road that comes down from your house.'

'I – I think he must have been mistaken.' She sounded unsure, but soon rallied. 'It must have been one of the men from the cottages that he mistook him for.'

'He was quite adamant.'

The door behind the counter opened and Mrs Brace stepped out. 'Right, we have some lovely potato rolls just baked, but they are limited. Are you next, Mrs Price?'

'Aye, that I am.'

With attention away from them, Elizabeth murmured, 'How come you were so quick?'

'There was no reply. I imagine Mrs Bowen and her daughter have gone out to buy supplies.'

If only they hadn't, thought Elizabeth. The last thing she needed was her mother falling out with Gwilym's. She wondered if Mrs Owen was right about her father. He had told them he was going to the mine, but that could have been to avoid a row with her mother.

'I'll leave you here to deal with Mrs Brace,' said Margaret. 'You know what we need. I'm going to the greengrocer's. That way we'll be quicker.'

Her mother left, shutting the door noisily enough that the other patrons turned towards it. This did not bode well. Her mother was in a mood and would likely be for the rest of the day. She anticipated another row and a frosty atmosphere at home that evening.

—

An hour and twenty minutes after they'd started walking, the men reached Tredegar. The Silver Band started up again after a break on the long walk. A few spots of rain fell, making Gwilym almost glad to be going into the court. He didn't want to ruin his Sunday suit. Because there'd been so many of them called for breach of conduct, he would be going in as their representative, and most of the rest of the men would have to wait in the wet.

They halted on the pavement outside the police court, the band still playing. Waiting there for them was Mr Evans, the agent, sent by the Miners' Federation to help deal with the dispute between the men and the colliery owners. Gwilym was relieved to see him.

'Didn't expect you to bring the whole damn colliery with you,' said Evans, lifting his cap to scratch his head.

'They've got a lot invested in this, seeing as it's in all our interest to get the minimum pay we're entitled to and the holidays we're allocated,' said Gwilym.

'Yes, well, you may be their rep, but leave the talking to us, boyo, and only speak when you're spoken to, *if* you're spoken to. They won't appreciate you going on a campaign in there.'

'Don't you worry, I'm more than glad to let you get on with it.'

When there was a lull in the music, Evans took out his pocket watch. 'Come on then, time to go inside.'

Gwilym called behind. 'We're goin' inside now, just those of you summoned.'

Noah Schenck handed his trombone to someone nearby and joined them.

'Good luck!' said Hywel.

The band struck up once more, so that Gwilym's reply was not heard. His stomach squirmed with anxiety. Who knew what position they'd be in by the end of the day?

–

Elizabeth placed the last of the provisions in the pantry, before returning the wicker baskets to their place on a shelf in the scullery.

'I'd have done that for you, Miss Elizabeth,' said Enid, striding into the scullery from the kitchen, carrying a large pan that she took to the sink.

'That's all right, Mrs Rhys. I could do with keeping occupied. I think I might change and go to the allotments.'

'It's not looking good out there.' Enid pointed out of the scullery's side window. 'Already spitting, it is.'

'A quick walk round the village to see where we are with things won't take me long.'

'When will you be wanting your luncheon, Miss Elizabeth? It's already half past eleven.'

'Whenever my mother wishes to have it, which is normally half past twelve.'

'She's going out, so I thought I'd ask.'

'Out?' Her mother had not mentioned anything to her. 'Where to?'

'I dunno, sorry.'

'Do you know where she is now?'

'She said something about making a telephone call first.'

'Thank you, Mrs Rhys.'

Elizabeth hurried through the kitchen, into the hall and past the stairs, in time to find her mother putting her coat back on. Her hat was already in place.

'Where on earth are you off to now, Mama?'

'Never you mind.'

Elizabeth went to the front door, standing in front of it. 'What's all this about? Is it something to do with Papa walking into Tredegar with the men?'

'I suppose you knew all about that.'

'I had no idea. He said he was going to the mine.'

Margaret yanked her gloves on. 'I do not have to discuss my business with you.'

'Were you hoping to leave before I came out of the kitchen? Is that why you asked me to put the food away?'

'Please move out of the way, I'm in a hurry.'

Other than wrestle her mother away from the door, there was nothing she could do to stop her. It wasn't the fact she was going out that worried her; it was that she'd been secretive about it. Nevertheless, she stepped to one side and even opened the door for her mother.

Margaret left without even a word of farewell.

Elizabeth felt tired to the core. The trouble with the men and the coal company, all the secrecy with her and Gwilym and the arguments between her parents had taken its toll on her.

Then it occurred to her where her mother might be going. She opened the door and rushed out onto the path, in time to see the motorcar disappearing down the lane.

-

The men were standing around the street in groups, chatting and shouting when Gwilym and the others came out. The chairman leading the case had decided to settle the matter in court today, so the hearing had been adjourned for a while as the various representatives and solicitors of the coal company and the Miners' Federation went away to discuss it.

Gwilym considered what good spirits the men were in, given they'd have to wait around a while on this gloomy day.

They'd been there around half an hour when a familiar vehicle appeared, just beyond where the throng of men petered out. Gwilym panicked, thinking at first that Elizabeth had turned up to support them. The Morris Oxford came no further, parking on the side of the road, but with its motor still running. Mr Meredith had spotted it too and hurried down the road towards it.

Gwilym was relieved to see Mrs Meredith elegantly alight the motorcar, but he suspected, by his expression, that her husband was not.

'What's going on there, then?' said Hywel.

'She's probably brought him some sandwiches for his *luncheon*,' said Idris, 'knowing what she's like.'

'So much for solidarity, eh?'

'Ooh, I don't know, actually,' said Idris. 'Looks like they might be having a bit of a barney. Wonder what that's about.'

Mrs Meredith's expression was indeed cross. Gwilym could imagine that her husband joining a march such as this would not go down well. It suggested that he hadn't told her and that she'd somehow found out. Perhaps Elizabeth would tell him tomorrow, on the afternoon walk they'd planned for after he'd finished work. He felt a little leap of pleasure at the promise of it, which he pushed firmly away. He had other matters to consider today. And who knew how they'd turn out?

The manager walked away from his wife and she got back into the car, far less delicately than she'd got out. She was soon off, her arm out, squeezing the bulb of the air horn on the side of the motorcar. The men shifted quickly as she speeded down the road, the horn still complaining.

'She's in a bad mood, and no mistake,' said Idris. 'Think she'd have run us over if we hadn't shifted quick.'

Meredith returned, standing alone on the pavement, looking thoughtful for a short while, but it wasn't long before he was off, talking to the men once again.

The Silver Band struck up once more, with a rendition of 'Calon Lan'.

Soon many of the men were joining in and Gwilym was glad of the distraction from thinking about Elizabeth and their situation.

It was two hours and five minutes before the man in the sombre black suit stepped out of the court door to usher the summoned miners back in, and only twenty minutes later when they were all back out again. The men surged forward when they saw Gwilym and the others appear.

Gwilym stood on the steps and gave a brief cough, hoping to make his voice loud enough. He then embarked on a brief rundown of what had been agreed.

'The resolution decided on will have to be passed by all of us in a mass meeting, and that is that no stoppage will take place in future at the colliery, until we've referred the matter in dispute to the management and the workmen's committee. If that fails, it's to be taken to the colliery agent and men's agent. If agreement can't be reached by them, it goes to the Conciliation Board.'

'That don't sound too bad,' a voice from the crowd called. There was a murmur of agreement.

'So, none of you is to be dismissed?' another voice called.

'No,' Gwilym reassured them. 'We've still got our jobs.'

A lengthy cheer went up.

'I'm that relieved it's over,' Gwilym told Idris. 'I did wonder if we'd suffer some penalty or other, or even get sacked.'

'No, mun, they're short of workers as it is. And at least we get to do the walk home before it gets dark. I 'ope there's some dinner left for me when we get back, that hungry I am.'

Now the worry was over, Gwilym realised he was hungry too, his stomach growling to confirm this.

When the cheering was over, Gwilym called, 'Let's get home then!'

The Silver Band started up once more, and they marched out of the town, the way they had come in.

The following afternoon, Elizabeth and Gwilym met part-way along Nantygalon stream. She had suggested it as a place where they were less likely to be spotted, for she'd never met many walking along its narrow banks on her treks. With the abundance of surrounding trees, they were unlikely to be seen from the village, despite the bare branches. She'd always enjoyed it here, finding the trickling water relaxing, and today she felt a heightened contentment.

'It makes a change to see a bit of blue sky,' said Elizabeth looking up, as Gwilym took her hand. 'If only in part.'

'At least it's not so gloomy as yesterday. Could have done with this bit of sun. Don't suppose we'll see too much more now, it being December next week.'

December. Christmas. How would that work out for her and Gwilym? It wasn't as if they'd be able to spend any of it together. The thought sowed a seed of despondency, marring her enjoyment.

'I'm so glad you and the other men who took the bank holiday off weren't punished yesterday,' she said.

'As Idris said, they're already short of men… Urm, yesterday, as we were waiting outside, your mother turned up. She looked unhappy.'

'I did wonder if that's where she'd gone after we returned from the shops. She'd only just heard that my father had joined the march, and, to say she was unhappy is an understatement.'

'They did seem to be having an argument, though we couldn't hear anything.'

'I'm surprised at her showing her annoyance like that in public, especially in front of the men. It illustrates how very vexed she was.'

'So, she found out from someone at the shops? I wonder how they knew, given he met us on the top road.' Gwilym placed his hand round his chin, as if puzzling it out.

Elizabeth was loath to admit what had happened next, considering it involved both of their mothers, but was surprised he hadn't heard already.

'I'm afraid… oh dear… well… we were in the grocer's when your mother was in there, and my mother was going on about it being you who organised the protest.' She tried to relate the conversation as well as she could remember, finishing with, 'and when my mother said it had nothing to do with my father, your mother asked why he'd marched with them in that case. Evan had apparently told her, after he'd come home limping.'

Gwilym threw his head back and let out a huffing sigh. 'I am so sorry, Elizabeth. It didn't even occur to me to tell him to keep his trap shut.'

'Why would it? It's just unfortunate that my father didn't tell her in the first place. Yes, she would have argued, but leaving her to find out made it twice as bad. And my mother should have known better than to throw accusations around about whose fault it was, not knowing who might be related to you.' Elizabeth felt even angrier about it now. And to think her mother was always going on about acting 'dignified' in public.

Gwilym moved closer to her, linking his arm through hers. 'Let's forget about them for a while. What's done is done.'

'I'm more than happy to. How is Evan now and why was he limping?'

'He tripped over a shovel in the mine. He rested up his leg when he got home yesterday, so it's not so bad today. He'll be all right, just needs to use his lamp to look where he's going.'

Gwilym placed his arm around her, and they stopped to share a kiss. When it ended, they kept hold of each other.

'I'm looking forward to the musical comedy play in Bargoed next week,' she said. 'Are you sure it's your cup of tea?'

'Why d'you say that? I've seen musicals before and found them entertaining.'

'I'm glad to hear it. My father isn't terribly fond of them, you see. So, shall I pick you up in the usual spot?'

'Yes. What are you going to tell your parents this time?' he asked.

'Not that it's yet another garden talk. I'll probably tell them the truth, but say I'm going with someone else again. Perhaps

Wilma Floyd, someone I worked with when I was a clerk in the overseer's office. I'll say I bumped into her, and she suggested an outing. Oh dear, I'm getting too good at this fibbing lark.'

'I think my mother suspects I'm walking out, but she doesn't ask any questions, which is handy. By the way, I saw an advertisement in the newspaper for a talk by the Cymmrodorion Society on the twenty-first of December. They're a society promoting Welsh culture and language, so I dunno if it'll be of interest to you.'

'I've heard of them. If you're asking if I'd like to go, the answer's yes.'

'I haven't told you what the lecture's about yet!'

'The answer's still yes,' she laughed.

The mystery of where this all might end flitted through her mind again, and once more, she batted it away. 'Let's continue walking. It won't be too long before it starts to get dark and we have to go back. And you can tell me what you know about the lecture.'

Chapter Ten

'Aren't you ready yet *fach*?' Gwen's father's voice called up the stairs. 'We'll need to leave soon.'

'Just coming, Da,' she called through the partly open bedroom door.

She turned back to the mirror that sat on the chest of drawers. Just a little more of the satin skin powder over the cream, to cover her yellow skin.

Taking the mirror to the bedside table, she sat down on the bed. Her back was aching, and she felt more tired than usual. It had been a heavy week at the munitions, with a lot of lifting. Anwen's celebration was something she'd been looking forward to, but all she wanted to do today was lie down on the bed and sleep. She undid the lid of the powder.

There was a knock at the door, and her mother, Ruth, pushed the door wide. 'Come on now, Gweneth. It's Anwen's and Idris's special day, celebrating Sara Fach's adoption. You look fine, *cariad*, you don't need any more paint.'

She replaced the lid and put the pot on the bedside table. 'All right, Mam, I'm coming.'

Following her mother down the stairs, she stopped as she experienced a moment's light-headedness.

'You all right, *cariad*?'

'Yes, yes, of course, Mam. Just a little tired after a busy week.'

'Here she is, Albert, so we're ready to go,' Ruth called from the dark hall, through the kitchen door.

He soon appeared, putting his jacket on. 'At last. Thought we'd never get going.'

'She looks a picture though, doesn't she, our Gweneth, in her purple dress?' She stroked the chiffon of the overskirt. 'Lovely. Just as fashionable as Miss Meredith.'

'Aye, very nice,' said Albert, who'd never understood nor appreciated fashion. 'Come on, get your boots on now,' he told her, shuffling her along the hallway.

She slipped her feet into her long, brown leather boots, then did up the laces. When she stood once more, she let out a long sigh.

Albert slung his cap onto his head. 'My goodness, *fach*, anyone would think you didn't want to go to Anwen's celebration. Normally love this sort of thing, you do.'

'Of course I want to go. Been looking forward to it all week, I have. I'm just tired.'

'Hope you're not coming down with anything, and just before Christmas too,' said Ruth.

Gwen slipped on her matching purple jacket and her coat, then picked up the sack bag that contained her handbag and a gift. 'Probably just a cold.'

Trudging up Bryn Road was an effort for Gwen, who'd been a nimble runner in former years. Halfway up, they met Violet and Hywel coming out of their house with the children.

'Oh dear, you're a little late too,' said Violet, trying to hurry her son along. 'Had a bit of an emergency with Benjy falling over and scraping his knee.'

'It hurt, Aunty Gwenny,' he sobbed.

'Oh, poor little mite.' Gwen felt his sadness.

Hywel took the boy's hand from Violet and swept him up in his arms. 'Come on, Benjy *bach*. I think there might be some cake at Anwen's house to cheer you up.'

'I like cake,' he said, though his chin was still wobbling.

Clarice skipped ahead, looking back to call, 'Come on Aunty Gwenny. Race me.'

'Gwen's not so well today, *cariad*,' said Ruth. 'I'll give you a little race.'

'What's wrong with you?' said Violet, her brow wrinkling.

Gwen brightened, even though she didn't feel like it. The last thing she needed was another lecture from her friends. 'I'm just tired. Heavy week at work.' And she had to go back tomorrow. She'd never felt less like it. No point taking any days off though: that would cut into her wages.

At the door of number thirty-four Edward Street, there was a warm welcome from Cadi as she gestured them all in and took their coats.

'It's so lovely to have friends come to celebrate the good news,' she said, tickling Benjy under the chin as Hywel stepped in.

'Is there cake, Aunty Cadi?'

'Of course there is, *cariad*. Been saving the ingredients a while now, and for other treats too.'

The idea of cake lifted Gwen's spirits a little. She'd always had a sweet tooth. The house smelled of baking, embracing her with a sense of comfort. If she could sit down for a while, she'd make it through the afternoon fine.

In the kitchen she headed for the first chair, at the end of the table nearest the door. Plonking down with relief, she greeted Gwilym's and Idris's mothers, and then old Mr Owen and Idris's da, nattering by the dresser. Elizabeth and Enid were standing in the doorway of the front room, chatting, the older woman bouncing Sara Fach on her slim hip.

'Cup of tea, Gwen?' It was Anwen, brandishing a teapot, her grin wide with joy.

'Ooh, yes, I'm gasping for one. Congratulations! I know I've already said it, but it's wonderful news. Here.' She bent down and pulled out the gift, wrapped in flowery paper, and placed it on the table.

'You didn't have to do that,' said Anwen, who was obviously touched all the same. 'Hang on, let me just pour a few cups of tea.' Completing her mission, she put the pot on the stand and moved the milk jug closer. 'Right.' She picked up the parcel, calling, 'Idris?'

He poked his head around the scullery door. 'Yes.'

'Come and see this present from Gwen.' She undid the ribbon and opened it, then carefully unfolded the tissue paper within. 'Oh my goodness, that's lovely, Gwen.' Inside the paper was a little white broderie anglaise dress, with frills around the three-quarter-length sleeves and around the hem.

Enid came over with the baby, leaning her towards the present. 'Look at that, Sara Fach, a beautiful dress for you.'

The little girl put her hand out towards it, but then touched Gwen's arm instead.

'It's like she knows it's from you,' said Anwen. 'Did you make it?'

'I did. I haven't made anything since I started at the munitions, but I found the fabric in the Bon Marché department store, in Ebbw Vale, and fancied having a go. Never done a child's dress before and didn't realise how much harder it would be.'

'Smaller proportions, isn't it?' said Enid. 'But you've done a wonderful job.'

Anwen's eyes filled with tears. 'I feel like I've received a second early Christmas present, with Sara Fach's adoption being the first one.'

Idris curved his arm round her shoulders. 'Aw, don't be sad, this is a happy occasion.'

'And these are happy tears,' she replied.

'Now come on,' said Cadi, clapping her hands. 'If you all spread out a bit, and chat for a while, we'll get the food out. You can go in the front room too. Help yourselves to the tea here.'

The group dispersed, joining in clusters of two or three to chat. Clarice and Benjy sat on the chaise longue, playing with Woof and Meow, pretending they were going on an adventure. Gwen stayed where she was. She noticed Elizabeth and Gwilym, through the door in the front room, looking very stiff and formal as they spoke to each other. No doubt it was about the allotments. There wouldn't be much else they'd have in common.

When Anwen returned with a plate of sandwiches, Gwen said, 'I don't suppose anything's been heard of Delyth.'

'No, they weren't able to trace her at all. I don't know how hard they tried, mind. Not that I care.'

'Do you think she'll wait for your father to come out of gaol?'

Anwen laughed drily. 'Highly unlikely, since he's got another eleven years to go. No, her sort wouldn't hang around. She's probably found some other mug by now.'

Gwen wondered what Madog would do when his sentence was up, whether he'd come back, looking for trouble, but she didn't say this to Anwen.

'To think she'll be a year old in ten days. She tried to walk a few steps the other day.'

'You'll have your work cut out now,' said Gwen.

'She gets around quick enough crawling, but at least she can't fall over... Are you all right, *cariad*? You look a bit dark round the eyes, like you need a good sleep.' Anwen rubbed her arm.

'Yes, I'm fine. Like I keep telling people, it's been a hard week at the munitions. I'm tired, which is why I'm having a sit down.'

'Sorry, I know you get fed up with people worrying about you.'

'I suppose it's nice to know people care.'

The women of the house finished laying the tea, and people tucked in, appreciative, even though it was half of what they'd have had even a couple of years back. Gwen, initially enthusiastic, found it hard even to get through the quarter of a sandwich she'd picked up. She nibbled at it, feeling a little nauseous.

'You all right, Gwen?' said Idris, leaning over to cut a piece of cake.

It was tempting to scream with the constant questions, but instead Gwen smiled sweetly. 'Been on my feet all week, haven't

I? Nice to have a sit down. You must feel like that, after a week in the pit.'

'It's not so bad now I'm an examiner. What I look forward to is some natural light.' He pointed towards the kitchen window. 'Not much today, though.'

'It's the same in the factory. We get out only for very short breaks. Are Jenkin and Evan not coming today?'

'No, they're down at the field beyond West Street Terrace, playing rugby with their pals. Can't blame them. This isn't their kind of thing.'

'I suppose not.'

'Gwen, what are you going to do when the war's over and the men come home?'

'I haven't thought that far ahead,' she said, surprised at the change of subject. It was something she normally tried not to think about.

'The dress you made Sara Fach is intricate. Have you ever thought of doing it as a trade?'

'Give over, Idris, I'm not clever enough for that.' She gave his arm a playful shove.

'I disagree. And there's Anwen, and her mam and mamgu, they're all good seamstresses too. You could set up together, be competition for Mrs Bowen.'

Gwen chuckled. 'I can't see her being impressed about that! Did you know Henry used to be rather fond of her daughter, Amelia? He never had the courage to ask her to walk out.'

'Aye, I suspected as much. She does rather think she's above the rest of us, though.'

'Yes, I don't suppose Henry would have stood a chance. The cake looks nice.'

'Have a bit, before it's all gone.' Idris joined Abraham and Albert, who were deep in conversation by the range.

Maybe something sweet would appeal more. She stood up, experiencing another momentary dizziness. When she got home, she'd take herself off to bed, have a good long sleep to prepare herself for the week ahead. Moving slowly to the side of the table with the Victoria sponge, she heard Clarice's piping voice say, 'Can I have cake now, Mam?'

Leaning over to retrieve a plate, Gwen was smiling at the little girl's enthusiasm, when what felt like a black veil fell over her. She experienced a moment's sick headache and breathlessness, then nothing.

–

Dusk was falling by the time Elizabeth arrived back at Anwen's house with Dr Roberts. Her hands were still trembling with the worry of what was wrong with Gwen. She'd fallen into a dead faint, only prevented from injuring herself by Gwilym passing by at that moment.

In the hallway, she stopped while the doctor went ahead to the kitchen. She'd done her bit so should go home, get out of their way.

Anwen came out into the hall and closed the door, biting her bottom lip.

'How is she?' said Elizabeth.

'She came round a bit, but she's – she's breathing – funny.' Anwen's face creased and she wiped an escaping tear away.

Elizabeth felt a lump in her throat, swallowing it back so she could reassure her friend. 'The doctor will find out what's wrong.'

'I keep thinking, what if she's been poisoned by the munitions? We did try to tell her.' The last sentence came out on a long whine. 'She just didn't want to hear it. And she's gone an even darker yellow recently.'

'Who else is here now?'

'Gwen's parents are with her. Violet's in the kitchen with Mam. The Owens went home, apart from Gwilym, who's with Idris in the front room, in case they need to carry her to the hospital.' She let out a sob. 'Hywel took the kiddies home, and Cadi's upstairs with Sara Fach.'

'If there's any other errand I can run, just say, otherwise I'll get home too, and get out of your way.'

As she spoke the last word, the door opened and Enid came out. 'We need some blankets to carry Gwen down to the hospital. Can you fetch the spare ones from the trunk in my room?'

Anwen scurried up the stairs. Dr Roberts leaned round the door. 'Ah, Miss Meredith. Would you be as kind as to run down to the hospital and ask them to get a bed ready for Miss Austin? We'll be along shortly.'

'Of course.'

Elizabeth wasted no time in departing, the nervous energy that had propelled her to the doctor's house still present as she sprinted down to the cottage hospital on West Street.

After completing her mission, she took the route home more slowly. She thought she might meet the men coming down with Gwen but didn't see them. What a day. It had started out as a celebration and turned into a calamity. The yellow skin – it surely must have something to do with that.

Still mulling this over as she entered the house, she could hear the annoyed rumble of her parents' voices. She removed her outdoor wear and unpinned her hat, placing it on the console table. Perhaps she would take it upstairs now, giving her an excuse not to enter the drawing room to say hello. Yet she wanted to tell them about Gwen. It might make them realise that their own petty gripes were pointless.

She'd only placed one foot on the first step when the drawing room door opened.

'Is that you, Elizabeth?' called her mother.

'Yes. I'll take my hat upstairs and then I'll join you. I have something to tell you.'

'No, you will leave your hat there and come in here now.'

She placed it down, hoping she wasn't expected to mediate between her parents as she had once before. It wasn't fair to put that burden on her.

Elizabeth followed her in, closing the door behind her. Herbert was standing in the middle of the room, hands linked behind his back, rocking slightly. He looked like he'd had enough of whatever it was already.

'Are you going to deal with this, or do I have to, yet again?' said Margaret, her back stiff and chin tilted up as she surveyed her husband.

'Look, before you start,' said Elizabeth, 'I want to tell you about Gwen Austin. Her father is Albert Austin, who's an overman at the colliery.'

'Yes, I know who you mean,' said Herbert.

'We're not discussing this trifling matter now!' hollered Margaret.

'It's not trifling, Mother! She collapsed at Anwen's today. She works at the munitions in Ebbw Vale, one of the Canary Girls, as they call them, and she's been taken to hospital. She's gone yellow, so I'm afraid it could be—'

'She's probably another of those strumpets who's got herself with child!'

Elizabeth pressed her fists into balls, jamming her arms into her legs. 'No, it's not that. And how can a woman get *herself* with child! Will you listen? I'm afraid it could be TNT poisoning, which I've read can affect some of the workers quite severely, and even cause death.'

'That is worrying indeed,' said Herbert.

'I'm sure it is, to her family,' Margaret said, brushing the matter away with a flick of her hand, 'but it does not concern us at this moment.'

'I beg to differ,' said Elizabeth, storming across the room.

'Where are you going?' said Margaret.

'To sit down!'

'Stay where you are. I don't intend for this to last long.'

'Well *I'm* going to sit down,' said Herbert.

Margaret frowned at him. 'I had a telephone call about an hour ago.'

'And what has that got to do with me?' She should leave, not be dragged into her mother's dramas. She looked at the fire, longing to sit by it quietly and read.

'It was from Anna Fitzgerald. I had to get your father home straight away.'

A chill ran down her back. 'Has Sidney been killed – or injured?' Better the latter, but it would still be awful.

'Not as far as I'm aware. This has nothing to do with him.'

Elizabeth made an 'O' with her mouth and blew out in relief as her hand went to her chest. 'Then what—'

'Have you nothing to explain this, this, outrage?' said Margaret.

'I'm not sure what I'm supposed to say. All you've told me is that you had a telephone call. I'm not a mind-reader.'

'Don't you be impertinent with me, young lady.'

'Margaret, she's a grown woman. There's no need to speak to her like that. And she's right that you haven't actually told her the problem.'

Her mother didn't regard her husband as she said, 'Grown woman she may be, but she's acting like a petulant youth. It's the kind of thing I expect of Tom, not her. I should have known you'd take her side.'

'What on earth—?' Elizabeth started.

'She must know of what I am speaking, but if we must play this game… You were seen with Gwilym Owen last week, outside the picture house in Bargoed, when you told me you were going with Rosemary Grayson.'

This was unfortunate, but she could hardly deny it. 'Yes, all right, so I went with Gwilym. So what? It was simply company. And how on earth would Lady Fitzgerald know Gwilym anyway?'

'It wasn't her who saw you. It was Ralph Tallis. He recognised him from when he came to visit the allotments. He couldn't remember his name, just said it was "that chap who ran the allotments" with you. He mentioned it to Anna when he saw her at a meeting.'

'What a' – she didn't say the word that came to mind first – 'brute. It's just him getting his own back for me finding out he was walking out with both me and Gwen, who I was just talking about.'

'Don't bring her into it again. Furthermore, he claims you were arm-in-arm! So what have you got to say to *that*?'

Elizabeth pressed her lips together, then spoke without looking at either of her parents. 'Caught red-handed, as they say. But then, if you weren't such a snob Mother, I wouldn't have to make things up. I enjoy Gwilym's company, and despite what you think, he is a well-read man.' The thought of him made her smile.

'This is not funny,' said Margaret, her eyes glaring as she went red in the face. 'He is a common miner, *and*,' she emphasised as Herbert was about to interrupt, 'Never likely to be anything else.'

'You can't possibly know—'

'And imagine that dreadful piece of news coming from the perfectly decent man you could have married. And via Lady Fitzgerald, of all people, whose son you're walking out with. I've no doubt she'll tell Sidney, and that will be the end of your chance at a good marriage!'

'I have told you a dozen times, Mother, I am *not* walking out with Sidney. He is simply a friend with whom I correspond.'

'And mixing with that Gwilym Owen of all people, him being the union representative and an agitator who took some of the men out on strike, then marched them all to Tredegar.'

'What, the march that Papa went on too?'

She saw her father raise his eyes heavenward. They had probably argued long and stridently about this already.

'That has nothing to do—' Margaret started.

'And the fact is, the men were keener to go than Gwilym was, because he was afraid it might prejudice their case, but he went along with it because it's what the men wanted. As for Ralph Tallis being a decent man, I refer you to my previous statement about him double-crossing me and Gwen.'

Margaret pinched her lips. Elizabeth wondered how on earth Tallis had seen them when she hadn't spotted him. Probably because she'd only had eyes for Gwilym.

'The answer to that problem, young lady, is that you just have to make yourself more interesting, and goodness knows, I'm aware of that.' She glanced at Herbert.

He shook his head. 'Don't start now, Margaret.'

'Elizabeth cannot be seen to be cavorting with the enemy, and *you* have been setting a bad example on that score.'

'It's up to Papa if he wishes to march with the men. He was one of them once.'

'I have said all I am going to on the matter. Either you stop seeing this man, or you will leave this house forthwith.'

'Don't I have some say in this matter?' said Herbert.

It was time her father made a stand. What was wrong with the man? He managed a whole mine, and did so very well, from what she'd heard. Why wasn't he putting his foot down?

'Yes you do,' said Margaret, 'and it is to agree with the very sensible demand I am making. You didn't get where you are today for your children to end up back in the gutter.'

'We didn't come—' he began.

'And you are not in a position to argue.'

He closed his mouth, looking down and nodding. 'Very well.'

It was on the tip of Elizabeth's tongue to refuse to give Gwilym up, to call her mother's bluff, but she remembered it was Christmas in nine days. Her aunt and uncle, Mama's sister and brother-in-law, were coming to stay. She was another who'd married 'well', although in her case it had been to a local solicitor. He'd gone on to buy into a practice in Worcester. It had irked her mother that Aunty Jennifer had done so well, which was why she'd been so pushy with Herbert and was forever striving to be 'better' than other people.

No, best not stir up trouble. Instead, she'd propose a compromise. It would buy her a little time to decide what to do, and she could discuss it with Gwilym when she met him for the lecture next Friday.

'Mama, I agree not to see Gwilym over the yuletide season. I do not want to cause bad feeling, what with Aunty Jennifer and Uncle Charles arriving.'

Her mother went to interrupt her yet again, but Herbert said, 'Let the girl finish,' as he pulled on his starched collar and loosened his tie a little.

Elizabeth continued. 'I realise you've been under a great deal of pressure, what with Tom's problems and him going off to war. I believe the few days over Christmas will give us both time to think and decide what is best.'

'It would be prudent of you to come to the right conclusion by new year. I'm your mother: I know what's best for you.'

'I believe that would be the wisest course of action at the current time,' said Herbert, rising. 'Now, if you'll excuse me, I'm going back to the colliery.'

Margaret frowned. 'I hope you're going to be back for dinner. It's Sunday, for pity's sake.'

'Which, due to the war, we now have some men working on. I'll probably be a little late. I wouldn't be home now if you hadn't made the situation sound so dire on the telephone.'

'Well, off you go, back to your *men*.' She waved her hand dismissively.

He walked to the door and entered the short passageway, wishing no one farewell.

Margaret smoothed down her dress. 'I don't know about you, but I have dinner to prepare.'

'I'm not hungry, so if you don't mind, I'll go up to my room.'

Her mother looked sharply at her. 'A little help would be appreciated.'

'And so would a little peace and quiet,' Elizabeth retorted. 'Excuse me.'

She skirted round her mother, who was in the way of the door now, and headed for the stairs. There was a lot to consider.

Gwen's eyes flickered, trying to focus. She wondered if she'd be able to keep them open any longer than the few seconds she'd managed so far. There was an unpleasantly tangy odour she couldn't quite place. She had a vague idea she was in bed but was too tired to figure out why, since there was daylight. Was it Sunday?

Carbolic, that was the smell. She'd always hated it. Hospital! What on earth was she doing here? She'd seen some faces. Her parents, and possibly Anwen and Violet. Elizabeth's voice came to mind, something about her not knowing if Gwen could hear her, but hoping she'd come round properly soon. Come round from what? And Esther Williams? There'd been nurses and Dr Roberts. What was going on?

She tried to recall what she'd been doing before waking up here. There had been a house, not her own. Anwen's! Lots of people. Why had she been there? An image of the white dress she'd made popped into her head. Sara Fach's adoption. That was it.

Her eyes stretched wide as she looked around, turning her head slowly. The fog in her head cleared a little. Sister Grey was at the bottom of her bed, her starched white apron, headdress and sleeve protectors pristine white.

'Nurse, fetch Dr Roberts please, he's in the other ward,' the sister called across the room. 'How are you feeling now, Miss Austin?'

'What happened? I don't remember coming here,' she croaked.

'You wouldn't, you were unconscious.'

Then she recalled she'd felt a bit dizzy earlier. 'What time did I come in, and what time is it now? It's sunny outside.' She looked at the window opposite.

'I'm afraid it's a matter of what *day* you came in. That was Sunday. It's Wednesday now.'

'Wednesday! I've got work!' She tried to sit up but felt sick.

Sister Grey came to her side. 'Do not try to move. I'm afraid you won't be going to work for a good long while.' The tone reminded Gwen of being at school.

She panicked. Would they keep her job open for her? How much money was she going to lose? 'What's wrong with me?'

'I'll leave the explanation to Dr Roberts. Here he is.'

The doctor, in a white, knee-length jacket, strolled down the ward to the second to last bed, where Gwen lay.

'Good, you're awake, Miss Austin.'

'What's happened to me?'

Dr Roberts came to the side of the bed and sat in the chair. 'You must have been aware that your skin was deeply yellow.'

'So is the skin of all the girls at the munitions. It's nothing unusual. The Canary Girls, they call us.'

'Haven't there been some women there who've left because they were ill – or worse?'

Gwen swallowed hard. 'A few girls have left over the time I've been there, some because they were unwell. But people get ill, don't they?'

One had died, but no one had said what the cause was. It was best sometimes not to ask.

'The skin being tinted, in itself, isn't dangerous, and fades with time, but it can be an indication of illness too. The chemicals get into your skin, and you breathe them in, and they're not good for the liver. This can lead to anaemia and jaundice.'

She was aware of the terms but didn't really understand what they meant. 'Isn't jaundice what newborn babies have?'

'Some have it mildly yes. But this is more serious. You have something called toxic jaundice, due to, well, basically your liver being poisoned.'

Gwen tried to gasp but ended up coughing instead. 'Will I die?' she managed through a strangled sob.

'No, you're one of the lucky ones, Miss Austin. I believe you can recover completely. But only if you don't go back to Ebbw Vale. A few months' bed rest is what you need.'

'Will I have to have an operation? Or have to take some medicine?'

He shook his head. 'Time will be your medicine.' He looked at his pocket watch, 'Now, it will be visiting time soon. You've been popular since you came in, always had someone by your bed, so you might want to get a bit of rest before it starts.' He gave her a smile before moving on to the patient next to her. 'Now, Mrs Jones…'

Gwen looked up at the ceiling, trying to take it all in. What would her future hold? There'd certainly be plenty of time to think about it.

–

As visitors started to pour in, Gwen tried to look past them, to see if anyone was coming to visit her today. Nurse Campbell had plumped up her pillows and helped her sit up a little, so she could talk to people better.

It wasn't long before a smiling face headed for her bed, sporting a shabby but clean coat, a little black hat perched on neat hair. Gwen's heart sank.

'Hello dear,' said Esther, sitting primly on the chair, putting on the airs and graces she used to be well known for. 'It's good to see you awake at last. How are you feeling?'

'Groggy.'

'That's to be expected. I've got my Christopher to write to Daniel, to tell him what's happened to you. He'll want to know, and I suppose it will be a few days before you can sit up and write.'

'Oh, yes. Thank you.' That was a point: she hadn't asked Dr Roberts how long she'd likely be in hospital.

'Now, I don't know if Daniel's written to you in the last few days, but I've brought a letter he's sent to Christopher. Thought it might cheer you up to know that at least he's all right.' She pulled the letter from her pocket.

'I, um, yes, I'm glad to hear that.'

Esther started the letter, obviously written for a younger sibling, full of the sounds of artillery and danger, but nothing gruesome. He spoke of discomfort, rank water and lice, making the experience sound unappealing, which she was sure had been his aim. When they'd had their trip to the Institute to see the operetta, he'd spoken of his little brother's attempt to sign up and how he 'hoped to God', as he put it, that the war would be over before he was old enough to fight.

She noticed Esther glancing over at the door several times as she was reading, which made her wonder if anybody she really wanted to see was coming in today. The thought had barely passed when the doors opened and her mother strode in, undoing her coat as her footsteps tapped on the wooden floorboards.

'You're awake! That's wonderful,' said Ruth, speeding up. 'You may leave, Mrs Williams. Gwen has her mother to keep her company now.' Reaching the bed, she leaned over to hug her daughter lightly.

Esther's posture became hunched. 'I was just reading this letter from Daniel as I thought Gwen might—'

'Gwen has her own letter from him, thank you very much.' She unclipped the handbag on her wrist and pulled an envelope from inside it. 'Goodbye, Mrs Williams.'

Shoving the letter back into the envelope, Esther stood. 'I'll be going, then. Cheerio, dear, see you again sometime.' She shuffled away, head bowed.

'The cheek of the woman,' said Ruth, when she was possibly still in earshot. She took her place in the chair.

'She's not doing any harm, Mam. I think she's a bit lonely.'

'Her own fault if she is. Never mind her, it's marvellous to see you awake.' She patted her arm. 'How are you feeling? How long have you been awake? Has the doctor told you about the jaundice?'

'So many questions, Mam. I woke up a coupla hours ago. I'm slowly remembering what happened. I'd had a bit of a dizzy spell during the day, and again when I got to Anwen's.'

'You never mentioned it.' Ruth's forehead puckered.

'I didn't want to make a fuss on Sara Fach's special day. I thought I was just tired.'

'Doctor reckons you'll be out well in time for Christmas, so we'll drag the chaise from the front room, and put it in the kitchen for you, near the range so you can keep warm.'

'No, don't do that. I'll be more than happy in one of the armchairs. I don't want to be lying down all the time.'

'All right, *cariad*. Whatever makes you comfortable.' Ruth stroked her arm where it poked out of the hospital gown.

'I'm sorry you've had to go to so much trouble. It's just, the money at the factory is so good.' She didn't add that she'd hated the actual job. Filling the shells and screwing on the tops had been tedious, and the lifting backbreaking. Plus, the place had a reek about it that was much worse than the hospital.

'Oh, I can understand that being a big attraction. I'm sure at your age, I'd have loved the opportunity to earn so much. But there's more important things than money, like your health.'

'They still send the men out to fight, even though it's not good for their health,' Gwen countered.

'If they became as ill as you have, they'd send them home, right enough.'

'And when they'd got better, they'd send them back. Perhaps when I'm better—'

'You're not listening, girl!' Ruth, realising her raised pitch had people looking at her, said more quietly, 'Didn't Dr Roberts tell you you're not to go back?'

'Yes,' she said reluctantly.

'Because if you do, you'll likely not survive this time. I dunno what else he told you, but I gather if you'd worked there much longer, you'd have been a goner, and no mistake.' Ruth pulled a handkerchief from her handbag and wiped her eyes as she sniffed back tears.

'Oh Mam, I'm sorry.'

'Never mind your sorries, it's me what's sorry. I should have insisted you stopped working there. I was never happy with that awful colour you went. Now, there's an end to it. Here's your letter from your – whatever he is.' She put the envelope in Gwen's hand.

'Friend, Mam, he's a friend. That's all. Thank you. I'll read it later. Is Da coming today?'

'He'll not long have left his shift. He said this morning he'd have a wash and pop round after.'

'Good.'

Ruth embarked on the account of what happened after Gwen had passed out. She half-listened, pondering at the same time what the future held for her.

Chapter Eleven

Elizabeth came down the stairs in a great hurry, not wanting to be late for the lecture, which she'd been looking forward to. One last chance to see Gwilym until after the Christmas period, by which time she would have hopefully worked something out. She was removing her coat from the hat stand as her mother marched into the hall from the study.

'Where are you going this evening?'

'I've already told you this, Mother. It's a talk at the Workmen's Institute in Bargoed, on Welsh culture.'

'Hm! It doesn't sound very interesting.'

'It is to me.'

Margaret continued to stare at Elizabeth as she did up her coat. 'Who are you going with then?'

'Wilma Floyd might be there.' It was a good thing she'd applied some rouge, as she was sure her cheeks were flushed. Still, if her mother had been more reasonable, she would not have needed to fib. And for all she knew, Wilma might turn up.

'The woman you worked with in the overseer's office? You went with her to the theatre, or so you said.' The last four words were said through gritted teeth.

It was not quite what she'd said, but it had done the trick at the time.

'I hope that Gwilym Owen won't be there.'

'I've no idea who else will be there.'

Elizabeth stood in front of the mirror and pressed her lips together, making sure the poppy stain was even. Closing her eyes briefly, she imagined the pressure on them was Gwilym's lips, triggering butterflies in her stomach. Next, she placed her hat on her head and cautiously applied the pin. She'd chosen to wear her dark green velvet skirt, which went only a couple of inches past her knees, and a new V-neck blouse with delicate embroidery down the front.

'You're going to a lot of trouble for a lecture.' Margaret folded her arms and frowned. 'Who are you expecting to be there, Lord Aberconway?'

'You never know whether some influential person will be there, like Anna Fitzgerald, for instance.' Though she sorely hoped the woman wouldn't be.

'*Lady* Fitzgerald wouldn't go to such a lecture.'

'A councillor, then.'

Margaret sniffed. 'What time does it start?'

Her mother was asking a lot of questions, suggesting she didn't believe her.

'Seven-thirty. Right, I'll be off.'

'I will see *you* later,' said Margaret, like it was a threat.

Elizabeth left the house and headed to the motorcar, parked next to the garden wall. In some ways she felt guilty, leaving Mama on her own. Papa was at the gentlemen's club this evening.

Having cranked the handle to start the motorcar, she got in and made her way towards the village. About to turn the corner over the stream, a motorcar loomed from the mist in the dip and went past her, up the hill. It was hard to be sure, but it had looked like Anna Fitzgerald's motorcar, a Wolseley-Siddeley Tourer. How strange. Mama hadn't mentioned her coming to visit. It was a little late for a spur-of-the-moment call. At least she'd have company and would be less of a worry.

She forgot about the pair of them as she emerged from the mist, into the village, imagining instead how it would feel to have Gwilym to herself again.

Always convinced that one of these days he wouldn't turn up, she was relieved to see him at the end of the village, under the last streetlamp, a scarf wrapped round his neck several times and his cap pulled down.

'I was afraid you wouldn't come with this weather,' said Elizabeth, as Gwilym got into the motorcar.

He leant over to kiss her lips. He lingered some seconds before sitting back up. 'It's only a little misty. And I'm looking forward to the talk.'

'That's why you're really coming, isn't it?' she joked.

'Of course. Spending time with you's only a secondary consideration.' He put on a mock serious expression.

Having him so close brought her senses alive, even more so than in her days at the Suffragette meetings. They'd been filled with the passion of their cause; this was an altogether different type of passion, one she'd never imagined would be so raw, so all-consuming.

He twisted round to kiss her again, this time the two of them clinging on to each other, as awkward as it was in the motorcar seats. The motorcar rumbled as it ticked over.

Gwilym was the first to pull away. 'We'd better get going. I dare say you'll have to take it a bit slower because of the mist. There'll be time afterwards if we want to pull up somewhere for a while.'

Elizabeth set off, a thrill swirling around her body as she anticipated further embraces from him later in the evening. They would be worth waiting for.

–

'The talk made it well worth tackling the inclement weather,' she said to Gwilym as the applause came to a close.

'Aye, it was,' he agreed. 'There were some ideas we could use there.'

'Indeed. And maybe useful for me, in the future.'

'Why's that?' he asked.

She'd never confessed this to anyone before, but who was a better person to tell than him, who shared her enthusiasm for growing vegetables?

'I was thinking, maybe after the war, of starting a market garden.'

His expression became one of bemusement.

'Am I being ridiculous to have such an ambition?' she asked.

'No, not at all! It's just, well, it was something I'd had at the back of my mind, as a possibility. I've been thinking for years about what I could do to get out of the pit. Maybe it is a ridiculous idea for me though.'

'Of course it isn't. Well, fancy that, us having the same ambition. Come on, we'd better get moving before the rest of the row wants to get out.'

As much as she'd enjoyed the talk, Elizabeth couldn't help but be thankful it had come to an end, for now she and Gwilym could spend some time together, just the two of them.

People rose to leave, the chatter around them positive. The two of them moved back towards the doors, discussing one of the matters raised. They walked slowly, heads down, following the sluggish progress of those ahead. She was in the middle of a sentence when she was halted by the sharp use of her name.

'Elizabeth!'

Her head sprang up to see her mother and Lady Fitzgerald standing behind the back row. Both she and Gwilym came to such a sudden halt that those behind almost bumped into them.

'I'm so sorry,' she said, as she and Gwilym moved to one side in the aisle. Several pairs of eyes were upon them, alerted to some trouble by Margaret's tone.

'You said you were coming with Miss Floyd.' Margaret's voice was accusing, her face twisted in fury. Beside her Anna half-smiled, as if gloating at her discovery.

Elizabeth composed herself, despite the tremor of fear in her chest. She did not want it apparent in her speech. 'I said she might be here, and I also said I had no idea who else was coming. Wilma didn't turn up. Gwilym just happened to already be—'

'Do not give me that! We saw you alight the motorcar together, so you clearly gave him a lift.'

Where on earth had they been, not to be noticed by her? But then, there had been several cars in Bargoed that evening, and it was still misty, so she likely had taken no notice.

'And you didn't say the talk was by an ardent Welsh Nationalist!' Margaret hissed. 'That's what mixing with the likes of a radical troublemaker like *him* does.' She jabbed a finger in Gwilym's direction. 'Next you'll be going on a demonstration!'

The conversation was garnering more attention now, with some tuts from those who plainly didn't like her mother's opinion of them. Gwilym shuffled his feet and twisted his cap in his hands.

Elizabeth pulled herself to her full height to claw back the higher ground. 'Mother, I can only assume you followed me here, which, given that I am now twenty-seven, seems an intrusion into my privacy.'

Margaret's mouth opened to speak, but Anna Fitzgerald beat her to it. 'You are an ungrateful daughter, indeed. Your parents have kept you in a manner to which you clearly have become accustomed, so that instead of going out into the world to do something useful, like my own dear daughters, you laze around, playing at gardening.'

Elizabeth's whole body glowed hot with the indignity of Anna's words. 'Perhaps you should ask Mama why it is I am still at home and treated to various threats when I suggest work I could do.'

With that, she took Gwilym's arm and marched him through the gawping crowd.

'Elizabeth? Elizabeth! Come back here this instant,' her mother yelled.

'I should see myself home,' Gwilym said softly, attempting to untangle his arm from hers. 'I don't want you getting into any more trouble.'

She slid her other hand through his arm to hold on tighter. 'I'm not giving in to her browbeating.' Her speed increased. 'Once out of here I suggest we rush to the car before my mother catches up. She is not one for running.'

Outside the hall, they did as she suggested, Gwilym throwing his cap back on his head as they went. At the motorcar, she fetched the crank and turned it, praying it would behave and start the engine promptly. It did. Jumping in, she soon pulled away, spotting her mother, her umbrella raised in threat, as they headed down the road.

'How dare she come to make a fool of me,' Elizabeth spat. 'And encouraged by that, that *woman*. Oh, so refined she acts, always crowing about how superior she is, yet she'd stoop to this.'

'I'm so sorry this has happened.' Gwilym took a long breath out, placing his head in his hands.

'Gwilym, it's not your fault.'

He looked ahead. 'I should have left you alone. What future is there for us?'

Wild thoughts entered Elizabeth's mind. She could drive off into the night, take her and Gwilym far away, where nobody would question their relationship. But where, in wartime? To another colliery village? For if Gwilym were without a mining job, he would be conscripted. Or could she move into a place in Dorcalon, get a job? She had some savings, but not enough to rent a house long term, and a woman's wages wouldn't pay the bills. Become a lodger? She could see her mother making a great deal of trouble for whoever rented her a room. Yet what could she do?

'As much future as there is for anyone,' she eventually replied. 'I love you, Gwilym, surely that's what counts.'

There, she'd said it. His silence made it hard for her to swallow.

'And I love you too, Elizabeth. I truly do. Never felt about any woman what I feel for you.'

She sighed with relief, but the tears fell anyway. 'Shall we run away together?'

'Running away's no solution. And I couldn't leave my family, especially with Da gone now.'

'No, of course you couldn't. I'm sorry, I'm being selfish. What are we to do?'

'Wait. See each other when we can.'

'My mother always seems to find out. It's like she has spies everywhere.' In a way she did, with her extensive network of ladies from various charitable committees. 'Damn Tallis! He is to blame for my mother finding out in the first place.'

'We should have been more careful after she threatened you.'

'It feels like everywhere we go, there's someone she knows who'll tell her.' She slammed the steering wheel with her fist.

'We've been pretty lucky up 'til now. Not everyone is ready to spy on us. I bet Anwen and Idris would be sympathetic. We'll find a way. In the meantime, you'd better drop me off here.' He pointed to the side of the road as they entered Dorcalon.

'It's not like I have to hide you from my mother tonight. And few people will be out. I will drive you to your street in case she sees you when Lady Fitzgerald drives her back. I wouldn't want her causing you more trouble.'

The motorcar grumbled a little as she took the hill up past Jubilee Green and turned onto Edward Street. At the end she stopped, looking around to make sure the road was empty. She leant over to Gwilym, kissing his lips quickly. When she pulled away his face was crumpled with concern.

'It won't be too bad for you at home, will it?'

'My father is much more understanding than she is, so I dare say he'll temper her anger when he returns.' She could only hope.

'If it becomes too bad, come and see me, please.'

'I will. Thank you, Gwilym. In the meantime, I think we'd better delay seeing each other again until the new year.'

'As loath as I am to agree, because I'll miss you, it will give things a chance to settle down a little.'

He leant over to give her a last peck, before exiting the motorcar. She watched for a moment as he disappeared down the side of the house, to go in the back way.

There was a face at the front window of the Rhys's house as she turned around and set off. It was Cadi, by the looks of it. She didn't think her the type to go tittle-tattling around the neighbours. At that moment she couldn't care less if she did. Let them all know. She wasn't ashamed.

When she arrived home, she was surprised to see the house in darkness. Anna couldn't have dropped her mother off home yet, otherwise she would most certainly be waiting up for her. With much relief, she went immediately to her bedroom. On finding the key in one of the dressing table drawers, she locked the door, something she rarely did. She undressed in the dark; with any luck her mother would think her already asleep and leave her alone until the morning. Or think she'd run away. After a night's sleep, she would be better prepared to deal with all that was undoubtedly coming.

Chapter Twelve

Elizabeth awoke early the next morning to distant shouting. At first she thought it was the lingering sounds of a dream about the night before. It was her door handle rattling that made her realise it was happening in the here and now.

'Margaret, that isn't going to help,' her father's voice appealed.

'Why has she locked the door? She must have that Gwilym Owen in there.'

'Don't be ridiculous. She's probably locked it because she knew you'd try to barge in, just like you are doing.'

Elizabeth sat up. She pushed the quilt and blankets back and slid her legs over onto the floor. Finding her dressing gown draped over the dressing table chair, she slipped it on.

The voices were quieter now, until her father said, 'And what was the point of coming to the club to get me and causing a scene there last night, after all the fuss had already occurred? It could have waited until I'd got home. Really, I should have thought Anna Fitzgerald would have had more sense than to have driven you there. You embarrassed me no end.'

Elizabeth blew out a breath of astonishment. She could imagine that not going down well at the gentlemen's club. A small part of her laughed at the idea of a woman turning up to cause a ruction. That's all those chauvinistic men deserved, in their closed male world, where women weren't allowed. What had possessed the very proper *Lady* Fitzgerald to do that?

Because she enjoyed humiliating those she believed were below her. She was no different to her own mother in that respect, except she was doing it from a higher position. If nothing else, the whole debacle should put her firmly out of the running as a wife for either of the Fitzgerald boys.

It was time to get this over and done with. She tied the cord of her dressing gown and unlocked the door. Stepping onto the landing, she saw her parents about to take the stairs down.

'About time,' her mother bellowed in an unladylike fashion. 'Where is he, that villain?'

'Villain? Do not be ridiculous, Mother. And I should imagine he's in the mine, working, since it is a Saturday.'

As Margaret lifted her arm to illustrate some further point, Herbert took hold of it gently and lowered it.

'Let us discuss this as adults and get it over and done with. I don't want to be long for I should be at the colliery already. Lizzie is twenty-seven years old and, as I have said before, can make up her own mind. Sometimes, Margaret, I think you have delusions about how high our station is.'

'And you think too little of our station; that is quite evident.'

Her father hung his head, shaking it a little.

'Now Herbert, if you want to maintain your position, and Elizabeth, if you want to continue living in this house, this is what is going to happen. You will not see Gwilym Owen in any capacity ever again. You will dismiss him from leading the allotments, or, alternatively, you will step back yourself. If this instruction is not obeyed, your father will dismiss Gwilym from the mine.'

'But Mama!' collided with, 'Margaret, for pity's sake.'

Despite her mother lifting her hand for silence, Herbert carried on speaking. 'It is not for me to dismiss a man because you don't like the look of him.'

'But if I tell the coal company he has assaulted my daughter, it will be taken out of your hands. I am sure they would trust my word over his, and that of my poor, overwrought daughter.'

'Mother, you wouldn't.'

'Margaret, this is ludicrous.'

'What is ludicrous is the craving this family has for cavorting with the lower classes. For goodness' sake, pull yourselves together. We are middle class now.'

A picture of Polly Coombes came to Elizabeth's mind, with her small but obvious bump, standing in their sitting room eighteen months back. This was so very different, but maybe what had occurred with Polly had prejudiced her mother against all her class.

'Well, what have you got to say?' Margaret pursed her lips as she looked down her nose at her daughter.

After the wonderful surges of hope she'd experienced the last few weeks, that there might be someone out there she wanted to be with, she now felt the weight of a new decision fall upon her. She heard Gwilym's voice in her head: *I should have left you alone. What future is there for us?*

'I'd say you give me no choice.'

'I knew you'd see sense.' Margaret displayed a triumphant smile as she did an about turn to face Herbert. 'You see, dear, it takes a firm hand to deal with these matters. Now you may return to work.' She flicked her hand in a dismissive manner.

'I need to have a word with Lizzie about those allotments you just mentioned. Some news from the coal company.'

'Very well. In the meantime, I have a committee to attend, to organise several events ahead. One is to raise money for the Welsh Soldiers' Fund and the other two for Netley Hospital, for our poor injured soldiers.' She wore the pompous smirk like a badge of honour. 'I mustn't keep the ladies waiting, especially as Lady Hortense Rees-Smithers is our chairwoman. She so relies on me to get the ball rolling. I will let you off today, Elizabeth, as you do look a state, but in future you will attend these meetings with me. It's about time you did something useful.'

'Yes, you're right, Mama. It is about time I did something useful.' But could she? Would she be able to go out on a limb, away from the life she was familiar with?

'I'm so glad we see eye to eye at last.'

Margaret headed downstairs, humming 'Santa Lucia', a recent gramophone record acquisition.

Herbert waited until she'd disappeared before saying, 'I'm afraid it's not good news, Lizzie. I had a visit from one of the company's agents yesterday, and from the first of January they're withdrawing permission for your general use of the land.'

'What? This isn't my mother's doing, is it?' Elizabeth's anger rose once more.

'No, no, nothing of the sort.'

'Then I'll convince them that having the allotments is for the good of their workers. Who shall I see?'

He shook his head. 'No point. They're fully aware that it's beneficial to have allotments, which is why they're going to divide up the land and rent it out to individuals.'

Elizabeth leant against the wall, wanting to cry, but not in front of her father. She took a while before she said, 'And that way, they make more money for themselves.'

'That's the long and short of it,' Herbert agreed.

She pushed herself away from the wall, a fury emerging. 'They're just greedy and want to make money out of the poor!'

'I don't disagree, Lizzie. But I'm powerless in this situation. What will you do?'

'What options do I have? I need to decide on a few things.'

They heard Margaret back in the hall, humming once more, before the front door opened and closed.

'I'll leave you to it and see you later.'

She watched him go down the stairs. He also went through the front door, then all was silent.

Elizabeth shuffled back to her bedroom like a wounded animal. She closed the door and leant her back against it. Was the situation really as bad as it seemed? After due consideration, she and Gwilym could work something out with her parents, surely.

An ache of despondency shot through her. She should have left him alone in the first place. Good sense had told her that, but she'd ignored it. She didn't want his life ruined by her. And now the allotments, her one success, and the very thing that had brought them together, were to be rented off. Everything, gone. The thought was like a spear through her heart.

Yes, it was about time she did something useful. And she knew now what that was.

She went to her dressing table and took a writing pad and fountain pen from one of the drawers, along with the last letter from her friend Rosemary Grayson.

—

'It's kind of you to let us pick the veggies for our use,' Ruth Austin called to Elizabeth, as she pulled a few more of the sprouts off a long stalk on the field on Edward Street. 'I'll need some nourishing food to get Gweneth healthy again, with her coming out of the hospital tomorrow.'

Elizabeth stood up from where she'd been bending to snip cabbages, enjoying the cool breeze. 'I'm glad she's well enough to come home, especially with Christmas in a couple of days. As for the vegetables, they belong to everybody, and I'm darned if I'm going to let the coal company get the benefit of them to entice allotment rentals.'

'I don't know why they couldn't have waited 'til the spring,' said Ruth. 'It's not like they can do much with them now.'

'Just greedy, they are,' said Mary Jones, as she passed by with a crate of parsnips. 'Put a lot of time into this, we have, and it pains me that they'd take it away from us. My Percy reckons they're getting their own back for the men striking in November.'

Her mother had said similar, except she'd worded in a way that implied it was a rightful punishment.

'If we can do some good with these and distribute them among some of the villagers, that will be something.'

Mary nodded. 'The people we delivered to last night were pleased as Punch.'

They'd had a brief meeting yesterday morning, at Anwen's house – she and Mary, Anwen, and Gwilym's grancher Abraham, all of whom had played a part in running the allotments since they'd started them a couple of years back. As had Gwilym and Idris, but they'd been at work. The group had decided to make a list of families who were suffering the most hardship. They'd divide the vegetables up and put them into boxes, sack bags and any other containers they could find, to drop around to the families chosen. They were going to set up a stall tomorrow morning, Christmas Eve, and give all the remaining vegetables to anyone who turned up: first come, first served.

Elizabeth looked around. 'It's good to see so many of the children helping out again.'

'It gives them something to do now they're on their Christmas holidays,' said Mary.

Rachael Owen came over with a crate she'd filled with cabbages. 'That angry my Gwilym is, about the coal company.'

The mention of his name produced in Elizabeth a strange mixture of longing and despair. 'We all are, Mrs Owen. At least we have the benefit of it being Sunday today, so most of our volunteers have been able to help. I see Gwilym has moved the chicken run.'

'Yes, he, Idris and Hywel missed chapel this morning to dismantle it and set it up in our garden. He's going to keep giving out eggs, though.'

'That's kind of him...' Her dear, thoughtful Gwilym. 'Oh no, this doesn't look good.'

Those nearby took a few steps onto the pavement, following Elizabeth. Steaming up it, his face puffed out in anger, arms swinging as if he were in a race, was James the Veg. Anwen, further down the field, walked up towards them.

'What is the meaning of this?' he blustered. 'I've just heard from customers that you're *giving* this away! No wonder I've not been so busy, and at Christmas too.'

'If you've heard that, Mr James, you must also have heard that the coal company are taking back possession of the fields, to let them out as individual allotments.' Elizabeth breathed deeply, the emotion of the unfair situation threatening to swamp her.

'What? I'd heard they were taking them back, but not why. That means people won't come to me at all if they're growing their own. And why is that an excuse to give the veg away? You could have sold this lot to me and I could have sold it on!'

'We wanted to get it sorted out by Christmas,' said Anwen. 'And we thought it more likely people would help if they were to benefit.'

'It's outrageous!'

'Tell that to the coal company!' Rachael shouted over.

'What's going to happen to the stuff still growing?' The greengrocer lifted his arm to indicate the field.

'We're inviting people to come after Christmas to dig it up and transplant it to their own gardens,' said Elizabeth. 'Don't be angry with us, Mr James, we're simply trying to make the best of it. Perhaps you could negotiate with some of the new tenants when they get started.'

'It won't be worth it, all of them doing their own little bits. I shall take this up with someone on the council.' He twirled round and hurried off back towards his shop, right at the end of the road.

'He can rave all he likes,' said Rachael. 'It's not going to make no difference. By the way, Miss Elizabeth, I forgot to tell you, Gwilym managed to arrange with Farmer Lloyd for him to bring his horse and cart over later, to help shift the crates from the different fields. We'll store them in our back garden, then tomorrow, we can put them round the front here.'

'That is going to be such a good help, Mrs Owen, thank you. I can't tell you how much I appreciate everyone's assistance, especially when you should all be at home getting ready for Christmas.'

'We'll appreciate it all the more for having done some good, as our Lord would want us to.'

'You all deserve a very happy Christmas after this.'

For her it would be the worst one she'd ever lived through. Her aunt and uncle were turning up today, so at least her mother would have to be on her best behaviour. She always liked to perpetuate the veneer of a happy family, especially with her more successful sister. The two of them would likely spend the three days playing a subtle game of one-upmanship.

'Everyone's working so well,' said Anwen, following Elizabeth back to the crates. 'I'm so proud of them all.'

'So am I.'

'What do you think you'll do after Christmas, with no more allotments? Or will you rent one?'

'No, I certainly will not.' Of that Elizabeth was sure.

'Do you have a new project of any sort in mind?'

She felt the weight on her heart and found it hard at first to speak. 'Possibly, but at this moment these vegetables aren't going to pick themselves, and it'll be dark in a couple of hours. Better press on.'

'Aye aye, Captain!' Anwen saluted before moving on.

Oh yes, she had something in mind all right. Whether she had the courage to see it through she had yet to work out.

Chapter Thirteen

Peace and quiet. After the bustle of the hospital, and then her parents fussing over her since she'd arrived home yesterday, Gwen was glad to be alone for a short while. Da was at work, Mam was helping distribute the last of the vegetables and Mamgu had gone to her knitting group down the road.

She'd had a nap and was now sitting in front of the fire. She adjusted the pads on the wooden armchair to make herself more comfortable and rearranged the blanket over her knees. Her mother had brought her a Mark Twain novel from the library. Reading was a luxury she didn't often have time for, so at least there would be some advantage to this home confinement. It was all right now, in midwinter, while she still felt unwell, but she feared she would soon tire of it.

Opening the book on the first page, she was snuggling into the blanket a little more when there was a knock at the front door.

Should she answer it? It wasn't like she couldn't walk, although she was somewhat slow at the moment. If it had been someone they knew well, they'd have come through the back door and called hello before entering the kitchen. Maybe Mam had locked the back door and they hadn't been able to get in. Despite looking forward to the peace and quiet, she wouldn't mind seeing Violet or Anwen.

She pulled the blanket back and rose, leaving the book on the table as she hobbled towards the hall. Through the glass she could make out a small figure in dark clothing. She opened the door to disappointment, and not a little impatience.

'Mrs Williams, I—'

'Oh my dear, I'm so glad you're in.' The woman was shaking, her face a picture of despair. 'I heard you were home, and I knew you'd want to know.'

'What on earth is wrong?'

The older woman held up a telegram, before bursting into tears.

'Come in, please.' Gwen felt breathless, but this time it was the foreboding of what was coming.

Gwen led her to the kitchen, taking her seat once more and inviting Esther to sit in the wooden armchair opposite.

'I'm so sorry to come when you're just out of hospital, but—'

'What's happened, Mrs Williams?'

'Daniel is missing, pres – presumed…' She couldn't get the last word out.

'I am so very sorry to hear that.' What else could she say? Did Esther expect her to be sobbing her heart out too? She was upset – at the loss of a young life, at yet another one of their men extinguished. Yet, she was not sorry for her own sake. How could she pretend otherwise? She hung her head and shook it as a compromise.

The back door groaned open, and a voice called, 'Hello, Gwen!'

Her mother. What was she doing back already?

The scullery door swung open. 'I was just saying to – what on earth are *you* doing here? I hope you're not upsetting my—'

'Mam! Mrs Williams has just heard that Daniel's missing, presumed… you know. She thought I'd want to know.'

'Oh, oh, um…' Gwen had never seen her mother stumped for words. 'Well, I'll um, get the kettle on, then.' Ruth hurried back to the scullery.

'There's always hope, Mrs Williams. It says missing. So there's always a chance.'

'I know what it means: They can't get to – to the bodies, or – or they're unrecognisable.' She inhaled noisily before letting out a low, strangled howl. 'What a Christmas present for me and my Christopher. I can't even tell him 'til he gets back from his shift.'

Poor Christopher. It was him Gwen felt the sorriest for, despite his brush with stealing earlier in the year. The poor lad wasn't even seventeen yet and look at all he'd gone through. From what Daniel had told her, he regretted his unlawful ways and wanted to leave them behind him. What would this new development do to him?

Ruth returned, brandishing the black kettle with its long, curving spout. 'Let's get this on, and you can tell us what you know, Esther.'

Her mother sat on a smaller wooden armchair, normally Gwen's. She leant over and patted the other woman's arm. 'I reckon you should have someone with you, when you tell Christopher – one of his friends, or better, an older man.'

They discussed, haltingly, who might be able to help. Gwen studied the woman's pale face and uncharacteristically dishevelled hair. Whatever her own problems, she knew she'd have to be on hand to help her through this.

–

As people started to arrive at the house, in the early evening of Boxing Day, Gwen felt guilty at the prospect of enjoying herself. Her mother had organised this get-together, with some games and treats, to give her a lift, but she couldn't help thinking about Esther and Christopher, at home, miserable.

Her mother was right though; cancelling wouldn't bring Daniel back, and there was little else they could do for the pair at the moment.

Gwen greeted the guests individually with a wave. She felt like an invalid, sitting in the armchair, forbidden to stand. Why had her mother invited so many people? Not just Anwen's and

Violet's families, but also Idris's and Gwilym's. Seventeen in all, counting themselves, plus the three kiddies. They had all been friends a long time, but it was rather overwhelming. She'd done her best to dress and make herself up as she would have done had she been well. Her mother had helped her wash her hair and put it up.

'Here she is, like a queen on her throne,' said Albert, pointing his arm towards her.

She felt more like an attraction at a freak show.

'How are you, *cariad*?' said Rachael, bringing in a sack bag of something.

'Better than I was, Mrs Owen, thank you.'

Each of the visiting men carried a chair in with them. How Gwen wished Henry were here. He loved a get-together.

'Thank you for bringing those,' said Albert. 'Should be room for us all to sit down now. Get yourselves organised. Some can sit 'round the table, and we'll make a kind of circle, so we can all hear each other.'

Clarice and Benjy were wildly excited, twirling round and round each other. Sara Fach, in Anwen's arms, caught the mood and giggled.

'Keep still now,' Violet said kindly. 'We don't want to knock anything over.'

'It's wonderful to see them so excited,' said Ruth. 'They make Christmas, children do.'

'Look Aunty Gwenny,' said Clarice, waving a cardboard packet around. 'We got wax crayons for Christmas. They're easier to carry 'round than paints.'

'Aren't you lucky? You'll have to draw me a nice picture each.' Gwen was reminded of a couple of years back, when Clarice had painted a picture of her with yellow skin. Even then, it had been obvious.

Gwilym placed his chair just behind the armchair opposite her, where Mamgu Bertha was knitting away and joining in various conversations. Gwilym was solemn, staring at the wall behind her.

'You all right, mun?' Idris asked him, placing his chair next to his.

'Aye, I'm fine.' The smile he displayed seemed strained to Gwen.

'Awful news about Daniel,' said Rachael. 'I know Esther was no friend of ours, but her son was a decent enough boy.'

There was a mumble of agreement.

Once everyone was settled, Ruth made a pot of tea. Everyone chatted in small groups. Clarice and Benjy, sitting on Hywel and Violet's laps, drew in their drawing books.

'So, what are we going to play first?' said Bertha, placing her knitting on her lap.

'We've got some games to play on paper, and a few for the kiddies, but how about The Minister's Cat to get us going?' said Albert.

'That's a funny game,' Evan called from the far end of the table, where he was settled in with Jenkin.

'You start,' Albert nodded at Gwen.

'All right. The minister's cat is... ancient!' She looked at Anwen to go next.

'The minister's cat is ancient and... bald.' Her answer got a laugh.

'Poor cat!' said Enid. 'Right. The minister's cat is ancient, bald and comfortable. It's got to have something nice in its life.'

And so it went on. Gwen joined in the laughter and groans but still felt vaguely uncomfortable about enjoying herself. It wasn't like she'd asked to get involved in Daniel's family, and she had her own problems. When she was allowed to leave the house, she'd go and see how Esther was. She left it at that and endeavoured to enjoy the games.

Chapter Fourteen

It had only been three days since Gwilym had seen Elizabeth, if only from afar on the allotments, and here he was, yearning to see her again. Hywel and Idris were trudging up Station Road with him, speaking of Sir Douglas Haig's promotion to field marshal. Gwilym only half-listened, more content with his own musings.

The whole shift he'd thought of nothing but Elizabeth, the warmth of her lips against his, the euphoria he experienced when she was near him. They agreed about so many things. All she had to say captivated him. Hywel and Idris's conversation faded into the background.

It was only a few days until the new year, when they'd said they'd find a way to meet again. How would they arrange it though, not meeting on the allotments anymore? Maybe she'd slip a letter through his door, or send a message via Anwen.

They'd reached the butcher's on Jubilee Green when a plummy, discordant voice called his name.

'Gwilym Owen! Stop immediately and explain this aberration to me.' Up the street strode Margaret Meredith. She was framed by the backs of the houses on James Street and the pit beyond, the grating of the pit wheel reflecting the tone of her voice. She was flapping a piece of paper in the air.

They all turned around. The other two looked confused.

'What the devil does she want?' Hywel mumbled.

Gwilym had a fair guess it was something to do with Elizabeth. But what now? It wasn't as though they'd met since that fateful evening. Had she happened upon him accidently, or had she been heading for his house? Whatever the reason, it was best to remain civil. She was Elizabeth's mother, after all.

'How can I help you, Mrs Meredith?'

'You know jolly well how you can help me. Where is she, then?'

'Who are you talking about?' said Hywel.

'That's none of your business, whoever you are.' She stuck her nose in the air.

'This is Mrs Rhys's brother,' Idris piped up, maybe thinking she'd show him a little more respect given Enid was working for them.

Margaret took no notice of him. 'Where is Elizabeth?'

'I have no idea.' Gwilym felt sick. Had she disappeared? And what was the paper her mother was waving around?

'She has packed a suitcase and left. Her wardrobe has clothes missing.'

His voice was unsteady as he said, 'I really have no idea what's happened to her. Why do you think I would?'

Margaret stamped a foot in frustration. '*Don't* give me that. You've been luring her away from us with, with, who knows what? You have nothing to offer!'

Hywel put a hand on Gwilym's shoulder. 'Come on, mun, better to walk away.'

'Don't you incite him to ignore me.' The colour rose in Margaret's cheeks. 'I'll have him sacked, and you. I don't care if you are Mrs Rhys's brother. Who are you to argue with the manager's wife? Now tell me where my daughter is.'

Gwilym had a flash of revelation. He pointed to the piece of paper. 'Is that a note from Elizabeth?'

'I found it this afternoon, when I returned home. Couldn't even tell me to my face.'

'Where does she say she's gone?' The possibility of her departure made his throat dry.

'She claims to have joined the Voluntary Aid Detachment as a nurse. I ask you! As if she'd be capable.'

He lost focus for a second, the certainty of Elizabeth's absence overwhelming him. Gwilym had no doubt that was indeed what she'd done. She'd had much admiration for the women of the VAD and had often talked of her friends who'd joined.

'I think you underestimate what she's capable of,' he said. 'And why you blame me, I don't know. We enjoyed each other's company, it's true, but I'm not the one who's driven her away with demands for this, that and the other. What does her letter say, exactly?'

Margaret placed it behind her back. 'That is none of your business,' she hissed, but she looked less sure of herself.

'Come on, mun, let's get going,' Hywel tried again, pulling on Gwilym's sleeve.

'That's it, take the ruffian away. But he hasn't heard the last of this.' Margaret unclipped her handbag and stuffed the letter in it. She turned on her heel and started back down the slope, leaving the two men alone.

'What was that all about, mun? You're not courting Miss Elizabeth, are you?' said Idris.

'I suppose I was.' Gwilym's stomach squirmed once again. Why had she gone without saying anything to him? Had he really meant as much to her as she did to him?

Hywel let out a long whistle and scratched his chin. 'Well, you are full of surprises, *bach*. Dunno how you expected that to end.'

'No, me neither.'

'Ah, there's Twm Bach,' said Hywel. 'I need to have a word with him. See you tomorrow.' He crossed over, calling Twm's name.

Gwilym and Idris started off once more up the hill.

'Do you want to talk about it?' asked Idris.

'Not really.'

'Fair enough.'

At Idris's house, Gwilym was lifting a hand in farewell and walking away when Anwen ran out of the door, almost knocking her husband over.

'Sorry, Idris. Gwilym! Wait a moment.' She ran up the road, stopping just short of him. 'Elizabeth put an envelope through the door for me this morning. It also contained this.' She held out a letter to him.

He was loath to take it, knowing he was not going to like the contents. His hand went out gingerly, removing the unwanted missive from Anwen's hand.

'Thank you. Has she said anything to you about joining the VAD?'

Anwen scrunched her eyes up. 'Yes, she said so in her letter to me.'

'It's what her mother said, too.' He looked down at his feet.

'Her mother?'

'I'll tell you over dinner,' said Idris, joining them. He leant sideways to look at Gwilym. 'If that's all right.'

'You might as well. The whole village will know soon enough.' Gwilym pressed his fingers against his forehead. He'd better tell his family too, before they heard from someone else.

'Would you like me to call round later?'

He looked at the letter then at Idris. Maybe it would be good to have someone to unburden himself to. 'In a coupla hours maybe.'

He walked past his house, taking the side path to the back garden. Leaning against the wall, he considered the letter before ripping open the back. He felt sick with anticipation, but there was no point putting off the inevitable.

> *My dearest Gwilym,*
> *I am so sorry to be leaving in such a hurry, and also to be conveying this in a letter, and not to you in person. I do not think it would have been a good idea to visit you, as that would have made leaving all the harder.*

The stress of leading a double life was tearing me apart, and I am sure it must have been the same for you. As you pointed out, running away together would not have been an option, and even in peacetime would have been difficult. We would both have ended up without the support of our families, and maybe you would have grown to resent me.

It was wrong of me to pursue this relationship. I can only blame myself for my persistence, which created the situation we found ourselves in. How could it have worked out, with our worlds so far apart?

I have secured a place at Netley Hospital, near Southampton, where I will be joining my friend Rosemary as a Voluntary Aid Detachment nurse. I have not, however, informed my parents of this decision, so would please ask that you keep it to yourself. They know only that I am going somewhere as a VAD nurse.

I wish you a wonderful life, Gwilym, and hope that you will find someone with whom to share your life who will prove less troublesome. We should have realised it would never work out for us.

Goodbye my love.

Elizabeth

He couldn't think of anything less likely than finding someone else. He'd never met anyone like her and it seemed unlikely that he ever would. He doubted she'd ever return to this backwater, having tasted freedom away from this closeted village and from her controlling mother.

He stuffed the letter in his pocket, then leant his head against the wall and closed his eyes. This was the wall by which they'd first kissed. His gut ached with longing and loss.

Swallowing back the pain, he composed his face. Life would never be the same, but it had to carry on regardless.

Gwilym dragged behind Evan, as they entered the back garden gate after their shift. His brother had walked home with him for a change today, instead of with his friends. He was jabbering on about the new year's resolutions he'd made, which Gwilym only half-listened to.

'What resolutions have you made for new year?' Evan stopped halfway down the garden, waiting for his older brother to catch up.

'I haven't made any of those for years, *bach*.'

'Haven't you got no ambitions?'

Gwilym knew that his strongest ambitions had been built on sand, and he wouldn't have confessed them to Evan in any case. 'My ambition was to do well with the allotments, and we did, but look what happened to them.'

'Reckon you were too successful, and the coal company could see how good the land was for growing stuff.'

'Aye, no doubt you're right.'

'What about work? Don't you want to become a fireman, or an examiner, like Hywel and Idris? Or make your way up to an overseer or something?'

It had never really crossed his mind. If anything, he'd had vague ideas of leaving the mine altogether, to do something else. 'Not really.'

'There's no harm in doing better for yourself.'

Gwilym raised his eyes. 'That's rich, coming from you, *bach*! Mam was all for you "doing better" for yourself. Wanted you to go into an office, or a bank, like Jenkin's parents wanted for him. But you both chose to leave school and go into the pit.'

'Mam wanted that for you too, but you went into the pit.'

'But it's not me saying as I want to do better for myself.'

'Wasn't walking out with the manager's daughter wanting to do better for yourself?'

Gwilym's huff was almost a groan. 'It had nothing to do with doing better for myself.'

If anything, it would have been Elizabeth doing worse for herself. That had been the reality of it, and a good reason for her to remove herself from the situation. He couldn't blame her, however much it hurt.

'And that's got nothing to do with you.'

Evan's head drooped. 'Sorry, mun, I shouldn't 'ave said nothing. Mam told me to walk back with you to cheer you up, but I've made it worse.'

Now it made sense why Evan had abandoned his friends. 'It's not your fault, *bach*. Come on, let's get in before Mam comes out and wonders why on earth we're hanging around in the garden.'

In the scullery, Gwilym called, 'Hello?'

Rachael came in, wiping her hands on her apron. 'There you are. I've got the bath ready.'

'I'll go and get in then,' said Evan. He was always first, due to being covered with less coal dust than his brother from his job as putter, pushing the coal trucks to and from the ponies.

'How are you, then?' said his mother, crinkling her eyes as she examined his face.

'Same as every other day, Mam,' he said in a light tone. 'Glad to be out of the pit.'

On past days he'd have been looking forward to working on the land. If only he still had that to concentrate on, but as of today the land was back in the hands of the Tredegar Iron and Coal Company.

'I'm sure, but how do you *feel*?'

She'd keep on until he'd given some sort of answer to what she was really asking. 'If this is about Elizabeth again, I don't wish to talk about her anymore.'

'No point bottling it up, *bach*.'

'I'm not, but I've got to look to the future.' He thought about Evan and his resolutions. 'In fact, my new year's resolution is to turn the garden over to vegetables when the weather gets a bit better, and maybe raise some more chickens, if I can have a loan of one of Mr Lloyd's cockerels.'

It had the desired effect, and her face brightened. 'That's good to hear. Look to the future. 1918. I wonder what the year will bring.'

'Don't see us any closer to peace, despite what they say.'

'We can hope. Now, could you undo this jar of jam for me? If you can call it jam, since there's barely any sugar in it. It's stuck fast. Wash your hands first though, they're filthy.'

'Well of course they are.'

He did as he was told, before struggling with the unwilling lid.

'Sugar rationing is in place now,' said Rachael. 'As if we'd had much recently anyway. I dare say they'll be introducing ration cards for it soon, and for tea, butter and margarine, like they have in some places.'

He finally managed to loosen the lid as Evan poked his head round the door, a smutty towel wrapped around his waist, showing he'd not done as good a job as he could have. 'Your turn, mun.'

Gwilym headed for the bath, divesting himself of his jacket and scarf, wondering what to do after he'd washed. He told himself to resist reading Elizabeth's letter, stashed away in a bedroom drawer, yet another time, touching the paper she'd held. But he knew it would be the first thing he'd do after he'd got dressed.

Getting over her was going to take a long time.

Chapter Fifteen

Gwen looked in the mirror on her chest of drawers, turning her face this way and that. Yes, the yellow had definitely faded. People kept telling her it had, but she sometimes wondered if they said it to cheer her up.

She wore a little less of the silk cream and powder than she had in recent months, then finished off with the rouge and lip stain. That would do. Anwen and Violet were popping over with the kiddies later, and her mother was allowing her to go for a longer walk than to the end of the garden.

She tipped back the net curtain at her bedroom window and peered out. The pit wheels were roaring as usual, standing tall above the chapel-like buildings of the pit. The long, thin chimney was belting out plumes of smoke, obscuring part of the blue sky that had emerged from this morning's clouds.

She picked up her book from the drawers, *Gwyneth of the Welsh Hills* by Edith Nepean, a present from Anwen at Christmas, and went downstairs for dinner.

'There you are, *cariad*,' said Ruth as Gwen entered the kitchen. 'Come and sit down. It's not much, but I managed to get a bit of tinned corned mutton and a small loaf from Mrs Brace. There's a scraping of Marmite left if you want it.' She brought the kettle from the stove to fill up the teapot, then covered it with a green and blue cosy. 'There's not much milk left until Morgan the Milk calls back round. Doesn't have a lot in the afternoons, though.'

'It's all right, I quite like it black. I'll leave some for Da, for he prefers his tea with it.' She opened the Marmite jar and peeped in. She'd leave that for when Da came in from his shift too.

'I noticed when I walked up to James the Veg, there's a few people out on the new allotments,' said Ruth, joining Gwen at the table. 'There are many what never lent a hand on the joint allotments. Funny how people can spare the time when it's something for theirselves.'

'I was thinking, Mam, come spring, I could maybe look for a job again?'

Ruth didn't look up from where she was slicing the tinned mutton. 'There's plenty of time to think about that. It's not like you've got anything to spend the money on at the moment.'

'Only because I'm not going anywhere.'

Her mother put her bread down. 'And what new things do you need to go out? You've got a wardrobe and drawers full of clothes.'

'If I wanted to go to an entertainment, I'd need to pay for it. And I have to pay my way here.' She didn't bother pointing out that her clothes would be out of fashion soon.

'There's no need to worry about that now, we're fine.'

'But I am getting so much better. I'm not going to want to be stuck in the house all day, every day, forever.'

Ruth finished chewing her food before replying, 'I suppose, if you're to meet anyone and have a future, you'll need to get out and about.'

'Oh, Mam! Why does everyone think that the only future a woman can have is marriage? It's a job I need. But not back at the pit, sorting.'

'No, that we can agree on. If you're determined to work again, at least wait until Easter. Perhaps one of the shops in Rhymney will need an assistant, or you could get a job in an office, what with the men abroad, like Miss Elizabeth did. Excellent, your English is, so that gives you an advantage.'

'What's the date today?'

'February fourteenth.'

Valentine's Day. Of course. A year ago today, Ralph Tallis had given her a beautiful card. She'd secreted it in a drawer and cherished it, removing it every night to read it and plant a kiss on it. Until, that is, she and Elizabeth had confronted him about walking out with them both at the same time. That night, she'd torn it up into a hundred pieces and tossed it into her father's compost heap in the garden. That would teach her to expect romance.

–

Anwen and Violet arrived at the back door with Sara Fach and Benjy as Gwen was drying the dishes. Gwen was sad she wouldn't see Clarice today, for she was at school.

'Off you go now,' said Ruth. 'I'll finish these off. Get out while the sun's shining. Best just take a walk to the gardens, then you can have a sit down.'

'Don't worry, Mrs Austin, we'll look after her,' said Violet.

'Yes, we look after Aunty Gwenny,' Benjy echoed.

'Oh, bless your little heart,' said Ruth, bending to stroke his cheek.

As they left the back garden and stepped onto Lloyd Street, Gwen held her face up to the sky and closed her eyes. 'This is what it must feel like, coming out after a gaol sentence.' She opened her eyes and took a sharp intake of breath. 'Sorry, Anwen.'

'Don't be daft. I don't expect people never to mention prisons. It doesn't upset me.'

'I wonder if that's how Rose felt when she came out,' said Violet.

'It's quiet, she's been, since leaving gaol,' said Anwen. 'Too quiet.'

'I don't suppose she can risk another spell inside, as it would surely be a lot longer next time,' said Gwen.

Walking slowly along the road, they matched Sara Fach's tottery and hesitant steps, with Anwen bent over to hold her hand. Like this, they took a while to turn the two corners to get onto the front of James Street. Benjy skipped ahead.

'What's up, Violet? You look a bit pale,' said Gwen. She'd noticed her placing her hand on her chest a few times.

'What? No, I'm all right. Just a bit of indigestion.' Violet patted her hand against her coat.

'Oh, I've had enough of this,' said Anwen, picking a complaining Sara Fach up. 'Come on now, otherwise we'll never get there.' She started singing 'Lawr Ar Lan y Môr', about a little girl at the seaside, as she jiggled the tot up and down. 'And maybe, one day, you will be a little girl at the seaside. That would be nice, wouldn't it, *cariad*?'

'Mamam,' was Sara Fach's reply.

Gwen and Anwen chatted, both intermittently adding to the song when Sara Fach became restless. Violet contributed little to the conversation as they went, concentrating on Benjy, as she was.

A movement, two buildings up, caught Gwen's eye as they crossed the road. 'Don't look now,' she muttered, 'But there's Rose just coming out of the butcher's.'

They carried on, ignoring her. On reaching the other side, they watched her disappear across the side road and into the grocer's.

'She didn't even hurl any abuse at us today,' said Gwen.

'I told you she'd been quiet,' said Anwen.

In the gardens, there was a carpet of yellow crocuses on the grassed area, while the daffodils pushed their immature heads up in the borders. Under one of the trees a few magenta cyclamens were gathered.

'Can I 'ave a run round?' asked Benjy.

'Yes, but don't tread on the flowers,' said Violet.

He looked hurt. 'I wouldn't harm flowers. I like flowers.'

'I know you do, *cariad*. Go and have your run.'

Violet and Gwen sat on the middle bench. Anwen held Sara Fach's hand as she tottered back and forth on the path next to them.

'By the way, have you heard from Elizabeth at all, Anwen?' said Gwen.

'I had a letter a coupla weeks back. She's still at Netley, and still hasn't told her parents exactly where she is. She sends the occasional letter to me to pass on. Mam takes them up and puts them on the mat when no one's looking, to make it seem someone's pushed it through the letterbox. I hate being so deceitful, but it's what Elizabeth wants.'

'Do you know if she's written to Gwilym again?' said Violet. 'I can't get over that, them walking out. I'd never have guessed.'

'Nor me!' said Anwen. 'Idris doesn't seem to think he's had any more letters. It looks like she broke it off, so it seems unlikely anyway.'

'Poor Gwilym,' said Violet.

Gwen wasn't so sure. 'Lucky Gwilym, if you ask me. Imagine having that lot as in-laws!'

'Couldn't be any worse than my former mother-in-law!' said Violet.

'Ah yes, the lovely Olwen. Have you heard from her lately?'

'She and Brynmore write and I give them news of Clarice and Benjy. They are still their grandchildren, after all. We're planning to meet in the spring, but only if I can take Hywel too. Brynmore has promised that Olwen will be on her best behaviour.'

'Well, there's encouraging. I like good news,' said Gwen.

'Ummm,' Violet started. 'Well… I have some more then. Hang on.' She stood up. 'Benjy, don't go near the gate, now.'

'No, Mam.' He called back.

She sat back down and stared ahead, pulling her lips in.

'What were you going to say?' asked Gwen.

'You see, it's just, Hywel and I have, like I said, some good news.' Her face flushed a dark pink.

Gwen cottoned on straight away, clapping her hands together. 'Oh, my goodness, you're expecting!'

'Are you?' said Anwen. Her face was a mixture of surprise and shock.

'That's why I have indigestion, though it's more of a morning sickness. I always suffer that.'

'Well, that's wonderful news, Violet.' Anwen came back to the bench to hug her. 'If it's a little girl, I have quite a few clothes I could pass on.'

'You might want them yourself,' said Violet.

Anwen pulled away, displaying the huge, forced grin that Gwen recognised straight away. She was pretty good at them herself.

'By then I'm sure your little one will have grown out of them, so it'll be fine.'

'Why don't we have a walk along Alexandra Street? I'd like to see what the new allotments are like there,' said Gwen.

'The allotments are busy, right enough,' said Anwen. 'But your mam said not to go too far.'

'I feel right as rain, honestly. And we can always stop for rests along the way. Now I'm out, and the sun is shining, I want to take advantage.'

Anwen glanced at Violet, before saying, 'All right, *cariad*. I'd probably feel like you too if I'd been stuck indoors for so long. But we'll turn back if you get tired.'

Gwen stood up. 'Thank you.' She was looking forward to a view of the valley and the hills, which she couldn't see from the house, what with the colliery at the front and other houses at the back. 'Come on then, and you can give me some suggestions for a new job as we go along.'

Chapter Sixteen

'Ooh, come on, mun, the carnival will be a good laugh,' said Evan, nudging Gwilym at the kitchen table as they ate their dinner. 'I bet Idris and Hywel are going.'

'They are,' Rachael confirmed. 'Enid told me yesterday at chapel, especially as Clarice and Benjy will be dressed up.'

'I was looking forward to reading my book this afternoon,' said Gwilym, knowing already he wouldn't win. 'And you'll be off with your pals anyway, Evan.'

'You've been reading all morning, *bach*,' said Abraham. 'You're in the mine all week normally, and now you've got an opportunity on a sunny Easter Monday to go outside, you want to be locked up indoors? You used to love being out.'

'It might be sunny, but it's not that warm, Grancher.'

'It's not too bad in the sun.'

'And there are the football matches after at the end of West Street,' said Evan, fidgeting on his chair in excitement, 'and the rugby matches too, opposite Mafeking Terrace.'

'I'm surprised you didn't get involved in the rugby, Gwilym,' said Ruth, 'since you've always been so keen.'

Idris and Hywel had badgered him about it, but he hadn't been bothered to go and practice with them.

'It's nearly springtime, *bach*,' said Ruth, her face serious. 'The weather's getting better and about time it is that you pulled yourself out of this winter gloom.'

By which she meant, it was time he'd got over Elizabeth. There was no point resisting, for they'd only go on and on. 'All right, I'll come along with you.'

'That's more like it, *boi bach*,' said Abraham.

–

When Gwilym and his family reached the top of Jubilee Green that afternoon, it was already packed with villagers on all three pavements, and the noise in the enclosed triangle was almost deafening.

'Glad to see you made it,' shouted Idris, tapping him on the shoulder. 'I thought from what you said, you weren't going to bother.'

'My family were rather persuasive,' he said, looking over to where Abraham and Rachael were chatting to Gwen and her mother.

'I'm glad you're here, anyway. Hywel's gone with Violet to walk with the kiddies in the carnival. That excited, they are. They wanted Sara Fach to go with them, so Anwen's gone over too.'

Mrs Bowen, the undermanager's wife, was pushing her way through the crowd with a bag of Welsh flags, selling them to people here and there.

'They must be left over from the flag day on St David's,' Idris laughed. 'It's all for a good cause, I suppose.'

'Aye,' said Gwilym, remembering the intended recipient of today's fundraising was Netley Hospital, and by extension the person he associated with it. *Elizabeth, oh Elizabeth.*

'I read in the paper that there's another battle on the Somme. Wonder if our boys from here are involved,' said Idris.

Several people said, 'Shhh,' and slowly the crowd became quiet. Gwilym looked around, wondering why this was the case, only to find Margaret Meredith standing at the top of the Institute steps, with a megaphone. His instinct was to step back into the crowd, to be out of her sight, but there was nowhere to go.

'Good afternoon, everyone,' said Margaret, in a benevolent yet condescending manner. 'I'm *so* glad that we have such a large gathering here for Easter Monday. As you know, the money raised today will go to funding the Dorcalon bed at Netley Hospital. And I should know how worthy a cause that is, since my dear daughter, Elizabeth, was a VAD nurse there these last three months.' She smiled charmingly at them all.

'I thought she didn't know where she was,' Gwilym muttered out of the corner of his mouth. 'And why "was"?'

'I'll tell you about it in a bit,' said Idris.

Gwilym dared not hope that Elizabeth was coming home.

'Shortly now,' Margaret continued, 'the Silver Band will start off on Gabriel Street. Then the carnival, resplendent with adults and children in fancy dress, will follow on, led by Mr Lloyd and his horse and cart, which I am informed will be decorated. They will all do two laps around the gardens, then head off down James Street. At the bottom, they will turn and make their way back here.'

She paused at this point, and Gwilym realised she was staring straight at him, her face expressionless.

Composing herself once again, she continued. 'Along the way, there will be helpers with bags to collect any donations you wish to give. Please be generous, for we never know when one of our own soldiers might turn up in the Dorcalon bed. Once back outside the gardens, the judges will decide who the winners of the adult and children's sections are.' She ended with a most superior-sounding, 'Thank you, and enjoy yourselves.'

She alighted the steps and seemed to disappear into the crowd. The noise level went up a little.

'What are you going to tell me?' said Gwilym, but Idris didn't get a chance before they heard a voice close by hiss, 'That's all I need.'

They both noticed Margaret at the same time, her pale face turning fuchsia.

'Especially after receiving a letter from Elizabeth this morning to tell me she's been posted to France.'

Gwilym took a few steps forward. 'France?'

'That's what I was about to tell you,' said Idris.

'What, to nurse on the front lines?'

'Well she's not going there to do the can-can at the Moulin Rouge!' Margaret pinched her lips into a button.

Gwilym, his face set firm, was about to say something – he wasn't sure what – when Idris jumped in first.

'I'm sure it's a worry to hear of Miss Elizabeth being sent to France, but knowing what an organised woman she was, establishing and running the allotments, I'm sure she'll do a very fine job.'

'That's my Elizabeth, selfless as always,' said Margaret. 'I'm sure she'd have done a lot more here, in the village, if it hadn't been made impossible for her to stay.' She glared at Gwilym.

'With all due respect—' he started.

'Come on, mun, let's go,' said Idris. 'I'd like to see the Silver Band push off.'

Gwilym's attention was momentarily diverted, and when he looked back, Mrs Meredith had disappeared into the crowd.

'She's a card, isn't she?' said Idris. 'The can-can at the Moulin Rouge! Not what I would expect a well brought-up *lady* like her to think of!'

'She's a hypocrite,' said Gwilym. 'She tried to run Elizabeth's life, but now talks as if she's taking the credit for her daughter's selfless act. So, what do you know about it?'

'Just that Anwen got a letter from Elizabeth yesterday to say she'd transferred to a hospital in France a week ago, and that she'd now admitted to her parents she'd been at Netley. I suppose she figured her mother could no longer turn up and make a fuss, so she might as well tell her. And it's not as if Mrs Meredith can get over to France easily, to drag Elizabeth home. And as you say, she's now playing the proud mother, so she's not likely to. But, and this is between us only, Enid said she kicked up merry hell when the letter first came from Elizabeth. Had a right row with Mr Meredith and blamed him, too. Enid heard it from the kitchen.'

'I – I hope Elizabeth will be all right out there.' It hadn't sunk in properly when he'd first heard the news, but now he felt sick with worry.

'I don't suppose the hospitals are that near the Front.'

The Silver Band struck up, signalling that the carnival would soon be starting.

'Come on, mun,' said Idris, 'Let's go.'

Gwilym nodded and followed on, but the afternoon had been tainted by a mixture of terrifying images, some related to him by the enlisted lads from the village, others he'd seen in *The Battle of the Somme*. Then there were the newspaper reports. The thought of Elizabeth in all that…

He grabbed Idris's sleeve. 'I'm sorry, mun, but I've got to go.'

'Where?'

'For a walk. Sorry. Tell my family I don't feel well, if they ask.'

Idris frowned. 'Shall I come with you?'

'No, you stay here with your family.'

Gwilym hurried off into the growing crowd, up Jubilee Gardens and on past the Workmen's Institute and the fire engine station, onto the slopes of Twyn Gobaith behind. He trudged up until he reached the brow of the hill, continuing until he was just over it. Here, he slumped onto the rough grass.

'Noooooo!' he shouted to the sky.

Having given rein to the frustration of being able to do nothing to keep his beloved Elizabeth safe, he slumped and let the tears fall.

Chapter Seventeen

There had been a brief gap in the flow of incoming casualties, though today so far had not been as bad as yesterday, where the ambulances had been non-stop.

Elizabeth sat next to Sister Coulter in the mess tent, on the long table that was always covered in a white cloth and several cruet sets, whatever was going on. It smelled of an earthy dampness and of the lamb stew they'd been served for lunch today with a slice of bread and butter. She took the first mouthful of her food, having learned to eat extra quickly since she'd been here.

'How have you found your first fortnight here, Nurse Meredith?' said Sister Coulter, in her Scottish burr. She had proved the friendliest of the trained nursing staff here so far, many of whom resented the Voluntary Aid Detachment 'nurses' being given the title.

'It's certainly been eventful. I thought Netley was busy, but it's been non-stop.'

'That's the way of it out here, near the Front. You seem to have held up well. Not like Nurse Denton, who scurried off back to Blighty pretty darn quickly once she saw what was really involved.' She raised her eyes and head upwards. 'Another one with a romantic view of her role as a nursing angel.'

'She did seem rather surprised she had to work so hard.'

'You have some skills, considering you were only at Netley three months.'

'I had excellent training by several of the nurses there.'

Although she'd started, as all VADs did, with scrubbing, emptying slops, disposing of soiled dressings and dealing with bedpans, one of the sisters there had soon realised she might have some skill helping with more technical jobs and, being short-staffed, had put her to work on wound care.

'And I've been reading nursing textbooks,' Elizabeth added. 'I thought it might help.'

'That's very commendable,' said the sister, giving an impressed nod. 'I'm afraid to say, with the war raging on the Somme once more, and the Germans gaining a lot of ground, there will be a lot more casualties to come.'

Elizabeth had no doubt of this. Always there was the distant thrum of explosions and artillery fire. There had been aeroplanes spotted overhead a few times too, both German and those of the newly named Royal Air Force.

The stew was passable, and she was glad of it after such an early start. But she still had half of it to go when one of the more experienced VADs, Doris Strong, ran into the tent and over to the two tables of nurses.

'Incoming casualties,' she shouted in her high little voice. 'Matron says you're all to come to the preoperative ward.'

'I thought it was too good to be true,' said Sister Coulter, standing wearily. 'Come on then, ladies, to your posts.'

There was a clatter as they rose as one and hurried out. There were several ambulances already parked, and more coming through the front gate.

In another large tent, there were already several rows of stretchers with soldiers, many of them moaning or calling out. There was a whiff of fetid soil and decay, and the men were muddy from head to foot.

Elizabeth was ordered to a stretcher near the entrance with Sister Coulter. The face of the man there was caked in earth and he seemed to be unconscious. She could just make out the three stars of a captain on his epaulettes. The temporary dressings, presumably applied by someone at his regimental first aid post, were already stained with extensive blood. There was also a tourniquet applied.

Sister Coulter lifted the specification tally, which had been pinned to his jacket. 'A bullet wound to the right leg. Oh dear, it's apparently exited, which will mean a much larger rupture. He's in a bad way.' She felt his pulse and put her hand against his forehead. 'Right, let's see what we've got here.'

As she lifted the dressings, there was the pungent stench of rotten meat. The wound had already started to produce copious amounts of pus. Elizabeth turned away briefly, on the edge of being sick. No, she needed to be strong. She'd faced similar before – worse – but it was never easy.

'Get the fabric cut off, Nurse Meredith,' said the sister, handing her a pair of scissors. 'Dr Turnbull, we'll need your assistance here,' she called over to one of the medics attending another man.

'Sorry, Sister, but this is an emergency and I need to operate.'

'Very well… Looks like we'll have to do what we can, Nurse. Right. You start on cleansing the wounds. We don't want sepsis setting in.'

Elizabeth got the hot water and antiseptic solution ready and started by washing the wound. It was then the soldier started to rouse with a long groan, which almost became a scream. He tried to move but the pain made him yelp.

'Settle down now, Captain—' Sister Coulter looked at the specification tally once again. 'Captain Fitzgerald. We need you to keep still.'

Elizabeth felt disorientated for a moment. 'Fitzgerald?'

'El— Elizabeth?' the soldier moaned.

'Sidney!' With all the mud on his face, she hadn't recognised him.

'You know this man, nurse?' The look on her face was asking how close she was to him.

'Our families know each other,' she said, to clarify.

'Then let's get him cleaned up and treated and not let his family down,' the sister said firmly.

'Wh— what happened?' said Sidney.

'Leg wound, Captain. So let us get on with it.' Her manner seemed frosty, but Elizabeth knew it was her efficiency and determination to get a patient well.

Sister Coulter got the drains ready to remove the pus. Elizabeth cleansed the extensive wound with soap and water, stemming the urge to cry. It was never easy treating any of the men, particularly when your efforts didn't save them, but at least there was normally a little distance created by them being strangers.

He continued to moan softly, until she started cleansing the wound with iodine, when he let out a sharp, 'Aaaargh!'

'I'm sorry, Captain,' Elizabeth said formally, 'but we do need to make sure it's all sterile.'

Sister Coulter started to irrigate the area with a saline solution. Elizabeth noticed the chattering of Sidney's teeth first.

'Sister, I think he might be going into shock.'

This was confirmed a moment later when his whole body began to tremble and his groans became gasping breaths.

Sister Coulter felt his neck. 'Yes, his pulse is rapid and faint. You know what to do, Nurse.'

Elizabeth ran to fetch more blankets and some hot bags. She placed the bags around his torso, covering them with the blankets to keep the heat in.

'He's lost a lot of blood if those dressings are anything to go by,' said the sister. She looked around the room. 'Matron!' she called over to the tall, thin woman in the grey uniform, attending another casualty. 'We could do with a blood transfusion here.'

'I'm afraid we're short of donors. You'll have to use a saline solution.'

'I'll be the donor,' Elizabeth said without hesitation, knowing how much better blood transfusions could work than saline infusions.

'I don't know. Yes, I suppose so.' As Doris ran by them, the sister said, 'Are you free, Nurse Strong?'

Her face was wrinkled with grief. 'Yes, we just lost our patient.'

'Then fetch us the cannulas and tubing. We're doing a blood transfusion.'

Elizabeth felt Sidney's forehead. 'Sister, the captain's still cold and quite clammy.'

'Quick, Nurse Strong, let's get this done. And let's hope we can get him into the operating theatre quickly.'

Elizabeth sent up a short prayer to the heavens. She hoped so too.

Chapter Eighteen

Margaret looked round at the ten members of the Dorcalon Social Committee, seated at her elegant mahogany dining table, as they got themselves settled.

'What a beautiful clock that is,' said Anabel Thomas, the Baptist minister's wife.

Margaret treated her to an indulgent smile. It was satisfying when someone appreciated the quality of one's furniture. 'It's a balloon clock. I particularly liked the inlay when we bought it.'

'It is attractive,' said Matilda Bowen.

Margaret gave her only a half-smile. As if she cared what the wife of the undermanager thought. This one was as much an upstart as Esther Williams had been in her time. The rest of the group were the wives of the ministers and shopkeepers, along with Farmer Lloyd's, Sergeant Harries' and Dr Roberts' wives.

Of course, given a choice, she'd much rather be mixing with the likes of Lady Anna Fitzgerald and Lady Hortense Rees-Smithers, but it was gratifying to be in charge of a committee for a change.

'I've always thought this whole room delightful,' said Agnes Banes, the wife of the vicar of St Peter's. 'The porcelain figures are exquisite, and how lucky you are to have so many photographs. The frames are beautiful.'

'Why thank you, Agnes.' Margaret glanced at the displays on the bookshelves and the mantelpiece, glad she had asked Brenda to give the room another polish this morning. 'Now, down to business. I believe you have the figures for the carnival yesterday, Anabel?'

'Yes. We made twelve pounds, fourteen shillings and sixpence in the collections, with a further one pound two shillings for the flags sold.'

'That is *excellent*,' said Margaret. 'Netley Hospital will certainly appreciate the sum towards the bed we sponsor.'

'I hear your daughter has now moved to a hospital in France,' said Anabel. 'How very brave of her.'

'We must all do our bit, mustn't we? Now, to look to the future.'

There was a tap at the partly opened dining room door and Margaret called, 'You may enter, Brenda.'

The young maid, dressed in the neat black uniform with white apron and cap that she wore in the afternoons, came in with the best silver tea service on a large tray. Margaret had bought the set the year before, enchanted by its fluted design and large, angular handles. This was despite Herbert's protestations that they already had a perfectly serviceable china one.

'If you'd be as good to pour a cup for everyone, please, Brenda?'

'Yes, madam.'

The young woman had turned out to be a competent maid, but only that morning she'd informed Margaret that she was remarrying and moving to Tredegar. Who on earth would she find now to take on these duties?

'In the meantime, ladies, we shall discuss our programme of events for the coming year.'

–

The meeting that afternoon had gone well. Margaret was still smiling to herself as she read through her notebook of the decisions made. She'd managed to manipulate Matilda Bowen into subordinate roles in all the events planned without too much trouble. She didn't want her getting above herself. Now she needed to go and discuss dinner preparations with Mrs Rhys.

Hearing voices at the front door, she rose from the table and entered the hall.

'Why Herbert, you're home early. What's that you have there?' She indicated what appeared to be a letter in his hand.

His expression was dark, the brows knitted. 'I met the telegram boy on my way up.'

Margaret clutched the front of her blouse. 'Oh Lord, no. Not Tom, not my beautiful boy, Tom.'

He glared at her. 'Lizzie's in France too.'

'I know, but she's unlikely...' She tailed off, not quite sure where the sentence was going.

Herbert tore open the envelope. Margaret was on the point of hurrying away, not wanting to hear the bad news, when he said, 'It's all right. No one's died.'

Margaret let out a long, noisy sigh, feeling weak with relief. 'Then everything is fine.'

'I wouldn't say that either. Tom is injured. He's at Devonport Hospital in Plymouth.'

She rushed to his side to snatch the telegram from him. 'An arm injury. That doesn't sound too bad. And he's to come home in a week or so! Well, that is good news.'

'How is it? He's injured!'

'It can't be that bad if they've only just told us about it. It will be a flesh wound, or a broken arm perhaps. Of course, it's not good to be hurt, but at least it means he'll be home for a while.' She thought of how comfortable she'd make him, and which of his favourite foods she might be able to acquire.

'Your logic shocks me sometimes, Margaret. Our son has been hurt enough to be brought back to hospital in this country, and you seem quite glad.'

She slammed the telegram down on the occasional table. 'Yes, I am glad he'll be away from the fighting for a while. He'll be safer here. What would you prefer, for him to have a minor wound or to be, to be – killed?'

Herbert didn't reply, picking up the telegram instead and placing it in his jacket pocket.

The letter box clanked, and three envelopes fell on the mat.

'Look, there may be more news in a letter.' Margaret bent her knees to retrieve them. 'There's one from Elizabeth,' said Margaret, cheering up, 'I shall read it and then write to her to tell her what's happened.'

'Don't I get a chance to read it?'

'I'll let you have it when I'm finished.'

'You do that,' he said, and headed off down the corridor towards the study.

Chapter Nineteen

At half past five the following morning, Elizabeth went to check on Sidney. She had sat up with him, after her shift, until midnight, despite her early start today. He was lying on his back, in striped pyjamas now, cleaned up and three-quarters covered with blankets, his leg slightly raised in a strap.

Sidney's operation had been a long one, the complication arising from the rupture at the back of his leg prompting some skilled surgery. He was breathing steadily now, though it was hard to see his skin colour in the light of the lamp.

He stirred, moving his shoulders, then, in a breathy under-tone she could barely hear, said, 'Watch out, Lieutenant!' He tried to turn but woke with a start.

Elizabeth was already up, pinning his shoulders down. 'It's all right, Captain. Keep still now.'

He came to. 'Where am I?' There was panic in his voice.

'You're at the casualty clearing station. You had a gunshot wound to the leg which was operated on. You're in the post-operative ward.' She looked up at the tent. It still seemed an odd place to call a ward.

'Leg?' he said confused. There was alarm in his eyes as he said, 'I've lost it?'

'No, they managed to save it. But you need to rest. The more you do so, the quicker you'll recover.'

Reassured, he closed his eyes once more. He dropped off, but slept fitfully, the odd sentence leaving his lips that she couldn't make out.

Despite what she'd told him, there was still a long way to go. She'd do her very best to make sure he didn't get an infection.

Chapter Twenty

Already Margaret had managed to secure some bread and margarine from Mrs Brace's grocery store and was walking across the road to make her way to Mr Schenck's bookshop. Her intention was to purchase some volumes she thought Tom might appreciate to occupy himself once home, maybe a P.G. Wodehouse or an Edgar Rice Burroughs.

Coming down Jubilee Green, from the other direction, she spotted two of her former maids, Jenny Richards and Anwen, reminding her once more of Brenda's news. Both were walking slowly, guiding toddlers along the pavement. She admired Anwen for taking on her illegitimate sister as she had done. Jenny's son — Frederick was it? — must be... She tried to work it out. Around two years old? Yes. She'd left McKenzie House to marry Pastor Richard's son, Joseph, but Margaret had heard rumours to suggest Jenny had already been with child at their wedding. Then Joseph had been killed in the mine disaster. Poor Jenny. She lingered in order to greet the pair.

'Good afternoon, Jenny, Anwen. I'm astonished to see how much your children have grown. I do not believe I've seen Frederick since he was a babe in arms.'

'Good afternoon, madam.' Jenny dipped her knee slightly, her face a little pink. 'No, you probably haven't. Freddie will be two next month.'

The little boy looked up at Margaret, with a cute grin. Her breath caught in her throat and it was all she could do to prevent herself from letting out a strangled whine. He was the spitting image of Tom at that age. No, not again, surely!

'Well, isn't he a handsome fellow?' Margaret managed, her pulse thumping in her head. 'And I see little Sara is walking now.'

'Yes, and very determined she is too,' said Anwen.

Laying her discomfort aside, she decided this could be a perfect opportunity. Margaret cleared her throat. 'I was wondering, Anwen, with little Sara being older now, whether you'd consider working once more. I ask because my current maid, Brenda Prothero, is leaving to remarry.'

She knew she should ask Jenny too, but she couldn't bring herself to. If her suspicions were correct, she doubted Jenny would want to anyway.

'I'm afraid Sara Fach is still too young for me to consider taking a post again, but, well, I do know someone who is looking for a job.'

'And who might that be?'

'My friend, Gwen Austin. Ill she was, from working in the munitions, so had to give up.'

'Of course, I remember Elizabeth mentioning her. But didn't she end up in hospital?'

'That was going on four months back. She's well now, and keen for a different job.'

Margaret unclipped her handbag and removed a notebook and a silver propelling pencil. 'What is her address?'

'Forty James Street.'

'Thank you. I shall look into your suggestion. Now, if you'll excuse me, I'm going to pay a visit to Mr Schenck.'

'Good day to you, madam,' said Jenny, at the same time as Anwen's more informal, 'Cheerio, Mrs Meredith.'

Margaret hoped the smile she was struggling with was indeed a smile and not a grimace. She watched them as they crossed the road, or rather, she watched young Frederick.

She hoped to God she was wrong. Looking around at the bookshop, she decided to leave it until later. The quicker she found a new maid, the better.

Gwen glanced at the old clock above the mantelpiece, wondering when exactly Mrs Williams would leave. Twenty to three. She'd wanted to walk into Rhymney this afternoon, to enquire about jobs. The woman's grief over her son's death had taken a new turn, one that Gwen did not know how to deal with.

'So you see, I can just *feel* that Daniel is still alive. It's a mother's instinct.' Esther bobbed her head up and down, agreeing with herself. 'A mother just knows.' She leant over from her place on one of the armchairs to take Gwen's hands. 'So you can take that pained frown off your face, for my son will return, and then you can marry.'

There was a whooshing in Gwen's ears and she felt her face heat up. This was terrible. How long would the woman hang on to her as a comfort, believing this? Maybe until the end of the war, when he didn't return.

'Of course, Mrs Williams, it's entirely possible that Daniel is alive somewhere. You hear of plenty of men being taken prisoner. But we shouldn't pin our hopes on that.'

Esther patted her hands. 'I know what's wrong with you, *cariad*. Sometimes it's easier to look on the negative side, and then you can't be disappointed.'

What else could she say to discourage her?

The woman shuffled forward a little closer. 'I'm told some of the Pals are back on leave tomorrow. Imagine if he just turned up! I think he might.'

'Let's not raise our hopes, Mrs Williams.'

There was a knock at the front door. Bertha, already in the hall, dusting, called, 'I'll get it.'

'If he comes home, I shall make sure he comes straight round to see you. In these times, no one wants to be wasting opportunities. Special licenses can be got.' She beamed, placing her fingertips to her mouth. 'How wonderful would that be?'

While Gwen hoped Daniel was still alive, for his sake, the thought of the proposed scenario panicked her. Had she taken this supporting of Esther too far? Had the woman known something about his feelings that Gwen didn't? It seemed unlikely, given he could barely bring himself to speak to his mother, let alone write to her.

The door opened, saving Gwen from replying. Bertha walked in, ahead of the mine manager's wife, who had a basket over the crook of one arm. This was truly turning into a bizarre day.

'Mrs Meredith here says she'd like a word,' said Bertha, sounding as confused as Gwen felt. 'I'll leave you to it.'

Margaret studied Esther with a slight sneer. 'I would like to speak with Miss Austin *alone*.'

'Oh, oh.' Esther bent to pick up her worn handbag and rose. 'Of course, Mrs Meredith.' She shuffled backwards a couple of steps. 'Bye bye, Gwen, I'll pop in again soon. Or you could come—'

'I haven't got all day,' Margaret huffed.

Gwen was tempted to give Mrs Meredith a ticking off for being rude, but given she had no idea why she was here, she decided to be a little more diplomatic. She stood up. 'I'll show you to the door, Mrs Williams.'

Bertha raised her eyes questioningly at her granddaughter as she passed by and received shrugged shoulders in reply. Gwen wished Mrs Williams a quick farewell, before going back to the kitchen.

'Would you like to sit, Mrs Meredith?'

'No thank you. As I implied, I'm in a hurry. I've just heard from Anwen Rhys that you are looking for a job.'

'Y-y-es, I am.'

'Brenda Prothero is leaving my service at the end of the week to remarry and I'm keen to engage a new maid as soon as possible. Would you be interested in the position?'

A maid? It was something she wouldn't have considered before. 'How much would you be paying?'

'Twenty shillings per week. Plus, you would receive luncheon and refreshments on your morning and afternoon breaks, of course.'

That was less than half what she'd been earning in the munitions, but was generous nonetheless, and more than a lot of women earned. She'd had no luck at the shops so far, and a couple of clerical jobs she'd applied for hadn't even offered her an interview.

'I would consider it, yes.'

'Splendid. Of course, I need to know whether you would be suitable.'

Whether she'd be *suitable*? Gwen almost laughed. Mrs Meredith was clearly desperate enough to go out of her way to call around the house.

'Firstly, I need to be sure you have recovered completely from your – ailment.'

'Toxic jaundice. As you can see, my skin is a healthy colour again, when it was yellow back in December. And I've regained my strength as well, and no longer get breathless.'

'And would you be prepared to work five and a half days a week?'

'I would.' She'd worked six full days before, so that was an improvement.

'In that case, I think you can start on a two-week trial. Although Brenda isn't leaving until Saturday, I'd require you in for a day before to learn what you need to do.'

That was awkward. 'The thing is, Mrs Meredith, my brother's home on leave tomorrow, and going back Sunday. I'd really like to spend the time with him.'

'I see.' She pinched her lips together. 'Since we heard yesterday that our son is coming home soon, I can understand your eagerness to want to spend time with him. I suppose, if you were willing to come in for a couple of hours say, on Friday, we could speak of your duties then, and Brenda could show you around the house.'

'Yes, I could manage that.'

'Let's say, ten o'clock?'

'All right.'

'Splendid. I'll show myself out.' She spun towards the door and left.

When Gwen heard the front door close, she slumped into the armchair. How had that happened? She hadn't even been sure she'd wanted the job. Still, not bad wages, and a five-minute walk, instead of the possible forty-minute walk to Rhymney. And she'd always fancied seeing the inside of the Big House.

'What was all that about?' said Bertha, brandishing a feather duster as she came into the kitchen.

'I've just been offered the job as maid up at the Big House.'

'That's wonderful, *cariad*!' Bertha placed the duster on the table and hugged her granddaughter.

'Come on then, Mamgu – now I haven't got to walk into Rhymney, I'll help you with the chores.'

Chapter Twenty-One

Three days after Sidney's operation, Elizabeth and the other VADs were serving lunch in the recovery ward he'd been moved to, a smaller tent with a dozen beds, all containing officers. Some of the patients were having to be fed.

As she looked down at Sidney, who was asleep, she touched the place on her arm where the cannula had been placed to draw out her blood.

'He's doing all right, thanks to you,' said Doris.

'The doctor says there's still a long way to go,' Elizabeth pointed out. 'I hardly like to wake him, but he needs some nourishment. It's still only beef tea at the moment, but it will help.'

'Yes, he didn't eat much of the porridge this morning. We'll prop him up on some more pillows, to make it easier... Captain Fitzgerald, sir, it's lunch time. Are you awake?'

There was a soft moan as he roused himself. 'Is it that time already?' He turned his head, and on spotting Elizabeth, came to a little more. 'Hello, there.'

'Here we go,' said Doris, as the two of them lifted him and added a couple more pillows beneath his head. 'Nurse Meredith's going to feed you some nice beef tea.'

'Elizabeth.' He smiled wanly, then screwed his eyes up tight and pushed his lips together.

'Does it hurt, Captain?'

He opened his eyes and breathed out a sigh. 'A bit, yes.' Which probably meant it hurt a lot.

'I could find the sister and see if some more pain relief can be given.'

'That would be appreciated. I am hungry though, so would welcome that beef tea.'

'I'll leave you to it,' said Doris.

Elizabeth brought the mug to his mouth and lifted it so he could take a sip.

'What's all this "captain" business?' he asked.

'It's the rules.'

'It wouldn't hurt to call me Sidney while the sister and matron aren't in earshot.'

'Just while I'm feeding you, then.'

'Fair enough.' He took another sip. 'I'm told it's thanks to you that I've made a recovery.'

'Along with Sister Coulter, Nurse Strong and, of course, the surgeons,' she laughed.

'No, but the sister told me you donated blood.'

'Oh, that. Yes. There were no donors available, and blood transfusions are better than the saline infusions, so it seemed the decent thing to do.' She'd felt guilty about the men who couldn't have blood, but she couldn't provide it for all.

'Well, thank you. When Mother said in a letter you'd come out here as a VAD, I never thought I'd be in a position to see you.'

Elizabeth was surprised Lady Fitzgerald had mentioned her at all. 'I started off at Netley hospital at the beginning of January. I've only been here a little over two weeks.'

'Mother was impressed you'd come. She had the feeling your – your mother had held you back from doing any voluntary work.' He took a couple of deep breaths.

Elizabeth could hear Lady Fitzgerald's supercilious voice spouting that to all who would listen. She wondered what else Anna had told him.

'The uniform suits you,' he said.

She looked down at the blue-grey cotton dress and white apron. 'The headdress makes me feel like a nun,' she said, though it was a white cap with fabric fanning out at the back.

'More like an angel. You all are… I hear you had a sweetheart in Dorcalon, who… who your mother did not approve of.'

It was a while before she replied. 'I did have, yes. But it's finished now. Drink up. You need all your strength, Sidney. You were in surgery for several hours and have a lot of healing to do.'

He looked down at his legs, covered with several blankets. 'Nobody has said. Will I walk again?'

'I haven't heard otherwise. The bullet missed the bone, which is good. Lots of stitches, though. You need to rest up here for another couple of days. Then you'll be sent on a ship to England, to a hospital there, to recover. I dare say they'll get you walking properly again. It was one of the jobs I had at Netley, to walk with the men as they exercised after leg injuries.'

'At least I still have my leg, I suppose. Not like poor Smythe-Harrington there.' He looked over to a second lieutenant, several beds away. 'Just wondering when I'll get back to the war. We've lost too many men as it is.' The last sentence came on a long, exasperated breath.

'The more you rest and do as you're told, the quicker you'll recover.'

He gave a small chuckle. His 'Yes, Matron,' was followed by a long whimper. 'I've had enough beef tea, thank you. I don't suppose there's any chance of anything a bit heartier?'

'I'll go and ask Sister. Then I'll see about some pain relief for you.'

-

'Well, I can't say it's been a pleasure to be here,' said Sidney, lying on the stretcher, in one of the tents used for patients being discharged, waiting his turn to be put into the ambulance. He was back in his uniform, which had been thoroughly cleaned by the orderlies, the buttons gleaming. 'But I'm so glad that you were here, Elizabeth, for it certainly gave some relief to what has been a painful and anxious time.' He took her hand.

'I'm glad you've made such a good recovery.' Elizabeth held her other hand over the top of his. 'I'm sure the hospital at Dartford will give you an opportunity to rest and recover. The doctor is pleased with how you're doing so far.'

'All right, sir,' said one of the orderlies. 'You're up next.'

Elizabeth followed the stretcher-bearer and orderly out as they conveyed Sidney to one of the ambulances.

Once they'd placed him inside the ambulance, she leant in as they went back to fetch another soldier. 'I hope your journey to Le Havre isn't too bumpy,' she said. 'And that you have a good crossing.'

'Thank you. I will write to you once I'm settled in. I do hope you'll continue to write to me.'

'Of course I will. And hopefully your parents will soon receive the letter you dictated to me and write back to you in Dartford. It was a shame Horace could not leave his post to come and visit.'

'The brigade was in the thick of it, so I'm not surprised. At least I had you here. And thank you, once again, for donating your blood.'

A new stretcher was brought back. Elizabeth stepped out of the way as they settled the other officer in with Sidney. She waved and called, 'Cheerio, good luck.' They closed the back doors of the ambulance, which was more like a truck than the smaller ambulances at home.

The driver got in and soon the vehicle moved off. She waved, even though Sidney would not be able to see her. As the ambulance disappeared from sight, Doris walked towards her.

'Here's a letter for you, from home by the looks of it.'

Elizabeth opened it as they walked to the mess tent together. 'Oh goodness, my brother's at a hospital in England, having sustained an arm injury.'

'How bad is it?'

'Can't be too bad, otherwise my mother's letter would be full of hysterics.' Of that she was sure. 'Maybe a bullet wound, like Sidney's, requiring some rest. He'll be home in a few days.'

'Do you want to apply for some leave at the same time, to see him?'

She thought about this. 'No. He'll want to rest and will get enough fuss from my mother. At least he'll be out of the war for a while. I'd rather take leave in France.' It was wise, for the time being.

Chapter Twenty-Two

'Hello there, Violet, Anwen,' said Gwilym as he joined the queue in the greengrocer's behind them. He breathed in the earthy smell of the potatoes in a barrel close by.

'You've come just in time for the new consignment of leeks,' Violet told him. 'Mr James is fetching them in.'

'I've got plenty of those in the garden. It's radishes my mother's wanting. I don't grow them, see. Suppose I should.'

'Hywel and I should sort out the garden. We could really do with more veggies now the meat's on ration and even more scarce. And there are certainly fewer veggies in here since we had to give back the fields.' Violet pointed to the half-empty crates.

Mr James came back and it was Violet's turn to be served.

'How are you, Gwilym?' Anwen said in an undertone.

He knew what she was getting at, with that certain look, the head on the side, eyes slightly creased.

'I'm fine.' He composed himself to say something that would hopefully stop her asking this question every couple of weeks. 'I realise it could never have come to anything, and at least Elizabeth is doing what she's wanted to do since the beginning of the war, and that's to make a proper contribution. Good luck to her.'

He wished he could feel as magnanimous as he sounded.

'I received another letter a week or so back. Would you like to read it?'

'Idris told me the salient points, so you're all right.'

The door opened and Matilda Bowen came in, chattering, followed by Mrs Meredith.

'Every cloud has an even darker cloud,' he muttered.

Anwen pulled him ahead of her. 'You go first,' she whispered. 'It might be best.'

Margaret greeted Anwen briefly but ignored Gwilym.

'So, your Tom is to be home shortly,' said Matilda, putting on the airs and graces that Esther Williams used to engage in when she was the undermanager's wife.

'Yes, and furthermore, I have had a letter from Elizabeth,' Margaret said in an over-loud voice. 'She's doing splendidly in France and has even met up with a nice young officer who she has known for many years: Sidney Fitzgerald.' She said the name as if everyone should know who he was.

The name caused a small jolt in Gwilym's chest. He was the officer Elizabeth had brought over to see the allotments, and with whom she'd been exchanging letters. And what did 'meeting up' mean? She'd come across him, or they'd purpose-fully organised a rendezvous? Even then, it could have been perfectly innocent. Hadn't she'd said she'd rather run away to the Front than marry either of the Fitzgerald brothers? But then, she had run away to the Front.

When there was no reaction to the name from Mrs Bowen, Margaret added, '*Captain* Sidney Fitzgerald. The son of *Lady* Anna Fitzgerald.'

'Oh, Lady Fitzgerald,' said Matilda, as if she were an old friend. 'Of course. So, they're involved, are they, Elizabeth and Captain Fitzgerald?'

'Of course, Elizabeth doesn't actually *say* that, but reading between the lines… His father owns a bank and a lot of prop-erty, you know.'

He noticed Anwen raise her eyes and shake her head subtly. This was clearly all for his benefit. Then again, could Elizabeth have changed her mind about Sidney?

If so, it was a definite conclusion to the drama that had been him and Elizabeth. But hadn't she made that clear in the letter she'd left for him after Christmas?

Mr James, who was giving change to Violet, called over, 'Sir Archibald Fitzgerald owns a lot of properties, all right.'

Margaret beamed to have her boast verified. 'He certainly does.'

'And he extracts large rents from the tenants, too,' Mr James went on, 'and isn't very sympathetic when they can't pay. I know, 'cos I have a friend what rents one of his shops in Tredegar… Thank you, Mrs Llewellyn. What can I do for you, Mr Owen?'

Gwilym didn't have time to look at Mrs Meredith's expression, but just the fact that she'd stopped talking, allowing Matilda Bowen to chatter on about something she'd seen at the theatre in Merthyr Tydfil, said it all. He took a brief pleasure in imagining her smug smile slipping, but it was soon replaced by the sadness in his heart.

–

It was Gwen's fourth day at McKenzie House, and she'd been kept busy getting the place ready for the return of 'Lieutenant Meredith', as his mother kept referring to him. Not that the house was in any way untidy. Brenda had been an efficient maid, and she only hoped she could keep up with Mrs Meredith's exacting standards in the same way. Currently, she was cleaning Tom's bedroom, giving his drawers a last polish. She admired the mahogany wardrobe with double, oval-mirrored doors. How she'd have loved it in her bedroom.

All her time in the house so far had been taken up with sweeping, polishing and scrubbing, but she was assured that once Tom was home, she would be changing into a smart uniform some afternoons to run errands. She looked forward to that. Tea breaks and lunch, as they called it, had been pleasant, spent in the kitchen with Anwen's mother, who provided good food, despite the shortages.

Yes, although hard work, it was so much easier than the munitions, and the days had passed well enough. On her first day though, she had overheard an argument in the study between Mr and Mrs Meredith, about her wanting to go down to Devon, to visit Tom in the hospital. He'd replied that it was pointless and that Tom would be better off resting rather than having her fussing around. And going there for the day would be too much of a trip, and where would she stay if she remained for longer? He must have won the argument because she hadn't gone.

Gwen wondered if she would have taken up the post if Elizabeth had still been here. There was no point spending the rest of her life thinking of the woman as a rival though, especially since Elizabeth had more recently been involved with Gwilym. What a surprise that had been! And it wasn't as if she harboured any feelings for Tallis, apart from disdain.

She rubbed the edge of the drawers. There, that should do it. She peeped out of the window, at the blue sky, then down at the pit. It didn't matter whether you lived in a small terrace or a big, detached house in this village; the pit was still what you saw out of the front window.

As she looked over to her own house, a movement on the path round the colliery caught her eye. Crossing the small bridge that went over the Nantygalon, was a motor ambulance, its large cross standing out. She ran to the landing, then took the stairs to the hallway more slowly, knowing Mrs Meredith did not like people running around the house. Where might she be?

Hearing voices from the kitchen, Gwen went there.

'Madam, I've just seen an ambulance coming over the bridge.'

'It's a little early. I wasn't expecting it for another hour. Quick, quick! You too, Mrs Rhys. You must come and line up to welcome Lieutenant Meredith home.' Margaret bustled her staff to the front door.

On the path, Gwen and Enid stood next to each other. Margaret went to the gate and opened it as the ambulance drew up, her hands gripped together.

The uniformed driver got out of the vehicle and came around to the other side, to greet Margaret.

'Good afternoon, madam.' He touched the peak of his cap. 'I presume this is the home of Lieutenant Thomas Meredith.'

'It is indeed. And we are eager to see him.'

'If I could just have a loan of one of your staff to help me.' He nodded towards them.

'I'll help, madam,' said Gwen, coming forward. Presumably he wanted someone to carry Lieutenant Meredith's luggage.

The driver opened the back door to reveal Tom on a bench on the left-hand side. His dark auburn hair, parted to one side, was slightly longer than it had been when she'd last seen him strolling around the village, before he'd signed up. The moustache was gone. His left arm was in a sling. He rose and started down the steps. 'You take his arm, miss. I'll fetch his rucksack.'

She was wondering which to take, then scolded herself. He wouldn't appreciate her clutching hold of his broken arm, she thought, having a quick look at it as she went to his other side. It was then she saw it. Or to be more precise, didn't see it.

It was missing from the elbow down.

Gwen felt slightly sick. Why had Mrs Meredith said nothing about this? She tried not to react, thinking how Elizabeth must have to cope with this kind of thing every day.

'I don't need any help,' said Tom, in a petulant tone. 'There is nothing wrong with my legs.'

'I know sir, it's just a precaution now,' said the driver.

'Very well,' he said in a huff of breath.

Looking over towards Margaret as they emerged from behind the ambulance, Gwen could see her leaning up, trying to see what was happening.

'Tom, at last!' She came through the gate, beaming, but stopped dead, two feet away. 'Oh my God!' Her hand went to her mouth. 'Where – where is your arm? Is it tucked into your jacket?'

It was a ridiculous question, for it clearly wasn't, but nevertheless Margaret surveyed the area around his arm.

'No, it's in an incinerator, somewhere in France.'

Margaret screamed, her face distorted with horror. Enid came rushing out through the gate.

The driver came round with the rucksack, confused. 'Didn't she know?'

Tom didn't reply.

'Madam, calm down,' said Enid.

'Oh my God, oh my—' but Margaret didn't finish the last word before she was half crying, half screaming once more, her arms flailing as she collapsed. Enid caught her but struggled to hold onto her. The driver ran to help.

Tom seemed unmoved, walking on quickly. Gwen attempted to keep up with him.

Nearing the front door, he pushed her helping hand away saying, 'Trust her to make herself the centre of attention.'

He might be severely injured, but Gwen deplored his selfishness and didn't even try to stop herself saying, 'Well no wonder, when you didn't tell her. How do you expect her to react? What is wrong with you?'

In the hall now, he turned, pushing his upper body a little forward. His dark brown eyes, so like Elizabeth's, were hard. 'I wouldn't allow anyone to tell her about it because I knew she'd have travelled to the hospital, letting her presence be known by one and all and she would have swamped me with her self-indulgent tears and wailing. Just like she's doing now. I needed the rest, to set me up for coming back here. Now, it's been a long journey and I'm tired and I'm going to my bedroom.' His long legs took the stairs two at a time.

She was tempted to retort, *You selfish rotter*, but went back outside to help with Margaret. She was now sitting on the wall, just as Mr Meredith arrived back.

'What on earth is going on? Where's Tom?'

'Arm, arm, missing,' Margaret groaned, like a wounded animal.

'What!' Mr Meredith looked at the ambulance driver, as if for an explanation.

'His arm is missing from the elbow down, sir. It was badly shattered by several bullets, and they amputated.'

Mr Meredith placed his hand to his head, closing his eyes. '*O Duw!*'

'There's a letter for you from the doctor. Your son has it.'

'Where is he?'

'Gone to his bedroom, sir,' said Gwen.

Composing himself, Mr Meredith looked at his pocket watch. 'Would you take the driver to the kitchen for some lunch, please.'

'Of course, sir.' She dipped her knee.

'That's right kind of you, sir,' said the driver, picking up the rucksack to carry it in.

'Mrs Rhys, can you manage my wife?'

'I can, sir. I'll bring her into the drawing room and fetch her some tea.'

'Right, I'm going up to see my son.'

'This way,' Gwen told the driver. 'Let's set you up for your journey back.' She led him to the kitchen.

What an utterly shocking turn of events. The idea of working here had seemed pretty straightforward to Gwen before. What would it be like now, with a sullen invalid and a hysterical mother? She knew she should feel sorry for Tom, and she did, but still… What on earth must the ambulance driver be thinking? She'd be polite and quick with his lunch, and maybe then he wouldn't think too badly of them all.

'Mother, stop fussing. I really don't want any lunch,' said Tom, keeping his eyes fixed on the dado rail from his recumbent position on the bed. 'I want to rest. I've had two weeks of people buzzing around in three hospitals, day and night. I just need to be alone for a while.'

'Come along, Margaret,' said Herbert, taking her arm. 'I'm sure he'll be hungry later.'

She pushed his hand away. 'I want to know what happened, and – and why he didn't tell us sooner.' She was sobbing.

'Believe me, what happened is not something you want to know,' said Tom. 'And I'm not going anywhere anytime soon, so I wouldn't worry about having to keep me company straight away.' His voice was flat. He was weary and longed for solitude. 'You'll be sick of me soon enough.'

'We'll see you later, son,' said Herbert, almost pushing the wailing Margaret out of the bedroom.

Tom waited for the sound of his mother's weeping to fade before he shut his eyes. Peace at last, from the shuffling of trolleys, the explanations of doctors, the bustling of nurses and, worst of all, the screams and moans of the patients.

But there was no silence, for in his head he could hear the blast of explosions, see the red, yellow and bright white of the light before the billowing smoke. His breathing became erratic. *Relax*, he told himself, like the nurse at Devonport had counselled. Think of nice things, from before the war, she'd said. He went back further, to his childhood in Georgetown, sitting on Mamgu Powell's knee while she sang to him and Lizzie, and they ate her pikelets with homemade bilberry jam.

Finally he fell into a shallow sleep. His dreams came quickly, as he pictured himself in the bottom of a trench, wrapped in a blanket, yet no sooner had this image appeared, then he was out in the middle of a muddy field, trying to avoid barbed wire as he ran, encouraging his men on. There was a round of shots, a machine gun, somewhere in the mist ahead. He looked around, dismayed to find several of his men on the ground, unmoving. Another round rang out and he found himself on his knees, an agonising pain ripping through his arm.

The relived torment woke him with a start and he immediately checked his arm. Not just a dream then. Sweat poured down his face, but he soon realised that some of the wetness was tears. Tears for his lost life, for what could have been.

He thought of Reading University, of his two years of study, the third year never likely to be completed. What would it even have been like to return, with half the young men he'd known there dead now?

He went to turn on his left side, but remembering it still hurt, he turned the other way. The vague tears became sobs, and in that way he eventually went back to sleep, to dream once more of scarred fields and corpses.

–

Margaret had woken up the next day, determined to be strong. She'd felt ashamed of the way she'd fallen apart the day before, with her son damaged and needing her support. No wonder he had spurned her concern, hysterical as she'd been.

She had made a fool of herself in front of the servants, so today she'd taken back control and issued some firm orders about what should be cleaned and what should be cooked. She'd imagined how Lady Anna would have coped with the situation, being such a disciplined woman. Margaret had taken meals up to Tom with a sympathetic yet pragmatic attitude, as he'd refused to come downstairs.

Mrs Rhys and Gweneth had been allowed to go home half an hour early, and Margaret was now alone in the kitchen. Slumping into a chair, she leaned her elbows on the table, pressing the palms of her hands against her cheeks. Why had all these troubles come at once? Her poor Tom, Elizabeth running away to the war, and then there was Herbert…

The kitchen door from the hall opened.

'Ah, here you are,' said her husband.

Margaret straightened herself. 'I didn't hear you come in.'

'Have Mrs Rhys and Gweneth gone?'

'Yes, I dismissed them early. I'd had enough of pretending everything is all right.' She felt her chin begin to wobble and pressed her lips together to prevent it going any further.

Herbert walked over to her, putting his arms around her shoulders. She shook him off. He took one step back. 'Margaret, I'm only trying to comfort you.'

'I saw Jenny last week.' She didn't look at him, examining the table instead.

'Are you wanting to employ her as a maid again? I thought Gweneth was meeting your requirements.'

'Yes, she is. And no, I would not re-employ Jenny, even if I was in desperate need of a maid.'

'Why is that?'

'She had her baby with her. Frederick, she named him. Not that you could call him a baby anymore, since he's nearly two. Two next month, in fact. I worked it out: Jenny must have been expecting for three months when she married.'

'Really? Well, it was good of Joseph to have done the right thing then. A pity he didn't survive.'

Margaret twisted around, causing the chair to grate on the stone floor. 'Oh yes, it was good of him, seeing as it wasn't his baby.' She kept her voice low, trying to keep a leash on her fury.

Herbert scrunched up his forehead as if in pain. 'What? What do you mean?'

'You know what I mean. That child is the spitting image of Tom at that age. I know, because there is that photograph of him and Elizabeth on my dressing table, which I look at every day. So, tell me truthfully, Herbert, is Jenny another victim of the carnal lusts of—?'

'Margaret, don't.' He walked to the end of the table and sat down, hanging his head low and closing his eyes.

'Don't what? Probe the fact that you knew there'd been another baby? Polly Coombes was supposed to be an aberration, a mistake never to be repeated. If anyone ever spots the likeness with Tom…'

'Yes, all right, I suspected it. But I concluded that the baby was Joseph's, as I didn't know she was carrying the child before she married him. And think about it: she would have – happened – before Polly, not since.'

'Does Tom know about this one?'

'I've no idea.'

'We are lucky that she married Joseph, and that she hasn't come looking for money since his death. And that Miss Coombes hasn't also come for more, since she is now in the village and her husband is in gaol. And how do you think I feel, every time I see either one of them?'

He fiddled with his fingers. 'I know.'

'Do you?' Margaret rose elegantly, looking down at Herbert. 'Now, although we will be living under the same roof, we will no longer be sharing a bedroom.'

'But Margaret—'

She put up her hand to silence him. 'I will not share a bed with you, not at the present time. Maybe, one day in the future, when you have regained my trust, I will reconsider, but for now, I would appreciate it if you'd move your belongings to the spare room.'

'Margaret this is ridic—'

'You can do it after dinner, which I am serving now.'

He dragged himself up from the seat, to lean on the table. 'Very well. I will take the cutlery into the dining room.'

'As you wish.'

She waited until he'd left the kitchen to serve the casserole Enid had made. She had to stop at one point, to sniff back more threatening tears. No, she'd save those for Tom's predicament. She wondered if he'd known about Jenny. It mattered not. Whatever had happened in the past, he needed her strength and energy now, even if he didn't yet appreciate it.

Chapter Twenty-Three

Tom watched through the bedroom window as his mother drove off down the road in the Morris Oxford. He sighed with relief at being left alone, before he remembered that Mrs Rhys and Gweneth were both in the house, executing their duties. Still, they wouldn't bother him, except to ask when he wanted his lunch and to tell him when it was ready.

He sat on the bottom corner of his bed. To be fair to his mother, she had ceased the hysterical behaviour of his first day home, but there was still that look of desperate concern etched on her face, even while her words were reasonable. Yet how else was a mother supposed to behave? It was him, his fault. He'd realised on his third day here that not allowing them to know what had happened until he'd come home had been a selfish act on his part. He felt bad about it now.

He'd forbidden them to write to Lizzie about the full extent of his injury. He would do the deed himself, making sure to persuade her not to come rushing home, that he was doing fine. And he was healing well. It was his mind that was a wreck.

There was a clatter on the stairs and he gathered Gweneth was coming up with something. He got off the bed and went onto the landing, in time to see her reach the top step with the vacuum cleaner. A couple of her blonde curls had escaped her bun and were bobbing either side of her forehead. As she looked up at him, a moment of surprise in her widened eyes, he was thrown off kilter for a split second by the intense blue of them.

'Good morning, Gweneth. Are you intending to clean my room today?'

'Well, sir, Mrs Meredith said only if you want me to, seeing as it hasn't been cleaned all week.'

'I'd rather you didn't, if you don't mind.'

'Of course, sir. I have other rooms I can be getting on with.' She did a little curtsy, the absurdity of which would have made him smile, had he been in a better humour.

'Thank you.'

He was about to go back to his room when she said, 'Mrs Meredith has also instructed me to help you downstairs at half past twelve for luncheon, if you should require it.'

He turned back, annoyed at the suggestion that he was helpless. 'There is nothing wrong with my legs and I'm perfectly capable of getting down the stairs on my own, should I want to.'

The maid frowned a little, her lips pressed together before she said, 'I'm sorry, sir. I was only trying to help.'

He regretted his tone. It wasn't her fault. 'I know. I'm sorry I was short with you.'

'That's all right, sir. I'm sure I'd feel the same, if – you know.' She looked uneasy.

'You have a brother in the 13th Battalion, I believe.'

Her face brightened. 'Yes, Henry. You were in the same carriage as him when you came home on leave, Christmas before last.'

'Of course, I remember now.' He recalled also that Polly Coombes's brother, Maurice, had been in the carriage. They'd all treated him with good humour, given he'd just become an officer. 'As for lunch, I think I will be taking it in my room, as usual.'

'Very well, sir. I will fetch it up at half past twelve, if that's all right with you.'

He nodded. 'Yes, thank you.'

Tom watched as she headed to his father's bedroom, as he gathered it now was. What had happened to cause this he had no idea, and at the moment, he hadn't the energy to find out.

He went back to his room and closed the door, leaning against it with his head back. Holing himself up in this one room was starting to feel as oppressive as being in the trenches. He had his life to think about, what lay ahead. But for now, he'd think about what he was going to do today.

—

Gwen started on what had just become Mr Meredith's bedroom with the vacuum cleaner, pulling and pushing at the bellows to get the dust up. She found it cumbersome and was sure she'd have done better with a dustpan and brush, but Mrs Meredith was keen on this new device.

She wondered why the mine manager had moved in here, not convinced by his wife's over-elaborate explanation of snoring and her finding it hard to sleep with Tom's injury worrying her.

She hummed to herself, as she often did to make the time pass. 'If You Were the Only Girl in the World' was what she started on, soon remembering that she'd first heard it when out with Ralph Tallis at a music hall.

'So what? I'm not letting you put me off it for evermore,' she muttered to an imaginary Tallis, and carried on singing. It would have been nice to have someone who thought of her in that way, that nothing mattered but her.

'Oh, this thing!' She stopped pumping for a while to give her arms a rest, then started again.

Tom had seemed a little bit brighter today, even if he had snapped at her. She couldn't get over what Anwen had told her a while back, that Tom was Polly Coombes's baby's father. And yet, why should she be surprised? She remembered a time when he'd strutted around the village, full of himself. Charming and friendly, yes, but clearly a cut above them all. Yet he'd taken quite a shine to Anwen at one point. He'd probably only been after one thing. Like Ralph, she'd realised when it was all over. She'd steer well clear of middle-class men from now on. Her pumping action became more determined with this firm decision.

Even so, it wasn't nice what had happened to Tom. If that was retribution for what he'd done with Polly, it was rather severe. It wasn't just the missing arm; she'd heard him calling out while having naps a few times. At least, she assumed he'd been napping, as it had reminded her of when Henry had called out in his sleep as a child, during nightmares.

Relieved when she'd finished with the vacuum cleaner, she fetched the caddy of cleaning items and proceeded to dust and polish the room. When she'd finished, she took a look at the clock on the fireplace there. Coming up to twenty-five past twelve. She struggled down the stairs with the caddy and the vacuum cleaner together, to be a little quicker.

'You finished upstairs, *cariad*?' said Enid, as Gwen rushed into the kitchen.

'Yes. Mr Tom didn't want his room doing, so I did the next on the list. I'll just put these away, then take his lunch up.'

'He's not coming down again today either?'

'No.' She dropped the bits off in the cupboard in the scullery and washed her hands. Today she'd be changing into the new uniform for the afternoon and had a list of instructions.

She re-entered the kitchen, coming to a sudden stop as Tom appeared through the opposite door.

'Well, Mr Tom, how nice to see you,' said Enid. 'What can we do for you, sir? Gwen was about to bring your lunch up to you. It's all ready.'

'That's all right, Mrs Rhys, for I've decided to come down for it after all.'

'I'll go and lay up the dining room,' said Gwen, going to the cutlery drawer.

'That won't be necessary,' said Tom. 'I've always preferred eating in the kitchen. It's warmer in the cooler months, and always cosier than the austere dining room.'

'Very well, sir,' said Enid. 'I need to be getting on with washing up and peeling in the scullery, so I'll leave you to it.'

'There's no need for that. I'm quite happy for you to be doing things in here. It would be like being at my grandmother's.'

'Thank you, sir, but I do need to get on.'

Gwen followed Enid into the scullery, in order to change her uniform. She hid in the pantry to do this as the older woman began the washing up. When she came out, she asked, 'Would you like some help with that?'

'No, *cariad*. You could see if Mr Tom would like a drink with his lunch, though. When I'm finished, I'll get our food ready.'

Gwen went back to the kitchen and asked the question.

'A nice cup of tea would be just the ticket,' he said.

She put the kettle on the range. While it heated up, she got a cup and saucer ready and fetched the tea and milk from the scullery.

Soon she had a pot on the table, with jugs of milk and hot water.

'Is there anything else, sir?'

'Not at the moment.' She was turning to go when he added, 'What are your instructions for this afternoon?'

'To pick up a book that's been ordered from Mr Schenck and to ask Dr Roberts to call in today or tomorrow for another check-up. I'm also instructed to pick up anything you might request and make sure you have everything you want.' She felt suddenly embarrassed, knowing what kind of thing a man like him might want, even with one arm.

He seemed to consider her words for some moments. 'I wouldn't mind going to the bookshop myself. But not today. I'm not ready to go out into the world, though I dare say what's happened to me has gone all around the village by now.'

'Not through anything I've said,' Gwen assured him. She'd told her parents and mamgu only, and then had sworn them to silence.

'I'm sorry, I didn't mean to imply anything. My father said he would let it be known, so that people wouldn't have a shock when I went out, and I wouldn't have to keep answering questions.'

'I see.'

'Do you play chess, Gweneth?'

She was thrown by the odd question. 'Well, yes, I do. Henry and I were taught by my grandfather and used to play a fair bit.'

'I might appreciate a partner for a couple of games this afternoon. Would you be happy with that?'

'As long as Mrs Meredith is fine with it.'

'I'm certain she would be. After you've had your lunch and done your chores, perhaps you'd come to the living room, and we'll have a game.'

'Very well, sir. Is there anything else at this moment?'

'No, I have all I need for now.'

'I'll be in the scullery if you change your mind.'

She left him to his lunch, considering how very different this job had turned out to be from what she'd expected.

–

It was the turn of Mrs Meredith's bedroom today, and, despite having to give it a full clean, Gwen relished the opportunity to spend time in such an elegant room. The inlaid, maple furniture was fairly new. How she'd have loved to take a peek in the two wardrobes and the drawers, especially the dressing table ones, but she wouldn't have dared.

This week had been eventful, with a visit to Merthyr with Mrs Meredith, to collect fabrics for Mrs Bowen to make her a new outfit. She had been the donkey of course, carrying the bits and pieces, but she'd enjoyed it nonetheless. Another afternoon, she'd been in attendance when Mrs Meredith's 'ladies', as she called them, had visited. She'd answered the door, then later had brought in the tea and served it. The much spoken-about Lady Fitzgerald had come, though Gwen had found her a pompous body.

Part-way through vacuuming the carpet, the door opened, and Mrs Meredith entered. She looked around the room.

'You're doing a splendid job here so far, Gweneth. And don't you find the vacuum cleaner just *such* a boon when it comes to getting the carpet clean?'

It would have been impolite to say anything but, 'Yes, madam.' She didn't think, *No, it's a wretched nuisance*, would have gone down well.

'I also wanted to say that I do appreciate you playing games with my son. I know they're *terribly* boring, but they do seem to cheer him up a little. He always did like board games.'

She could have told Mrs Meredith that she loved board games herself, and that learning draughts, a new game to her, had been entertaining, but then she might not be so appreciated. The fact that he'd won every game so far didn't bother her in the least.

'I'm happy to do what I can, madam.'

'Thank you Gweneth. I think you may turn out to be a gem.' Margaret swiftly exited the room.

A gem? Goodness, she'd never been referred to as that before, not at work, anyway.

When she'd finished with the vacuum cleaner, it was time to polish the dressing table and dust the ornaments and photographs that sat upon it. She hummed to herself as she worked, admiring the various pieces and enjoying the scent of lavender. The last one she dusted was a photograph. She'd only glanced at it before, vaguely aware it was two children who she assumed were Elizabeth and Tom. She examined it more carefully now, staring at Tom for several moments. The huge grin was immensely cute, but she had the feeling that she'd seen the face before. Maybe there was another photograph like this, somewhere else in the house. Did he maybe look like Polly's son, Herby? No, she couldn't see it. The child was quite like his mother, with her blonde hair, rather than the dark auburn hair.

She put the photo down. It must just be that there was a likeness to Tom as he was now, that's all.

—

Gwen leant her head back as she walked along James Street with Anwen and Violet, face up to the sky.

'What are you looking at?' said Anwen.

'I'm just enjoying the sun. The weather hasn't been so good the last few days, so it's nice of it to oblige on my day off.'

'It is, and—' Anwen looked behind. 'You all right, Violet?'

Their other friend had stopped for a moment and looked a little pale.

'I am now.' She caught them up. 'I still feel a little sick at times, even though I'm more than five months gone.'

Gwen looked down at Violet's stomach: her pregnancy was starting to show quite a lot now. They carried on with their walk.

'How is Tom doing?' Anwen asked Gwen.

'He's coming out of his room every day now, and we've played a few more games.'

'It's all right to be paid for playing,' Violet quipped.

'It is!' said Gwen. 'Of course, it would have been better if Tom hadn't lost his arm, and it does cause a strain on the household, as you can imagine.' She was regretting taking this line, since much of the strain was between Mr and Mrs Meredith, and she felt she shouldn't tell anyone about that, not even her best friends.

'It would do,' said Violet.

'He's talking about walking into the village next week, so that will be good for him… providing he doesn't get any comments.'

'But he's adjusted to being home?' Anwen asked.

'I think so. But not to his condition, and who would? He seems… humbler than he was before he left.'

'He was always charming,' said Anwen, 'if sometimes a little needy. It was a shame he blotted his copybook with Polly Coombes. Oh look, there's Jenny.'

Gwen and Violet looked across the road to the bottom of the triangle on Jubilee Green. Jenny, walking towards them on the other side of the road, was just passing the entrance to the gardens. Toddling along beside her was Freddie, holding her hand.

Anwen crossed the road ahead of them. 'Hello, Jenny. Look at this: three maids or former maids of McKenzie House together,' she joked.

'How are you getting on at the Big House?' Jenny asked Gwen as she caught up.

'I'm quite enjoying it, really. It's probably better for me, since you two had to put up with peevish Rose.'

Jenny's eyes darted heavenward. 'She was a one. Quiet she's been lately, and so polite when she serves in the butcher's.'

'A little *too* quiet, if you ask me,' said Gwen.

'Have you seen the posh clothes she wears when she goes out now? I reckon her father's had to make it up to her, not paying for her to stay out of gaol.'

'I wouldn't be at all surprised,' said Anwen, 'with Rose *and* Gertie on at him.'

'I was sad to hear about young Mr Meredith.' Jenny's mouth drooped and her eyes were sad. 'Such a nice young man, he was.'

'It is a terrible shame,' Gwen agreed, then, to change the subject so she wouldn't be asked any awkward questions, she carried on with, 'My goodness, Freddie's got big now.'

'Aye, nearly two, he is,' said Jenny.

Gwen hunkered down in front of him. He held out his hand, in which was a shabby, but clearly well-loved teddy bear. 'This

Arthur,' he said. 'He my friend.' He plunged the teddy against his chest and cuddled it, treating Gwen to a cute smile.

It was then she saw it. That photograph on Mrs Meredith's dressing table: it could have been Freddie. Even the dark auburn hair was the same colour as Tom's.

Wobbly with the shock of this revelation, she managed to say, 'He's a lovely friend.' She stood once more, still gazing at the child.

'And where are your littl'uns?' Jenny asked.

'With their das,' said Anwen, 'playing games. So we've been let out for a coupla hours' walk.'

'You've picked a nice day for it,' said Jenny. 'I'm staying with a friend at the moment, as my aunt has the influenza and is quite bad. I don't want Freddie to get it.'

Anwen nodded. 'Idris's mother mentioned that a coupla people on Alexandra Street have influenza too, and a family on West Street.'

'It's a bit late in the season, isn't it?' said Jenny. 'Anyway, have fun.' She passed by, carrying on across the road beside them and down towards Owain Street.

Gwen, still a little shaken from her possible discovery about Freddie, didn't realise Violet was speaking until she tapped her arm.

'Well, Gwen?'

She came to. 'Sorry?'

'We thought, rather than go in the gardens yet again, we'd take advantage of not having the kiddies and go for a longer walk on the hill.' She pointed towards Twyn Gobaith.

'That would be lovely,' said Gwen.

She was probably imagining the likeness and anyway, surely Joseph Richards wouldn't have married her had she been expecting another man's child, especially with him being a minister's son.

She quickened her pace. 'Let's go, then.'

Chapter Twenty-Four

Gwen looked up at the sky as she left McKenzie House. It was nice having nearly three hours of daylight to look forward to when she left work, now they were fast approaching the middle of May. Even the colliery wheels, in the dip before her, churning on in their eternal groan, could not spoil the relief of it being home time.

It had been a strange afternoon. She'd been hoping to play another game or two with Tom, but Mrs Meredith had spirited him away in the motorcar around half past two, amid much whispering. The only thing she'd gathered was that they were heading to Cardiff, though he had not seemed keen.

She had her mam's cawl to look forward to this evening, with some of the veggies her da had harvested in their back garden. Her mouth was watering at the thought, when she spied someone on the bridge, looking down at the pit. It was Esther Williams.

The older woman must have seen her from the corner of her eye as she turned in her direction. Her usual downhearted version of a smile was a little brighter.

'Oh Gwen, I'm so glad to have caught you. I was afraid you might have left early.'

Esther walked towards her, meeting her in the middle of the bridge. 'I've got some good news.' She grabbed hold of Gwen's hands.

'You've heard from Daniel?'

'No, but someone has told me he's alive.'

Gwen felt a wave of relief. 'Who told you this?'

'It was Mrs Tudur at the end of Station Road.'

'Mrs Tudur?' Gwen's brow was creased in confusion. 'How would she kn—' It was then she remembered: Mrs Tudur claimed to be a medium.

'Mrs Williams, I don't think Mrs Tudur is a reliable person. She's made claims before that haven't been true, like when there was the mine accident in 1906 and she told Florrie Harris that her husband was still alive and they'd find him. Well, they found him all right, but it was clear he'd been killed instantly from the fall. I was only twelve, but I remember my mam talking about it.'

'But she's right this time, I just know it. She says she can't find him in the spirit world.' As she said this, her voice became more excited. 'I can feel he's still alive.'

'I do hope you're right, but I wouldn't pin any hopes on it.'

'But this is wonderful, Gwen, wonderful! You must be excited, surely?'

'I'm sorry, but I believe that Mrs Tudur is a charlatan.'

Esther was not to be discouraged. 'Oh, I know you don't want to build up any false hope, but you'll see, he'll come home, and then you can be together. You'll be wanting to get home now, no doubt, to tell your parents the good news.'

Esther walked with her, chatting on the way about how excited Christopher would be when she told him.

Poor Christopher, thought Gwen as Esther walked away, a spring in her step. Hopefully he wouldn't be as gullible as his mother.

–

Gwen always loved cleaning the drawing room, as Mrs Meredith referred to it, especially after she'd finished the windows and the vacuuming, and could concentrate on the furniture. She imagined now that she was the lady of the house, as she flittered the feather duster across the top of the cream Chesterfield settees and polished the shelves and occasional tables. The two windows in here, one to the side and one looking over the back garden, were large, not like the one poky window in her kitchen at home, where they spent most of their time. Oh, to live in a house like this!

Enjoying herself so much, she started singing. It was her interpretation of a song she'd heard Tom playing on the gramophone many times in the last few days. That seemed to be his latest interest. She thought maybe the song was Italian, as it sounded like the language she'd heard the family at the Perilli Bros Refreshment House speak to each other in. And it was perhaps called 'Oh Solo Mee-oh', but she couldn't be sure.

Singing softly to begin with, but remembering that Mrs Meredith had gone out, she sang a little louder. With the sun shining, and not having been bothered by Esther since she waylaid her on the bridge two weeks before, her mood was light. They'd also had a letter from Henry, who was currently in the back lines, for which she was thankful.

She was giving the song her all, making up words in between others she'd learned, polishing the mantelpiece furiously. She turned to get some more polish and jumped in fright. There, by the door, was Tom, his eyes raised in surprise. He was still wearing his arm in a sling, though Gwen wasn't sure it was necessary anymore.

'Oh my goodness, Lieutenant Meredith, I didn't hear you come in.'

'Evidently. I could hear you from the hall.'

She felt the hot flush travel across her face. 'I thought you were in the kitchen, having morning coffee.'

'I was, until I finished. Please, don't stop singing. You have a good voice.'

'Thank you, sir. I don't really know that song though. 'Oh Solo Mee-oh', or whatever it's called.' She shrugged.

"O Sole Mio',' he said in a lilting accent, very like the Perilli family. 'It's by Enrico Caruso and means, 'Oh my sun', as in, the sun in the sky.'

'I see. I heard you playing it quite a lot and just picked up a few words. Do you speak Italian, then?'

'I learned a little from a book, when I thought of travelling to Italy in August 1914, with a couple of university friends. One of them had an Italian mother and helped me a little. But then the war started.' His voice became monotone and he looked away. After a few moments he composed himself. 'Why not sing me a Welsh song instead? You can carry on cleaning, as I don't want to get you into trouble, but I'll sit here and listen.' He sat on one of the armchairs.

She thought for a while, then started on 'Bugeilio'r Gwenith Gwyn'. By the time she'd come to the end of the song, she'd finished the mantelpiece.

He clapped his one hand on his thigh. 'Sorry, that's the best I can do for applause. So, do you think of me as a young and foolish lad yearning after some young maid?'

'I – I didn't think you spoke Welsh,' she said, 'Or at least, not much.' That was even worse, for now it sounded like she'd picked something she thought she could sing as a joke without him knowing.

'It's my first language.'

'But your accent – it's English.'

'Yes, sadly it was flattened into Anglo tones to prevent me being teased at Reading. I suppose I should have stuck to my guns and to hel— heck with them.' At this point, he spoke in Welsh. 'You must have heard Lizzie speaking Welsh, as I know she often did, working on the allotments.'

'I – I suppose I thought she'd learned it, to fit in,' she replied. Though looking back, she should have realised she was too fluent. 'Why don't you speak it in the home, then?'

He let out a short and mirthless laugh. 'Why do you think? It's been banned,' he said, in a dramatic voice. 'Has been since my father became an undermanager.'

She supposed he meant Mrs Meredith had banned it but thought it best not to say so. 'I'm sorry about the song; it was just the first one that came to mind.'

'I'm only teasing. Though maybe I am a foolish lad. Maybe all men are.'

She wasn't sure what to make of that, until it occurred to her: his dalliance with Polly. And maybe Jenny as well.

'If you are, I'm sure it's your own business, sir.'

'I'm sorry, Gwen, I didn't mean to embarrass you. You see, that's what I mean: I take a joke too far. What I actually came in for was to ask you whether you can play backgammon.'

'No, sir, but I'm a quick learner,' she said with some pride. 'Would that be this afternoon?' She hoped so, as she did enjoy playing games and it was better than cleaning or running errands.

'I'm afraid not, for my mother has other plans for me this afternoon. Another trip to a doctor in Cardiff.'

'About your arm?'

He huffed a brief laugh. 'No, about my mind. Dr Roberts recommended him. He thinks I might have shell shock, but I think I'm just – just having difficulty getting over what I've seen. Anyone who's taken part in the war would be. I've seen men with shell shock in the trenches, and this doesn't compare with their suffering.' He shook his head mournfully. 'But mother is keen for me to go.'

'I hope it goes well, sir.'

'That reminds me of the other thing I wanted to say. All this "sir" and "Lieutenant Meredith" lark, I had enough of that in the army. And it's not like I'm ever likely to be a lieutenant again. Anyway, Tom will do.'

'But Mrs Meredith—'

'Yes, I know. When she's in earshot, I suppose you'd better comply with her wishes.'

'Very well, sir – Tom.'

'I'll leave you to it, Gweneth.'

'Gwen.'

'Sorry?'

'Everyone else calls me Gwen. Except when Mrs Meredith is in earshot, of course.' She hoped *she* hadn't gone too far.

Tom threw his head back and let out a mighty roar of laughter. 'Touché! Gwen it is, then!'

He left the room still chuckling.

–

Tom ate his lunch slowly, since eating quickly wouldn't get him to two o'clock and his trip to the village any quicker. Outside, the early June sun was shining in a cloudless sky, and he couldn't wait to bathe in its warmth. His mother was chatting away about how the members of her committee were considering putting their planned events on hold, because of the influenza epidemic.

'I do feel they're taking it a little too far. Life has to go on.'

'There have been a lot of cases now though, and a few around here have proved fatal, I've read in the newspapers.'

'No deaths in our village, though.'

'Yet,' he said. 'Perhaps it would be better to curtail your trips, especially those outside the village, for you don't want to catch it. And I certainly don't. Once was enough, and this version seems worse. As it is, I'm not getting too close to people when I'm in the village.'

'Talking of which, I don't know why you can't postpone your trip to the village until tomorrow, when I'll be home to come with you,' Margaret intoned in an irritated manner. 'But I really *must* attend the meeting this afternoon.'

Which was why he'd picked today. Their last foray into the village had consisted of her milking the 'poor Tom, but look how brave both he and I are being' aspect of it. She was making him out to be a hero, which he wasn't, and at the same time inviting admiration of herself. He didn't want people's pity. He'd foregone visiting any of the shops for fear she would do the same in every single one.

'I'd really like to go this afternoon, since it's sunny.'

'Tomorrow I could take you out in the motorcar somewhere better than this. Monmouth, maybe.'

'What did I just say about not going out of the village during this influenza epidemic? It's enough to have to go to Cardiff each week. And you know what Sergeant Harries said about wasting petrol.'

'Then we could take the train tomorrow.'

'I want to go out today, and I'd prefer to stay in the village. And tomorrow might not be so nice.' He could hardly say it was *her* he didn't want to go with. He smiled, knowing the outward appearance of him being content satisfied her.

'When we go back into Cardiff next Friday, perhaps you'd like to buy some more gramophone records. You must be tired of playing the same ones over and over.'

By which she meant, *she* was tired of hearing the same ones. 'I'm quite content with what we have, thank you.'

'Some more books, then.'

'We'll see.'

The truth was, so little engaged him now. The only sunny spot in his day was his time spent with Gwen. She was bright and sparky and didn't refer to his amputation as if it were the most abhorrent affliction, but as a matter of fact, something to take into consideration but not brood over. It was what he needed. Even his father had that pained look about him when he considered Tom. What a shame Elizabeth hadn't been home for he was sure she'd have dealt with the whole sorry business a lot better.

At last he'd finished. He'd largely lost his appetite these days, which wasn't helped by the poorer choice of food on offer. Would he ever get his gusto for life back?

–

He was relieved when two o'clock arrived. He'd spent the last twenty minutes tidying himself up, declining his mother's offer to help him before she left for her meeting. It was harder dressing with one hand, especially doing up buttons, but somehow he had managed it. In the hall he considered himself in the mirror. The grey, worsted suit was one from before he'd enlisted. If Mother had had her way, he'd have worn his uniform, which she'd had cleaned, but he would have felt a fraud in it. He lifted his arm, only bandaged today, but covered with his shirt and jacket. The left sleeve on both had been folded and sewn to accommodate. He heard the kitchen door shut.

Gwen appeared from around the corner. 'Are you ready, Tom?'

'I am. So you're wearing your uniform, are you?'

'I always have to when doing errands and afternoon jobs.'

'I feel like I'm being taken out by a nursemaid,' he said, peeved by the black dress and the cap with its bit of frill. Or someone in mourning, he thought.

She looked down at herself. 'At least I've been allowed to take off the apron.'

'Come on.' He lifted the straw boater off the hat stand and opened the door.

He enjoyed the warm air on his face. There wasn't the stench of gunfire and TNT here, even if the colliery did have a smell of its own. What a shame they didn't live right out in the countryside, or by the sea.

They spoke only sporadically as they took the road round the pit. The first few people they encountered greeted him with reverence, all of them avoiding looking at his arm, whether from revulsion or respect.

It was as they reached the crossroads of James Street, Jubilee Green and Station Road that they spotted the men rolling up the road from the colliery.

'The early shift's over,' said Gwen.

Tom considered them, sooty skin and clothes from head to foot, yet chatting amiably, even laughing. 'You'll be relieved when your brother is one of those coming up the road.'

'Yes, strange, isn't it? For it's not the life I'd choose for him, or anyone really, but it would be preferable to where he is.'

'Indeed.' He took a step to the side and almost bumped into one of the miners. 'I am so sorry.' He moved away quickly.

'No, my fault, not looking where I'm going, like. Oh good afternoon, Mr Meredith, Gwen.' The man lifted his cap, revealing auburn hair a little lighter than his own, but curly.

Tom knew he'd been one of the leading allotment workers, but he couldn't remember his name. He was saved from embarrassment by Gwen saying, 'Afternoon, Gwilym.'

Of course, Gwilym Owen. The 'rascal' who'd sent Lizzie scurrying off to be a VAD, if their mother was to be believed. But the letters from his sister had indicated otherwise. 'Good afternoon, Mr Owen. I was sorry to hear of the allotments being taken over by the coal company.'

Gwilym looked embarrassed, probably because of the past situation with his sister, but Tom was not going to hold it against him. His mother was the intolerant one.

'Aye, yes, sir. A sad business. And I'm glad to see you're out and about and getting better after your injury.'

'Thank you. Have a good afternoon.'

'I will, sir. And you.' He went on his way.

'Let's go in the bookshop, so we're out of the way,' said Gwen. She opened the door and they slipped inside.

He took in a deep breath. Books, paper. Yes, that was an aroma he felt at home with. A shame the books themselves interested him less these days.

'I've always enjoyed coming in here,' said Gwen. '*A whole world of discovery in two rooms*, as Mr Schenck calls it.'

As if hearing his name, the shopkeeper popped his head round the door from the next room. 'Mr Meredith the younger! How good to see you again, out and about. I had a delivery of new books yesterday and have acquired quite a few older ones to fill my shelves once more, which you might be interested in. And welcome to you also, Miss Austin.' He performed his customary bow.

Tom looked around. 'I'm amazed you've put this place together again so quickly. It hardly looks any different.'

'I was fortunate indeed that there were so many wonderful people in the village willing to help with the work, given that builders are so far and few between these days. Now, please, look around at your leisure, and do ask if there's anything I can help with.'

Mr Schenck withdrew, going to the counter at the back of the shop.

'I think I'll go and look at the history books,' he said, pointing at the other room.

'I'll have a look at the children's books. It's Benjy's fourth birthday in a coupla months, so I'll see if there's anything there.'

He remembered Anwen speaking of Benjy and… Clarice, that was it, when she'd worked at the house, and he was sure he'd seen them playing on the allotment as their mother worked. Violet. Yes.

Gwen went ahead to open the door into the other room. He wished she wouldn't, for he had a perfectly good hand to do such things, but he accepted that she was being kind, and acting in the way a servant should. He couldn't imagine himself ever having his own servants. But then, he couldn't see himself ever leaving his childhood home now. What would be the point? He was unlikely ever to marry.

He heard Gwen, ahead of him, say, 'Oh, hello Polly.'

He came to a standstill.

'Well, don't you look smart in your maid's dre…' Her voice trailed away when she noticed Tom standing there. She stared at his arm as she said, 'Good afternoon to you, Mr Meredith.'

'Good afternoon, Miss Coombes. I mean, Mrs Smith,' he replied, very formally. What else could he do? There was something different about her now. The gaudy colours and frills were gone. Her clothing was quite plain and her face held no make-up. She was still pretty, yet looked – worn out.

She was staring at the arm, so he said, 'Excuse me,' and went towards the history books.

He pulled out several volumes awkwardly, taking each to the table in turn so he could rest them there as he perused them.

The women chatted, mainly about the child. He glanced over a couple of times, trying to see if there was some family likeness. When he heard the boy referred to by name he stared, wide-eyed, unable to believe that she'd named him after his father. Herby. It had to be short for Herbert. Did his parents know? Polly had agreed to keep the name of the father to herself, for a tidy sum of money, and here she was, using a family name. Not that there was anything unusual about it, but still…

He tried to forget them, reading the contents pages of the books to distract himself, but it was no good. It occurred to him that his days of courting women were over. Not that they'd really begun as he'd been more concerned with his studies. Who would marry him now, unless they liked the idea of the apparent 'war hero'? More likely they'd see him as damaged and not a good provider. That's what women wanted. Look at his mother. He slid the book he was holding back into the gap on the shelf.

'I'm going to look at the novels,' he told Gwen. 'You don't need to come through yet. I'll tell you when I've finished.'

'Very well, sir.'

He went through to the other room, quickly finding the modern novels. The first one he picked up was a book of short stories by P.G. Wodehouse. That they'd be both amusing and short decided him. He went quickly to the counter.

'I read this recently,' said Mr Schenck, wrapping it in brown paper and tying it with string. 'Very amusing, it was.'

Bookshop owner. Now that might appeal to him as a career, thought Tom. Or not. How would he deal with stacking books every day, with one hand? He'd end up dropping more than he shelved.

Gwen was leaving the other room as he placed his change in his pocket. Catching her up, he said, 'I think, instead of walking around the town, I might like to take a walk up the hill, if you don't mind.'

'Of course not. I go there all the time.' She went ahead to the door, waving to Mr Schenck as she opened it for Tom.

It was a relief to Tom to see that the miners had all disappeared to their houses. He and Gwen spoke little as they walked past the Institute and the fire station, to Twyn Gobaith behind.

'Shall I take the book for you?' she said.

'It's fine. I have one good hand so I may as well use it.'

'I'm sorry, I didn't mean anything by it.'

'Don't apologise, Gwen. It's me in a bad mood. Well, not bad, more, thoughtful.'

'I'm a good listener. But only if you want to share it, of course.'

'I've been wondering what I'll do, eventually, that's all. What it is I even *can* do.'

'You've got a good arm, and it's your writing arm. Couldn't you get a desk job, especially being educated, like? The man whose job Elizabeth had for a while, at the overseer's office, lost his knee but could still do the job. I know that's not quite the same, but you could do something like that, I'm sure.'

'Maybe.'

'What were you doing at university?'

'A law degree. Not that I wanted to. I'd like to have done history, or literature, but my mother had a plan.' He raised his eyebrows. 'I didn't finish it as I got influenza.'

'I remember Anwen saying.'

'Not that many others would have finished, as most of them enlisted.' And not many were left to finish now, he thought but didn't like to say.

'If you like literature, perhaps you could be a writer,' she said.

'I've always rather fancied that, but you can imagine what my mother would say.'

'But you're a...'

He stopped as they reached the brow of the hill. 'What?'

'I don't want to speak out of turn.' She fiddled with her hat, although it was perfectly in place.

'Go on. I value your plain speaking.'

'You're a grown-up, not a child. How old are you, exactly?'

'Twenty-three.'

'Only a bit younger than me. I was twenty-four recently. My parents, they like their say in my life, but they recognise I'm an adult, see, and let me make my own decisions too.'

'I envy you, Gwen, I really do.' He started off again and she caught him up.

'What, me?' She pointed to herself. 'I'm just from a working-class home.'

'Yes, you. You have riches I don't have. I used to. Being better off financially isn't always what it seems.'

'Oh I know that all right. You know I had a job at the munitions, with real good wages. But look what happened to me.' She'd told him one afternoon, over a game of chess.

'There, you see, you already know what I mean,' he said.

'Yes, I suppose I do. Money doesn't always make you happy.'

He stopped halfway down the hill, looking towards the road, and beyond, to Rhymney. 'You're so easy to talk to, Gwen. You listen. You make helpful suggestions. You don't judge. You remind me of Lizzie in that way.'

Gwen chuckled.

'Why is that funny?'

'Ralph Tallis.' Surely he knew about it already.

'I vaguely remember my mother going on about him. Let's walk down to Rhymney, then come back via the road, and you can tell me more.'

'All right. As long as you don't judge me.'

'I won't. Go on.'

'Well, you see, Elizabeth and I went to the picture house...'

Chapter Twenty-Five

Elizabeth sat in the mess tent, wilting over the table, half-heartedly spooning the porridge into her mouth. It had been a night filled with incoming casualties.

'I could pop my head onto the table and fall asleep,' said Doris.

'Me too,' Elizabeth admitted. 'I'm so hungry but am also the weariest I've felt since I got here.'

'We're so short-staffed now, I doubt we'll get much rest today.'

Sister Coulter arrived at the table with a couple of nurses and three of the VADs. 'You all did very well last night,' she said.

'That's not what Matron seemed to think,' said one of the VADs, referring to a period in the night where she went around telling staff they needed to buck their ideas up.

'I dare say she was as weary as us,' said the sister. 'And now one of the post-op wards has detected three more cases of influenza, while there are another two on a recovery ward. We've been lucky not having too many cases up 'til now, and being able to isolate them. They've also displayed fairly mild symptoms, whilst these are more severe and prolonged. You all need to be vigilant, so that if any symptoms are detected, we can try to isolate the soldiers involved. And don't forget to wear masks when dealing with these patients, for we are already short-staffed and do not want to go down with the disease ourselves.'

'Wouldn't that just be the icing on the cake,' said Doris.

Elizabeth pondered this problem. 'There have been lots of cases reported in the local newspapers I've been sent from home, and my friend Anwen has written of several cases in the village. They all seem quite mild, though an older resident was in hospital for a while. Spanish 'Flu, the newspapers are calling it.'

'There have been cases in my hometown too,' said Doris. 'I suppose some unsuspecting soldiers who've caught it here have taken it with them when on leave.'

Several people joined the discussion, detailing what they'd heard from their own families. Soon Elizabeth's mind wandered to the letter she'd received from Sidney. It had been nearly two months since they'd discharged him from this casualty clearing post. He'd been in the hospital in Dartford for four weeks, before going home for three weeks' leave. He was now travelling back to France, to join his battalion. She wondered if it were too soon, though he'd seemed satisfied in his letter. Finally, she finished the last spoonful of porridge and took a draught of her tea.

'I wonder what Matron wants,' said Doris, spotting her coming into the tent. 'She looks quite stern.'

'When doesn't she?' whispered one of the other VADs.

'Nurse Meredith,' Matron announced. 'You have a visitor. I will allow you fifteen minutes to speak with him.'

It surely couldn't be Sidney. Who else, though? She left the rest of her tea and followed Matron's retreating back, all the way to her office. It was one of the small huts, filled with files and with clipboards hanging on the wall. A man turned as they entered, standing by the desk. It was indeed Sidney.

'I'm only allowing this as it was requested by an officer,' Matron said sniffily. 'Like I said, fifteen minutes.' She left them to it.

'Sidney, how lovely to see you so well.'

He limped towards her and she noticed he had a stick. 'Not entirely, not yet, but I've been allowed back for a clerical role in the back lines. At least I can be useful.'

'It was lovely of you to visit.'

'I was on my way back to HQ, and the driver was kind enough to divert here. Elizabeth, I'm not going to beat around the bush. Your presence when I was brought here for treatment was what kept me going, especially your company when you were off duty. It was kind of you to spend some of your spare time with me. Not to mention your selfless deed of donating your blood, of course. Your letters have been a bright patch in a dark time. And that day out we had at the Brecon Beacons – I can't tell you how much I enjoyed it.

'I know this is rather precipitous but – would you do me the honour of marrying me on my next leave? I wouldn't expect you to give this up, but at least we could spend some leave together, and we'd have some future to look forward to.'

To say she was surprised would have been an understatement. She had never dreamed he would ask such a question, even though he had clearly enjoyed her company while he was here.

'I – I don't know what to say.'

'I know it is sudden, and under normal circumstances I would have courted you for some period of time before such a matter would be considered. But these are not normal circumstances, and who knows when, or indeed if, such times will return? I'm not usually what you'd call a spontaneous person, but I feel that if I do not grab this opportunity while I can, that it may slip through my fingers.'

Did he perhaps fear he might be killed and not have a future beyond the war? She sometimes felt that same fatalism herself, even though she was a little further away from the action.

'Would you mind if I took a walk around the camp to think about it? Five minutes, maybe. I can't answer, just like that.'

'Of course. I know it's a huge thing I ask of you, since we have not been walking out. Yet, I realised, even when I came to visit you at your home last time, that I admired you greatly.'

'I'll be back soon.'

She left the office, her emotions churning. How on earth could she say no without upsetting him too much? Yet, would he really expect her to accept? As she contemplated the best way to let him down, she also thought of Gwilym, and how that could never have worked. Then what was she going to do with her life after the war? Even if she started her market gardening business, would she always be alone? Would marrying Sidney be so bad? She'd discovered he was a far more gallant man than she'd taken him for. He had values, many of which matched her own. They also shared some interests. She'd known of marriages based on far less.

By the time she got back to Matron's office, she'd made her decision. As soon as she closed the door, she said, 'Yes, Sidney, I will marry you.'

'Oh, my dear!' he almost sang, limping rapidly towards her. 'I will make you happy, I promise. Where are we now? Sixth June. Hopefully we will be able to organise this by July or August. Now I must be on my way. May I beg a brief kiss, before I leave?'

She nodded, lifting her head up. He bent down and brushed her lips with his, before kissing her for a couple of seconds. It did not produce the tingle of the kisses she had shared with Gwilym, but it mattered not, as she was sure that would come in time.

'Thank you, Elizabeth. You have made me very happy. It has been worth the injury, to leave with this prize. I will write when I am able to get leave, so you can arrange yours too.'

She saw him to the waiting motorcar. He called, 'Until next time,' and got into the passenger seat. Once more she waved him off, hoping there would be a next time.

–

'I'm not sure what the point is of putting patients with different infections in different tents, and separating them with barbed wire, if we nurses are still to attend them all,' Elizabeth complained to Doris, as they made their way from breakfast to the area that had been divided off.

'I did say the same thing to Sister, but she said it wasn't her decision, but Matron's.'

'Meningitis, dysentery, trench foot, a couple of cases of diphtheria and now this Spanish 'Flu. They should be at a different hospital. How are we to get the other injured men well if they risk getting other diseases?'

'I quite agree. But there aren't enough nurses to divide them up in that strict way, and now we've had one nurse down with dysentery and another with influenza we're even more short-staffed. And moving the men would be detrimental to their health.'

'I suppose you're right,' Elizabeth conceded.

'At least it's summer.' Doris looked up to the clear, blue sky. It was already warm, though only twenty past six in the morning. 'Come winter, we'll be struggling even more, with the cold, wet and mud.'

Elizabeth didn't look forward to that. Conditions were desperate enough as it was. However, it was what she'd signed up for, so she'd have to learn to put up with it when the time came. However bad it was, it would be even worse for the men in the trenches.

They stopped just before they reached the entrance to the influenza tent.

'Right, masks on,' said Doris. 'At least we can minimise our risk of catching anything.'

Elizabeth nodded and pulled her eucalyptus mask out of her pocket. Luckily, she liked the smell, but there were several nurses who didn't. Their first job would be to disinfect everything – yet again. Then it would be breakfast for these men – those who could manage to eat anything.

But on entering the tent, they found a young and newer VAD panicking at the far end. 'Oh, thank goodness you're here,' she whined. 'I – I think…' her words faded away.

They rushed to her side. Doris felt the man's neck. She went to work, trying to revive him, but it was no use.

'What's happened, is Harry all right?' a man called from three beds away, the only patient apparently awake.

'You get some more rest before breakfast, corporal,' said Elizabeth. 'We're dealing with it.'

'Oh no,' the young VAD whispered. 'That's the first death we've had from the influenza. I thought it was supposed to be mild.'

'There have been a few deaths reported in the newspapers, nevertheless,' said Doris. 'So we can't assume anything. I'll inform Matron. You two know what to do.'

Elizabeth looked over at the awake soldier, making sure he'd settled down once more, before placing the sheet over their patient's head. She could see the young VAD was trying not to cry.

'You're meant to be off duty now,' Elizabeth said kindly. 'Get along and have some breakfast and I'll finish up here. And don't forget to wash and sterilise your hands.'

The young nurse nodded. 'Thank you, Nurse Meredith.'

As she wandered off, her head down, Elizabeth looked around the beds. She hoped with all her heart that this wasn't going to be the first fatality in here of many.

Chapter Twenty-Six

Gwen found pumping the vacuum cleaner as she dragged it across the floor in the dining room even more cumbersome than usual. She felt a bead of sweat drip down the side of her face so blew upwards to cool her forehead.

She had a few errands to run for Mrs Meredith later, written on a list she'd left for Gwen on the kitchen table. They included seeing what she could do with the vegetable patch that Elizabeth had started to cultivate in the garden last year. Gwen wondered how much use she'd be though; it wasn't like she was a natural gardener, even though she'd helped on the allotments a bit.

She heard footsteps on the stairs. A few moments later, several doors opened and shut at various intervals.

Gwen had started on the vacuuming once more when the door opened. Tom peeped around. 'Good morning, Gwen.'

'Good morning – sir.' She felt self-conscious, with her face damp and her hair straggling down a bit.

'Have you seen my mother around?'

'She's gone off to a meeting. Something about sorting out the new rationing books that are being issued. Then she's having lunch with some of her ladies in Monmouth.'

'Monmouth?' He came into the room properly. 'She must have forgotten about my appointment in Cardiff today.'

Of course, it was Friday. 'She'll surely be back before then.'

'She'll be cutting it fine from Monmouth. Darn it. The first time I've slept in since I enlisted, and it had to be today. I suppose I could go on my own. I'm just a little nervous about going so far at this juncture, with my arm as it is. Or rather, isn't. I'm still rather self-conscious about it.'

'If she doesn't make it back, I could accompany you, if you really feel you need someone with you. I have a list of jobs, but I'll try to get through as many as I can.'

'I'm sure Mother wouldn't mind if some of the jobs were left until another day if you were helping me, and I would be grateful,' he said. 'I need to catch the twenty past one train from the station here.'

'I'll make sure I'm ready.'

'I'll leave you to get on. Oh, and don't wear the black uniform. Did you come to work in something tidy? You always seem to.'

'Yes sir, a nice skirt and blouse.'

'Would you change back into it please, rather than you looking like my servant, or worse, my attendant?'

'Very well.'

He left. It was a good job she still liked to look her best. She'd even worn a hat and gloves this morning, and had brought her second-best shawl since it was chilly first thing.

A trip to Cardiff. She'd settle for that over the list of chores. In her lunch break she'd be sure to neaten up her hair.

—

When the train reached Queen Street station in Cardiff, Tom opened the door ahead of Gwen, despite her getting up first. He seemed determined to show he could manage things himself. She admired him for that. He wasn't so different to her in that regard, with her determination to do things her own way.

She followed him down the steps onto the wide platform with its high glass ceiling and its slim columns. It had been a few years since she'd been to Cardiff. There weren't as many people here as the last time she'd come up on the train, before the war, with Anwen.

They came out of the main building onto the wide street in front.

'Where exactly is the place you've got to go?' Gwen asked.

'It's on Charles Street, three streets away. I don't need you to come in. Mother always does, but I'd rather she didn't. Queen Street is just around the corner, with the shops, if you want to wander around them.'

'I've been here before. I'll be fine.'

'Be careful about getting too close to anyone, especially if they're coughing or sneezing.'

'My mother says the same thing, even in Dorcalon.'

'Your mother is very wise.'

'What time will you be finished?' she asked.

'Half past three. We'll meet somewhere at twenty to four.' He considered her for a second. 'Let's meet at The Dutch Café on Queen Street. Do you know it?'

'I know where it is, yes.' Though she'd never been in.

'I'll treat you to afternoon tea, such as we can get now, for putting yourself out and coming with me.'

'That's very kind of you, sir, but you don't have to.'

'No, but I want to. And please, it's definitely Tom while we're here. Twenty to four, then.'

He went off first, heading down a street in front of them. Gwen watched him for a while, then turned right, to walk to the top of Queen Street. She looked down at its splendour, with its imposing buildings, most of them five storeys high. Many of them had their wide, white canopies out, which fluttered in the slight breeze. There were many shops here she'd liked to have visited, but with time short, she hurried down the pavement. She spotted The Dutch Café, where she was to meet Tom later. It stood out among the other buildings, with its timber frame, looking rather like a Tudor house.

As Queen Street became Duke Street, the walls of the castle grounds loomed into view, the verdant trees peeping their heads above the battlements. A tram squealed as it came down the road. It was rather alarming, and she wondered how people put up with the noise all day. Was it any different to the constantly grinding pit wheels in the village though? And at least here, with the hustle and bustle of people and motorcars, the town felt… alive. Yes, that was it. And modern. Not like Dorcalon, with its gossipy women and moaning old men, its tiny shops, few in number, with little choice of items for sale. No, there was so much to see here, and to do. Marments drapery store was the first place on her list. She expected there'd be less to see these days than the last time she was here, but it would be more than they had locally.

As she entered the store, the scent of the fabric put a smile on her face. She worked her way around the shop quickly, perusing linens, cottons, silks and the new artificial silk they called rayon. Further along there were a few delicate organzas, chiffons and crepes. She wondered about making her own clothes once more. With more money in her purse and less time in the evening when working at the munitions, she hadn't felt the need. But now, it might help her keep up a little with the fashion more cheaply. The only piece she'd made in ages was Sara Fach's dress. She had a look at the Butterick patterns, spotting one that illustrated long, loose, sheer blouses with smocking and tie-around belts. It was all she could afford today with the money she'd brought. She conveyed it to the counter, where the assistant took her money and sent it in a carrier across the shop on a wire. Not long after, a receipt and her change were sent back and the pattern was placed in a paper bag.

Outside, she carried on, stopping opposite the castle entrance. What a shame it wasn't open to the public. She'd have loved to look around the building and its extensive grounds.

Turning back a little on herself, she took the route down the High Street, intent on a quick walk through the market. The place was packed with people, both on the ground and around the balcony, the noise of rowdy chatter deafening. She was surprised to see several people wearing masks.

The customers might still be many, but the produce was far less abundant than when she'd last been here. The fish stalls, vegetable stands and butcher's pitches had maybe a third of what they should. She saw someone handing over one of the new rationing books and wondered whether, even with those, there'd be enough to go round.

How she wished this horrid war were over, with its shortages and nasty bomb factories and her brother in danger and several local lads dead and Tom with his arm missing and, and… She felt the fury build as she walked around. Not to mention this blasted Spanish 'Flu. She mustn't let it upset her today, but enjoy her brief escape.

She took a glance at the clock tower in the middle of the large hall. Ten minutes to two. If she had a quick look at the second-hand book stall, and flitted round the rest of the market, she'd have time to visit David Morgan's department store and Howell's as well, and go through a few of the arcades.

She set off, a woman on a mission.

—

Aware she was a minute or two late, Gwen hurried back to Queen Street to meet Tom outside The Dutch Café.

'I'm so sorry, I got carried away in Morgan's Arcade.'

'The arcades here are attractive.' He removed his fob watch from the pocket of his waistcoat. 'And you're hardly late at all.'

He opened the door of the café, letting her go ahead.

They were shown into a long room by a man who must have been in his seventies, as was another waiter. The rest of the staff were women.

The walls of the café were covered in a dark, reddish-brown wood. There were large plates displayed on some shelves on one side. In the centre of one wall in the middle of the room was a tiled fireplace. The windows were high, and leaded, with tiny panes of coloured glass among the clear ones.

After escorting them to one of the square tables for two by the unlit fireplace, the waiter started to pull out a chair for Tom.

'I can manage, thank you. See to the lady.' He was polite, but Gwen spotted the tightness of his mouth.

'Very well, sir.'

When they were seated, the waiter brought them a menu. 'I'm afraid it's been very much reduced in the last year or so. If you're looking for cakes, we only have the fruit cake and a plain sponge, both un-iced or otherwise decorated, due to the shortage of sugar.'

'I don't suppose a café au lait is available?' Tom asked.

'I'm afraid not sir, due to the scarcity of milk.'

'Just a black coffee then. And no cake. Gwen?'

'I'll have a pot of tea please.'

'Anything to eat, madam?'

Madam. It made a change for someone to give her the title.

'Don't forgo the cake just because I'm not having it,' said Tom.

'Well… I think maybe a piece of the fruit cake, please. I am partial to sweet things, and there haven't been so many.'

'Very well, madam.'

It wasn't long before a waitress brought over the pot of coffee, glancing at Tom's arm several times. When she came back with the tea, she gave Gwen a sympathetic look as she laid the items on the table.

Tom must have noticed, as when she left he said, 'She must believe we're a couple and is sorry for you.'

She coloured a little at the idea of being his sweetheart. 'It's not me who's injured.'

'But she assumes you'll have to deal with it.'

'There'll be many women who'll have to deal with a lot worse before this war is over.'

'Sadly true. The women already married, who'll be trapped with a man they have to nurse, one who'll no longer be fit to keep his family.'

She wondered what the country would be like, with so many missing and injured men, and more with the memory of the horror. Even now, the lads who came home on leave had changed, their youthful cheer gone, including Henry.

'I'm sorry,' he said, 'my gloom is making you sad and spoiling the afternoon.'

She poured her tea. 'I was already thinking about the men in the village who are fighting and those who are lost.'

'You spoke of this Ralph Tallis, but you've not said if you have a sweetheart now. Maybe one overseas?'

She hesitated. 'No, I don't, but there was someone who thought he was my sweetheart. Well, his mother seemed to think so. I didn't give him that impression, not on purpose, but just went to a show with him when he was on leave, to cheer him up, as a friend.'

'A local lad?'

This was awkward. Why hadn't she just said 'No' to his question? 'It was the son of Edgar Williams, you know, who used to be the undermanager, before he was sent to gaol.'

'What, Daniel Williams?'

'Yes. I agreed to write to him as he seemed lonely. I thought I was being kind, but it backfired, if he shared his mother's view that we were sweethearts.'

'You are kind, Gwen.' He patted her hand but withdrew his own quickly. 'I'm sure Lizzie wrote to me that Daniel had been killed, back in…'

'December, just before Christmas. The telegram said missing, presumed dead. But Mrs Williams has it in her head that he's still alive, because she went to see a medium. She thinks he'll come back, and that I'll marry him.'

'I suppose he could have been taken as a prisoner of war.'

'You don't believe that mumbo jumbo, do you?' said Gwen, alarmed.

'You do hear some strange things. But it is more likely they just didn't find his body. Sometimes it's hard, with all the…'

'All the what?'

'You don't need to know the horror of it, Gwen.'

'If it's anything like it was on the film, *The Battle of the Somme*, I can understand why they might not find some people.'

'Of course, I forgot you went with Lizzie to see that.'

'Yes. I wish I hadn't, but in a way, I was glad to see just what it's like for you all out there. Anyway, I tried to tell Mrs Williams that Mrs Tudur was a charlatan, and had got things wrong before, but I suppose she's still hopeful.'

'You can't blame her. Let's speak of something other than the war while we're out. Tell me about your trip around the shops.'

She began with Marments and worked through them in the order she'd visited.

–

Gwen and Tom were coming up the lane to McKenzie House when she noticed the Merediths' car was in its place, outside the house.

'At least my mother's back now,' said Tom, opening the gate.

Gwen was shutting it behind her as Mrs Meredith came rushing out, her face puckered, as if she was suffering a great deal of pain.

'Oh Tom, *there* you are!'

'I left a note, Mother, placed on the hall table.'

'Such a terrible, terrible thing!'

Gwen shrank back, sensing she was in trouble for leaving her post.

'Calm down, Mother. How is it terrible? You clearly forgot about my appointment, and I simply asked Gweneth to accompany me. She was kind enough to agree since it's not part of her job.'

'I'm *so* sorry, it slipped my mind. Yes, it was kind, very kind of you, Gweneth.' She got more agitated as she spoke. 'I thought you'd be back before now.'

'What is the problem, then?' Tom's voice came out in a rumble, as if losing patience.

'It's not you going to Cardiff. Oh, oh dear.' She bent over, her hands on her knees in an unladylike fashion that was so out of character. 'I've tried to telephone your father at the colliery, but they must be having problems with the line again.' She started sobbing.

Tom and Gwen looked at each other, both his ire and her worry turning to concern. Gwen went towards her employer.

'What is it, madam? I could run down to the pit for you, if you want.'

Margaret straightened herself slowly, pulling a piece of paper from her pocket that was now badly crumpled. 'How could this happen to my children again? Dear Edward, dead, my darling Tom maimed and now...' She shook her fist with the paper in it.

'Has something happened to Lizzie?' said Tom, his eyes wide with worry.

'It's a letter, from the matron of Elizabeth's hospital in France. Sh— she has the influenza. Not like the one you had, but that Spanish variety they've been talking about. Sh— she's very bad with it. And has dysentery as well.'

'Oh my God!' Tom went to his mother, placing his arm around her as he took the letter and read it.

Gwen went cold, emitting a small shiver. 'I'll go now and fetch Mr Meredith back.'

Without waiting for a reply, she rushed out of the gate and was soon running down the hill.

-

Gwilym trooped down Jubilee Green on a cloudy but warm evening, looking forward to a game of billiards at the McKenzie Arms – as much as he looked forward to anything these days. Mrs Moss had managed to buy a second-hand table to put into one of the small rooms downstairs, and Idris had reserved it for the early part of the evening.

Such distractions had been welcome since Elizabeth had left, even though his heartache eased for only fleeting moments while his mind concentrated on the activity in hand.

About to cross the road to the McKenzie Arms, he spotted Gwen hurrying round the corner of James Street, onto Station Road, looking upset.

She didn't notice him until he ran over, calling, 'Is everything all right, Gwen?'

Whirling around, while still running sideways, she said, 'Oh Gwilym, I've got to fetch Mr Meredith.'

'Is there an emergency? Can I help?'

She turned forward once more and ran, while Gwilym kept pace.

'I don't know if I should – well, you'll find out soon enough. It's Elizabeth. She's caught the Spanish influenza, in the hospital in France. And dysentery. She's very ill.'

Gwilym came to a standstill and Gwen carried on.

Very ill, with the 'flu? And dysentery? It was as if his body had been wiped of all feeling, a second before a wave of emotion swept him up. He was sinking in a pool of despair, unsure how to save himself from drowning.

'Hey, Gwilym.' A hand thudded down on his shoulder, and Idris's voice said, 'Coming over for the game, then, mun? Well, what's got into Gwen, running down to the pit?'

Gwilym took three deep breaths, feeling distant and weak. 'It's Elizabeth. She's gravely ill, with the Spanish 'flu.'

'*O Duw.* Are you all right? You look a bit wobbly.'

'No, I'm not all right.'

'Here, mun, let me walk you home. You're clearly not in any state to play billiards.'

'No. I – I'm sorry.' Even now it was unreal. Perhaps he'd wake up soon, from a bad dream.

'Don't be daft. I'll take your arm.'

They went a few steps before Gwilym stopped, pulling Idris back. 'No, I need to walk. I don't want to have to explain to Mam and Grancher yet. I need to clear my head first.'

He knew if he went now, he'd end up crying, or worse.

'All right, mun, as long as you're sure.'

He nodded.

'See you tomorrow then,' said Idris, who seemed reluctant to leave. 'Or later, if you decide to pop into the Arms.'

Gwilym lifted his arm in farewell, heading back up to Jubilee Green. Idris crossed over to the public house. At the crossroads, Gwilym carried on, up past the Institute and onto the hills, where he'd gone when Elizabeth had left. He needed to be alone again, like he had that day, and give his heartbreak free rein.

Chapter Twenty-Seven

Gwilym was digging a patch in his garden, slamming the spade into the soil, made hard from the dry, July weather, but still not in need of quite as much effort as he was putting in.

It had been over two weeks since he'd heard about his darling Elizabeth's grave illness, one she'd apparently had for some days before her family had received the dreaded letter. He'd relished the long, heavy shifts at the mine since then, working relentlessly both there and in his garden at home, channelling his fear and anguish into physical labour. This frantic activity hadn't distracted him from the shock of the news as much as he'd desired, leaving a constant, grinding ache in the pit of his stomach.

But there was news now, and unexpectedly hopeful news at that. His prayers had been answered. Elizabeth had survived, and today, she was due home. But she still had a long way to go, if the four letters Gwen had seen were anything to go by, letters written by a fellow nurse of Elizabeth's called Doris.

He'd thanked God every day since he'd heard she'd taken a turn for the better, had kept on praying for her to make a full recovery. If only he could have been there to meet her when she arrived home, just to see her the once.

Of course he wanted much more, but he'd never have that. If she could only recover, he'd told the Almighty, to have a worthwhile and long life, he'd make the sacrifice of leaving her to that life.

'Hello, Gwilym.'

He looked up to see Gwen on the other side of the fence, her hands resting on the gate.

'Gwen. Hello.' He speared the spade sharply into the ground and laid his hands on its handle.

'I've just finished work and thought you'd like to know that Elizabeth arrived around half past two.'

The anxious expression on her face might have been for him, or it might have been for Elizabeth.

'How is she?'

She hesitated, making his gut churn with anguish.

'She was weak and very pale, considering how much colour she had from working outdoors so much. And she was quite thin. She went straight to bed. It was strange, I mean, not in itself, but because it was like a repeat of when young Mr Meredith came home.'

'The family's not had a lot of good fortune recently, that's for sure,' said Gwilym. 'Did anyone say how long Elizabeth would take to recover? Or mention anything about her ongoing condition?'

'Not to me. I'll try to find something out from Tom – that is, young Mr Meredith.' She looked embarrassed at the casual use of his name. 'Part of my job at the moment is to play chess and whatnot with him, to cheer him up, since he has a bit of the melancholia. But that's only between us two.'

'It seems rife among the soldiers, from what I've heard... I'd appreciate being able to keep up with how Elizabeth's getting on. I don't suppose she'd appreciate me knowing, though.'

'Mrs Meredith thinks only *she* knows what's right for her children, so I wouldn't rush to believe that Elizabeth left because of anything you'd done.'

'Then surely she would have said that in the letter she left me. No, it sounded pretty final.'

Gwen shrugged. 'Won't you go and see her?'

'No,' he said without hesitation. 'I can't imagine I'd be allowed anywhere near her.'

'I'll keep you up to date, Gwilym. I'd better get home before my family wonder where I've got to.'

'Aye. And thanks, Gwen. I do appreciate it.'

She nodded, looking glum, and carried on down the path.

He started on his task once more, taking his pain out on the earth. The briny sweat pouring down his neck reflected the salty tears running down his cheeks.

—

Elizabeth dragged herself out of her bed and coughed a few times. Feeling cold, she reached for her dressing gown on the chair to one side of her bed and put it on. She went to the window to look out across at the village. Having slept most of the day before, after arriving home, she at least wanted a walk around the garden on this sunny July day. If her mother would let her. She went back to the bed to sit down, weary already. How would she even get down the stairs, feeling like this? It had been a struggle getting up them yesterday, with Gwen helping her.

Tom had been there when she'd arrived, but she'd only seen him briefly. Even knowing what to expect, it still shocked her. She'd cried herself to sleep over the sight of his missing arm. It still seemed unreal, like it was one of the men back at the casualty clearing station.

There was a knock on the door. She hoped her mother wasn't going to come in, telling her she must stay in bed.

'Yes?'

'It's Gwen, Miss. Mrs Meredith wants to know—'

'Come in, Gwen.'

The door opened tentatively. Gwen looked round it, before coming in fully. She left the door ajar.

'Good to see you're looking a bit better, Miss.'

'Am I?' she croaked. 'And what's all this "Miss" business? You can call me Elizabeth, as always.'

'I'd rather not in the house, you know, Mrs Meredith…'

'You mean you'll get told off.' Elizabeth suspected Gwen felt more comfortable being formal with her, and that made her sad. 'How are you? I understand you were ill, too.'

'Yes, toxic jaundice, the doctor called it. But I'm much better now, thank you.'

'I'm glad to hear that.' She took a deep breath. 'Your skin is certainly a better colour. Almost back to normal.'

Gwen nodded.

'And how is everyone in the village? I've had some news in my letters from Anwen but have been rather out of touch this last couple of weeks of course.'

'Things are much the same.'

Elizabeth knew she'd have to be more specific. 'How is Gwilym?'

Gwen seemed surprised she'd asked, though from what Anwen had told her of events after her departure, she must have known.

'He always seems to keep hisself busy, with the union stuff and whatnot.' Gwen came a little closer. 'And that garden of his is full of vegetables. I believe he's sold a few of his extra veg to Mr James too.'

'That's good. He'll be missing the allotments.'

The door swung open, her mother standing in the entrance, a smile on her lips.

Gwen can't have seen her as she added, 'And Gwilym has the chickens as well.'

Margaret glared. 'Gweneth! I did not send you up to speak of that ruffian to my daughter.'

Gwen swung around, wide-eyed.

'Mother, it's not her fault. I asked after him, so please, do not take it out on her.'

'I sent you to find out if Miss Elizabeth required a cup of tea. Would you please do your job and report the reply to Mrs Rhys.'

'Yes, I would appreciate one, thank you,' said Elizabeth.

Gwen scurried away. Margaret shut the door.

'Why you'd even want to speak of him after the good news I've just received, I have no idea.' She held up a letter, the smile on her lips once more.

'But you've not told me what it is. What would be good for me is a change of scenery, even if it's only sitting in the drawing room with a view of the garden. I've been in bed for too long. Or a sit in the garden would be better. Where's Tom? He could sit with me. I'd like to talk to him.'

'He's taking a walk in the forest. Now don't be coy, this letter came this morning, from Sidney Fitzgerald, who clearly thought we were acquainted with the situation.'

Elizabeth's breath stalled. Sidney. With being so sick, she'd almost forgotten about him. Poor boy. There were apparently two letters from him, packed in her case by Matron, which she hadn't got around to reading.

'He'd only just heard about your illness, via his mother, who was as ignorant as I of your betrothal.' Margaret beamed. 'I'm so thrilled. And Lady Anna will simply have to put up with it.' Margaret seemed to revel in getting one over on the woman, who surely wouldn't relish her as a daughter-in-law. 'So much for your insistence that you weren't interested in him. Anyway. He has leave soon and is coming to visit you.'

'I see.'

'I know you're unwell, but at least sound a little bit excited. There's a letter for you enclosed. Would you like me to read it to you?'

She was about to open it, so Elizabeth said, 'No! I will read it later.'

Margaret looked disappointed but handed the letter over.

'Maybe you could get a special license and have a small wedding, food rationing being what it is. Then, after the war, you could have a proper celebration.'

Margaret gabbled on about what the 'proper celebration' would be like. Elizabeth breathed a sigh of relief when there was a tap at the door, and Gwen entered with a tray.

'Place that on the bedside table here. Elizabeth, you get back into bed now. I'll leave you to pour, Gweneth, then leave Miss Meredith to rest.'

'Yes, madam.'

When her mother departed, Gwen did as she was ordered in silence.

'I'll be able to manage now,' said Elizabeth. 'You'd better get back to your work.'

Gwen curtsied and left. It was time to see what Sidney had to say to her.

–

A week had gone by, but Gwilym hadn't managed to bump into Gwen until two days ago. He could have called around to Gwen's house but hadn't wanted his interest to be too obvious. At least Elizabeth had asked after him. He'd been mulling this over all day at work, wondering what to do.

As he left the pit that afternoon, coming up to the top of Station Road, he saw the Morris Oxford drive past from James Street to Gabriel Street. Mrs Meredith was at the wheel. A spark ignited a determination in him. If she was going out to one of her meetings, she'd likely be a while. He could wash and dress quickly, then walk round to McKenzie House. He'd still have to negotiate Mrs Rhys and Gwen to get to see Elizabeth – oh, and Tom – but they might be more sympathetic than Mrs Meredith. If Elizabeth didn't want to see him, then so be it.

He rushed home now, relieved to see he'd arrived back before Evan, who was no doubt dawdling with his friends.

'What are you in such a hurry about, Gwilym *bach*?' said Rachael.

'I need to get out somewhere, so if you don't mind, I'll have the bath first today.' He rushed into the kitchen, where he knew the tin bath would be ready, and wasted no time stripping down for his wash.

His clean clothes were all laid out, allowing him to dress quickly. He gave his hair a quick comb and went to the scullery.

'All done, Mam. I'll see you later.'

'Don't you want any dinner?'

'When I get back.'

Evan came through the back door as Gwilym made for it. 'You already done, mun? Where you off to?'

'Never you mind.'

He rushed out and down the path at the side of the houses, figuring he'd be less likely to meet anyone that way, and be delayed. Walking over the small bridge and curving onto the road near the cottages, he spotted some of the old boys who'd worked with him on the field behind McKenzie Cottages. He knew they'd clubbed together to rent one of the new allotments there, so he guessed that was where they were heading.

'Ah Gwilym!' said Billy Thomas, who was their informal leader. 'Haven't seen you in a while. We was having a good old discussion about the Russian royal family. The papers reckon the czar's been executed.'

'So I read.' He glanced up towards McKenzie House, wondering how he could move on quickly without being rude.

'I know he were a tyrant, but there doesn't seem to have been a trial of any sort,' said Billy.

'No, you're right.'

'We was wondering what might have happened to the rest of the family. Papers reckon the czarina, young prince and the princesses were taken somewhere safe.'

'We can hope so, for the children's sake.'

His stomach had a knot in it in with his eagerness to escape. Normally he'd have been happy to talk with them about these matters. They'd often chatted about such things when working close together in the field.

'Seems to be mayhem in Russia if you ask me,' said one of the others.

'Can't help that there's a war on,' said Gwilym.

'Not that they're fighting anymore, given they signed that treaty with Germany.'

'It's certainly complicated.'

'Well lads,' Billy called to his pals, despite their advanced years, 'we'd better get up to the allotment and get on. See you, Gwilym.'

'Cheerio,' he said, with some relief as they headed up the steps to the field beyond.

On his way again, his heart fluttering with anticipation, he saw a figure with blonde hair come down the steps in front of McKenzie House. It was Gwen. Maybe she'd know how long Mrs Meredith would be out.

She approached him, clutching a basket, stopping to say, 'Afternoon, Gwilym. Are you off to the forest for a walk?'

'No, not really. You were asking last week if I'd call in to see Elizabeth, so I thought… Well, actually, I thought I might, you know, do just that. See how she is for myself. Especially as I saw her mother go out.'

'Oh, right.' Gwen bit her bottom lip and pulled a face. 'The thing is, Gwilym…'

He slumped. 'Has she said she doesn't want to see me?'

'It's not that. Mrs Meredith made an announcement yesterday, and we're supposed to be keeping it secret until they make the official announcement, but it doesn't seem fair not to tell you.'

'Is she going somewhere else to recover?'

'No.' Gwen's pained expression showed she was having difficulty getting the words out.

'She is still getting better, isn't she?' He gripped his clammy hands.

'Yes, yes of course. She's much better. It's – it seems that, while she was in France, she became engaged to Captain Sidney Fitzgerald.'

'Sidney?' Mrs Meredith had mentioned that they'd seen each other in France, but he'd thought she'd said that more for his benefit. Elizabeth had seemed quite disparaging of him and his brother.

'Are you sure? That's not just Mrs Meredith making it sound more than it is?' There was always hope.

'No, I'm sorry, Gwilym. Elizabeth was there when she announced it, and she didn't deny it. I'd better get on and get these groceries I've been sent out for.'

'Of course.'

He watched her walk down the hill. What to do now? The knowledge of her betrothal hurt like hell. But wasn't it better for her, to be with someone of her own class, to be in a situation that wouldn't tear her away from her family?

He'd made a deal with the Almighty, saying he'd leave her to her life if she recovered. She was recovering, so that part of the bargain was being kept.

He became aware of the rumbling of a motorcar engine. Sure enough, there was the Morris Oxford on its way back over the bridge. His heart sank.

Mrs Meredith slowed down to take the corner, looking straight ahead and ignoring him. If Elizabeth had been driving, she'd have given a cheery wave.

Elizabeth.

'And now you've got to keep your side of the bargain,' he said to himself.

Chapter Twenty-Eight

Margaret studied her daughter, sitting in one of the winged armchairs placed by the back drawing room window. She was alternately looking out at the sunny garden and reading her book. She didn't seem to be able to concentrate much on anything, though she was at least getting a little stronger.

'It's your turn, Mother,' said Tom, indicating the back-gammon board in front.

She wasn't fond of games and had been glad when Gweneth had shown an aptitude for them and been willing to play. Now it didn't seem right, the maid being in here of an afternoon, with Elizabeth present and unwell. Margaret considered the board before taking her turn.

'I think I'd like to take a short walk this afternoon,' said Elizabeth, 'further than the garden. Maybe down to the stream. Or beyond, if I feel well enough.'

'It's too soon for that,' Margaret said quite sharply, remembering seeing Gwilym Owen walking along the road just yesterday. It was too easy for her daughter to come across him.

'I won't get stronger unless I make the effort,' said Elizabeth.

'And if you do too much, too soon, you'll get ill again. There's plenty of time.'

Elizabeth looked back down at her book. It wasn't long before she got up. 'Excuse me, I need to visit the bathroom.'

'Do you need any help going upstairs?' said Margaret.

'No. Thank you.'

When she'd gone, Tom said, 'Mother, you've got to let her do things. It's a lovely summer's day. I'm sure a walk would do her good. I'll go with her.'

'What if she fainted? How would you pick her up with one arm?'

He looked crestfallen and she regretted saying it. He was despondent enough without her pointing out his shortcomings.

'I'm just being practical, that's all,' she added, to try and make it better.

'Gwen – Gweneth could come with us too. I know you're concerned for Lizzie, but there's no point stifling her with it. That's why she ran away in the first place.'

'Nonsense! It was that rogue bothering her.'

'I don't think so. From Lizzie's letters to me, it sounded more like she'd encouraged the relationship. And it sounds like he was very good to her.'

'He might have been good *to* her, though I doubt it, but he certainly wasn't good *for* her. No. And it's academic now, for she's betrothed to Sidney Fitzgerald.'

'I do know his surname, you know. You don't have to add it every time you say his name.'

A few minutes later there was a tap on the door and Margaret called, 'Enter.'

Gwen came in. 'This letter has just arrived for Miss Elizabeth.'

'Bring it over.'

She did as she was ordered, handing the letter to Margaret.

'My, that looks like Sidney Fitz— Sidney's writing. Thank you, Gweneth, you may go.'

She left as Elizabeth was coming back in.

'There's a letter for you, from Sidney.'

Elizabeth took it, walking away as she opened it. She went to the window to read it. 'He says he's arriving here on Sunday to see me.'

Margaret rose. 'Oh my, in three days' time. We'd better prepare things for him.'

'Prepare what?' said Tom. 'A bit of tea and cake? That's not going to take three days.'

'He might want to stay a night or two.'

'He says he's coming for the afternoon. It's not as if he has far to travel from home,' said Elizabeth.

'Surely he won't only visit his fiancée on one afternoon. We could drive the pair of you into Monmouth and he could buy you an engagement ring.'

'Let's not make plans until he gets here.'

'I will ring Anna Fitzgerald when we've finished this game, to check.'

She was aware of a look passing between Elizabeth and Tom but ignored it. They simply did not understand such matters.

–

Elizabeth stood in the middle of the room, determined not to look like an invalid to receive Sidney. Tom had heard a motorcar drawing up outside the house a couple of minutes before and her family had gone to welcome him. Her heart raced, making it hard for her to catch her breath.

She tried inhaling and exhaling slowly, but her out breath always caught, causing her to gasp in once more.

It will be all right. He will be a good husband to you. If he too isn't lost before the war ends, she thought.

She neatened the dress her mother had chosen for her to wear, a green skirt with a cream, lacy blouse. It had been too loose when she'd tried it on three days ago, so Mama had paid Mrs Bowen extra to come to the house and take it in.

From the passageway, Elizabeth heard Sidney say, 'That's right. The Welsh division's been in the back lines for a bit now, but I've a feeling things are about to kick off shortly.'

Her father opened the door, leading Sidney in.

His dark hair was immaculate, the longer hair on top parted to one side and oiled. His bronze eyes were full of concern as he rushed to her. 'Oh, my poor darling.'

'We'll leave you to it and serve tea later,' said her father, who left and shut the door.

'Oh Elizabeth, if I'd known, I would have tried to get leave sooner.' He took her hands in his. 'You are paler, and thinner, my poor sweetheart.'

How kind he was. A good man, more understanding than his brother would have been. Yet…

Bursting into tears, she pulled her hands from his and clutched them to her mouth.

'Oh darling!' He tried to enfold her in his arms, but she turned away. Instead, he held her hand. 'That's it, let it all out. You've been through such a lot.'

She thought about Anwen, holding out for Idris after he broke off their engagement, determined he was the one for her and suspecting that he was trying to save her from having to cope with his illness. Then there was Violet, kept from Hywel by a cruel mother-in-law who couldn't understand why she needed to move on from her dead husband. Their feelings for each other were what you called love. This brought to mind her first kiss with Gwilym.

The truth was, she didn't love Sidney. She liked him and admired him, but she was afraid she would grow to resent him over the years for not being the person she wanted to be with.

She took out a handkerchief from her skirt pocket to wipe her eyes and delicately blow her nose, then placed it back.

'Sidney, I must speak plainly. I'm sorry, but I can't marry you, and I should never have said I would.' She felt herself about to sob so carried on quickly. 'I was swept away by the moment, by being surrounded by the horrors and the thought of something positive, by the real possibility that life was short and we must make the most of it. Can you forgive me?'

He looked towards the fireplace, his face glum. After some moments he spoke. 'Yes, I can forgive you, Elizabeth.' He now looked her in the eye. 'I suppose I was rather carried away too, though I do have feelings for you. Do you have none for me at all?'

'As a dear friend, yes, especially when I got to know you while you were in the hospital. I suppose, before then, I saw you only as someone my mother was trying to foist upon me, you and Horace.'

'He suspected as much and was quite amused about it. I wasn't, because I felt sorry for you. I know what it's like to have a domineering mother. Maybe, if you are still free, we could examine our relationship again in the cold light of peacetime. Will you promise to write to me, when this war is over, to tell me what conclusion you've come to?'

'Yes, Sidney, I will do that.'

'I will leave you now, if you don't mind, and not stay for tea. I wish you a speedy recovery, Elizabeth. And, if we do not meet again, I wish you a wonderful life beyond.'

'Thank you. And I wish the same for you, Sidney.'

He lifted her hand and kissed it, before exiting the room swiftly.

Elizabeth took a few steps to the Chesterfield and collapsed onto it. She breathed out a long breath of relief.

It wasn't long before her mother was in the room, rushing to sit beside her. Her wide eyes and ridiculously broad grin spoke of excitement. 'We heard Sidney leave. Has he gone to fetch a special license? There's so much planning to do!' As her father and Tom followed on behind, she said eagerly, 'There's to be a wedding!'

'No, there isn't,' said Elizabeth.

'You're putting it off until better times, then?' asked her father. 'That seems wise.'

'No, there's to be no wedding at all.'

'Of course there is, you silly girl,' said Margaret. 'You and Sidney are engaged.'

'*Were* engaged.'

Margaret's mouth fell open. 'He broke it off? I bet that's his mother inter—'

'No, I did.'

'What?' Her mother stood abruptly. 'Don't be ridiculous! He's a wonderful catch. You will give him half an hour to get home, then you will telephone him and tell him you've made a mistake as you weren't feeling well.'

'Margaret, it's up to the girl,' said her father.

'No it isn't, when she's being foolish!'

Elizabeth didn't have the strength for this showdown, but she'd have to see it through. 'Mama! I am not going to marry Sidney, for although I respect him and am very fond of him, I do not love him in the way I want to love my husband.'

'Love has got nothing to do with it! If you respect him and are fond of him, love will follow.'

'Mother, it's up to Lizzie if she wants to marry him,' said Tom.

'He is the best chance of a good life she is likely to get. She's twenty-seven now and her options are swiftly shrinking. She's a stupid young woman, and if I find out that Gwilym has anything to do with this—'

'How could he have?' said Tom. 'She hasn't even seen him.'

'How do I know that? The staff seem to know him well. One of them might have let him in while I was out.'

'I've been here most of the time, and I can assure you they haven't. You don't think much of them, do you?'

'As I said,' Margaret continued, 'if I find out he has anything to do with this, I will have him driven from the village – along with his family.'

'Don't be absurd,' said Herbert.

Elizabeth rose. 'Since you don't seem to need me to have this conversation, I'll leave you to it.'

Shuffling to the door, she felt herself welling up once more, heart-sore to have caused yet another row in the house. She was aware of her mother following her, but her father got ahead, and as soon as Elizabeth left the room, the door was slammed shut by him, preventing her mother going any further.

What could she do to escape? The only option was to go out and hope her mother would be stalled long enough by her father to allow her to get away somewhere. Forgoing her hat or even a shawl, she left the house quietly and went through the gate. Which way to go? The village, where she had so far been forbidden to visit. She'd take it slowly, greet people, answer queries about her health to suggest she was feeling much better.

She set off.

–

Margaret was *not* going to let her daughter get away with this, this wanton act of destruction on her own life. Rising just after Elizabeth did, she followed her daughter to waylay her and bring her to her senses.

Almost reaching her, she was shocked when Herbert stepped in front and slammed the door after Elizabeth's departure.

'What are you doing? Fetch her back now!' she demanded.

'No, I will not.' He stood with his back against the door.

She tried to get around him, to the door handle, but he wouldn't budge.

'I know I've done things in our marriage that you have not been in control of, Margaret, but picking on Elizabeth and trying to control her instead is not going to make things any better.'

'It has nothing to do with that. But you are certainly in no position to take the moral high ground.'

Tom came towards them. 'Mother, perhaps it's time to forgive Father and to move on with life. If there's one thing I've learned in the trenches, it's that life can end at any time and you have got to grab it with both hands. Father made one mistake. You might not forget it, but you can surely forgive it.'

Margaret's head thumped with indignation. Tom clearly had not guessed about the second indiscretion. She'd avoided telling him, because of his condition, and maybe never would have, but now...

'But it's not just one mistake, is it?'

'Let's not go into that now,' said Herbert. 'We've enough on our plate.'

'Tom needs to understand why I've been so hard. I came across Jenny's child the other day, and he looks just like you at that age, Tom.'

'W— what, what are you implying?'

'Do I have to spell it out? Your father suspected, but thought it must be Joseph's, since Jenny married him.'

'Father?'

'Yes, all right, I admit it.'

'For God's sake, Father! I was willing to take the fall for you and let Anwen think *I* was the father of Polly's baby when she saw her come to the house, carrying a child. I thought, better that they think it's a young, single chap, than the married manager of the colliery.'

'And I was grateful.'

'But, what, you'd already had a... dalliance? With Jenny? For she left to get married months before Polly turned up.'

'That's right,' Margaret replied, when her husband didn't answer. And maybe now, at last, Tom would see why she was so brittle all the time.

'People took me for a cad, even though I'd done nothing but be friendly with women. And I certainly wouldn't treat my wife like you have.'

'You never know what you might do until the situation arises, son.'

Tom pushed his face towards his father's. 'But one error wasn't enough? And what if other people have heard I'm the father of Polly's baby, then see the family likeness with Jenny's? They'll assume I'm that baby's father, too!'

Herbert rubbed his forehead, his eyes closed. 'I'm sorry.'

'And so you jolly well should be,' said Tom. 'However, our concern currently is Lizzie and giving her the freedom to choose her own life, or inevitably losing her forever. For now she's had a taste of freedom, she won't stay once she's better, I'm sure of it.'

'All I've done is for her own good,' said Margaret. 'To raise her status in society.'

Tom lifted both palms in a questioning pose. 'For her own good? More likely yours. Lizzie doesn't care about status, it's only you.'

'You didn't do so badly from my efforts, going to university. My father's savings have come in handy for your education.' He seemed to have forgotten that.

'For all the good it will do me. Perhaps the money would have been better used on Lizzie as well as me. What's left could be split. And if you hadn't been so ambitious for us and given us so little other care, then maybe this situation with her wouldn't have happened. Now, both Lizzie and I have decisions to make about our futures, for God knows I've been hanging around too long feeling sorry for myself. And if you're both wise, you will support us in whatever decisions we make, not try to control them.'

Herbert nodded slowly, then left the room. Margaret felt the blood leave her face and the urge to be sick. Was that what Tom and Elizabeth thought, that she didn't care for them, only what status they could bring her?

'I'm going to find Lizzie,' said Tom. 'She might have gone for a walk in the forest, since she implied she wanted to.'

He left the room.

A surge of hopelessness overwhelmed her. She stumbled back to the nearest Chesterfield and took a seat. They didn't understand that she had their best interests at heart. She couldn't let Elizabeth just wander around in her condition. If Tom had gone to the forest, she should go in the opposite direction.

Having reached halfway down James Street, Elizabeth decided that she should not walk too much more before taking a break. The gardens on Jubilee Green would be the ideal place to do this, so she carried on down the other half of the street. *Poor Sidney*. Yet, even as she thought this, the whole incident felt like it had happened to someone else.

She passed a few people, who displayed surprise. Since she knew none of them well, she gave them a simple nod in greeting and moved on. It wasn't until she entered the gardens that she noticed Violet and Anwen sitting on the top bench, with their husbands. Clarice and Benjy were chasing each other on the small lawn, while Sara Fach toddled around after them. There were other families here today, one seated in the middle, while a few others were sitting on the grass.

Anwen, spotting her, ran down the path. 'Elizabeth, hello! Is there nobody with you?' She looked beyond her.

'Hello Anwen, it's lovely to see you. It's my first walk out and I wanted to come alone. It's almost the end of a warm, sunny July, and I feel I've not seen any of it. I do need a sit down now, though.' She sat on the bench closest to the bottom gate. Anwen sat with her.

'Quite a shock, it was, when we heard. Mam said you were getting stronger, but that Mrs Meredith wasn't allowing anyone to visit yet, otherwise I'd have come.'

'Mama said that? I did wonder why you hadn't called by.' Had her mother been intent on shutting her off from everyone?

Violet started waddling down the path, the bump of her pregnancy quite obvious.

'Hello, Elizabeth. This is a long way for you to walk. You look a little pale.'

'Do I?' She coughed. 'I've still got a way to go until I'm completely well but getting out on a lovely day helps.' She wasn't sure now that coming so far had been a good idea.

'Here's Gwen now,' said Anwen, looking down at the gate as her friend entered.

'I thought that was you,' she said to Elizabeth, as she approached. 'Hasn't anyone walked down with you?'

'To be honest, I left without them knowing,' Elizabeth confessed. 'I was so fed up with my mother forbidding me to leave the confines of the garden.'

'Wasn't your fiancé coming this afternoon?' said Gwen. 'I'm sure that's what Mrs Meredith said.'

Oh dear, how could she explain that? The urge to cry came again, because she'd hated hurting his feelings. 'He's already been. And he isn't my fiancé. I'm afraid things got a bit muddled.' That would be explanation enough. Maybe when some time had passed, she could relate it more dispassionately.

'Oh?' said Gwen, frowning, suggesting that Mama had gone overboard in emphasising their betrothal.

'Please, do tell me what you've all been up to. You look well on in your pregnancy, Violet.'

'Yes.' she rubbed the bump. 'Only a coupla months now.'

Gwen and Violet sat down. And so the conversation continued, Violet and Gwen more distant and respectful than Anwen, who was like an old friend. Elizabeth settled down to what felt more like normality.

–

Gwilym closed his front door behind him, grateful for such a lovely day on his Sunday off. Normally, he'd be straight out into the back garden, tending to the vegetable patch, but he'd have plenty of daylight and warmth to do that in the late afternoon and evening. No – for a change, he was going to go and spend some time with his friends.

Idris and Hywel had said they'd be in the gardens this afternoon and had suggested he come along too. And why not? He'd hidden himself away for too long. Gwen had come to tell him that Elizabeth's fiancé was arriving today, on leave. It still hurt, like a mighty sack of coal dropped into his gut, but what could he do about it?

Reaching the top gate of the gardens, he spotted Idris and Hywel on the top bench with the children close by. Anwen, Violet and Gwen were sitting further down.

He stopped dead. Seeing Elizabeth there with them, he lost orientation for a second. He looked around the garden. There was no sign of any of her family, or of Sidney Fitzgerald. This surely was his opportunity.

He greeted Hywel and Idris briefly, before running past. When Elizabeth spotted him coming towards her, she did a double-take. He slowed down.

'Gwilym! How are you?' she said.

'Never mind how I am. How are you? You don't look well. Should you be out?' He was aware he sounded terse, but he was worried.

'That's what I wondered,' said Violet.

'Has your fiancé not come down with you?' He looked around, as if expecting him to emerge from the bushes.

'I'm sorry,' said Gwen. 'It was me who mentioned you were betrothed. I thought Gwilym ought to know.'

Elizabeth stood up. 'Yes. Then he should also…' She wobbled a little, causing Gwilym to leap forward and catch her before she swooned.

'Elizabeth!' He lowered her to the ground gently. The other three women gathered around her.

By this time, Idris had also made his way down. Gwilym was vaguely aware of others in the garden standing and murmuring, and of the sound of the gate opening, but he was too wrapped up in worry to pay any heed to either… Until there was the bellow of a strident voice.

'Elizabeth? Elizabeth!' Margaret came charging up the path. 'I *knew* something like this would happen. I should have guessed *you'd* be involved, Gwilym Owen! You two had this arranged all along. Out of the way!'

He had no intention of moving from the spot until he knew Elizabeth was all right. The three women didn't budge either.

'Mrs Meredith, nothing was arranged,' said Anwen. 'We saw Elizabeth come in, and Gwilym came here because Idris asked him to come and meet us. None of us knew she'd be here.'

'That's right, madam,' said Gwen.

'I hope you have not been involved in passing messages between them, Gweneth.'

'No madam, I haven't, honestly.'

There was a groan and Elizabeth stirred. Her eyes fluttered open as she muttered, 'Gwilym. I'm sorry. I'm obviously not as fit as I thought I was.'

Now she was awake, he relinquished hold of her to Anwen and stood. Margaret elbowed him out of the way and knelt down beside her daughter.

'I'll run to the house,' said Idris, 'and ask Mr Meredith to fetch the car down, if he's in.'

'Yes, he is,' Margaret confirmed.

'And I'll fetch Dr Roberts,' said Gwen. 'Hopefully he'll be at home.'

Gwilym walked backwards, up to the seat where Hywel was standing.

'You all right, *bach*?'

'I will be when I know she's going to be all right. But it would be better if I watched from here.'

Gwen arrived back first with Dr Roberts. He was soon talking to Elizabeth, who nodded and shook her head. Not long after that, the Oxford Morris appeared. Idris got out the same time as Mr Meredith and joined Gwilym and Hywel.

Dr Roberts got Elizabeth on her feet and walked her to the car with her father's help. Content that she was in good hands, Gwilym turned on his heel and made his way to the top gate again, without a word. He'd have been better to stick to his garden, and that was where he'd go now.

Chapter Twenty-Nine

'They had to carry a couple more men home today,' said Idris, having his wash in the tin bath by the fire after his shift.

'Not more with this Spanish 'Flu?' said Anwen, sewing at the table. 'I thought it was fading away now.'

'There aren't as many men off work as there were, that's for sure, but there are a few. I'd still be careful when you and the babby go out, and keep away from anyone coughing or sneezing.'

'I'm always careful. Gwen said she saw a few people wearing masks when she was in Cardiff, back in June.'

'Suppose it might help.'

Anwen finished the last stitch in a new dress for Sara Fach and laid it out on the table. She fanned herself, being a little overwarm with the fire in the range and it being a humid day.

'That's very pretty, *cariad*,' said Idris. 'You can try it on her when Cadi gets back from the shops with her.'

'Little madam probably won't want to take it off though,' she said affectionately. 'You know what she's like with anything new.'

'Getting a right little personality now,' he said with a grin.

'Trying to get the kitchen scrubbed, I was, this morning, while Cadi was doing the washing, but Sara Fach does like to have more attention now, and isn't content to simply sit and play with her toys like she used to do.'

Idris climbed out of the bath and wrapped a towel around himself, wiping his arms as he took a closer look at the dress.

'Don't drip on it, now.'

'I'll be careful. I'm always amazed how neatly women can sew. I'm sure I couldn't do it.'

'Only 'cos you've never had to!' she said. 'You don't even have to do it in school, which doesn't seem fair. But you get men who are tailors, so it's not like men can't sew, is it?'

'You and your mam though, you're dab hands, and Cadi in particular, you're all so gifted when it comes to needlework. I was saying to Gwen, after she made that lovely dress for Sara Fach, that you could start a proper sewing business, since the village only really has Mrs Bowen, who can be a bit expensive.'

'Gwen said she heard Mrs Meredith complain because Mrs Bowen was charging even more as she'd said her costs had gone up.'

'There you go then. You could do second-hand clothes as well, brighten them up a bit, like Cadi does with things.'

'But Mamgu already does a bit, as do several women, though only for pin money.'

'Exactly. Your skills are all worth more than a bit of pin money. And you're a good organiser and looked after the accounts for the allotments before Gwilym took over. You could even employ Violet to do something.'

'Well, since we're looking to rent our own house, I suppose we could do with a bit of extra money. And there'd be extra rooms to work in with two houses.'

'And having a child – or children if Violet joins in – you can help each other out with their care.'

'My goodness, Idris, you have it all worked out.' She looked up at him and chuckled.

'What you laughin' at?'

'Your hair. It's all over the place from where you've been towelling it. You'd better comb it before it dries like that. Anyway, you with all your big ideas, why don't *you* start a business?'

'What would I do? Gwilym's the one who talked vaguely about starting a market gardening business after the war, but I don't know if he's interested anymore.'

'He's still growing loads of veg.'

'Hm. But he uses his garden work as an excuse to hide away, I reckon. Talking of which, any more news about Elizabeth?'

'None since yesterday, when Gwen said she's up and moving around the house again. It's a shame Mrs Meredith has banned anyone from coming to visit her.'

'Always very sociable, was Elizabeth… Anyway, you have a ponder about my suggestion. I think you'd enjoy running a business.'

'I think I might.' She'd mull it over later. 'The others'll be back soon, and they won't want to see you in the nuddy. Get yourself dressed and I'll finish the dinner.'

'Lovely. I'm starving.'

He got dressed and sat down, picking up the *Cambria Daily Leader*, which was perched on the next chair.

'It's starting to look better,' he said.

'What's that?' She turned to find him pointing to the front page of the newspaper.

'The war. Looks like our lads are making some good advances, and that the Germans are dropping back. It might all be over soon.'

She ladled some stew onto a plate and brought it over to Idris. 'That would be wonderful. But how many times have they said that in the last four years?'

He put the newspaper down with a sigh. 'Aye, true.'

'So I'll believe it when it actually happens.'

–

As Gwen came round the corner, over the Nantygalon stream, she saw Anwen waiting at the end of the last row of houses on James Street. She came forward when she spotted her on the bridge.

'Have you come to meet me?' she asked.

'Yes. First of all, how is Elizabeth?'

'She was let out into the garden today, for a walk around.'

Anwen raised her eyebrows. 'You make her sound like a pet dog.'

'Mrs Meredith says it's for her own good, but I know there have been arguments between her and the two men about it. Please keep it to yourself, but I'm worried about her. I heard Tom say that if his mother keeps her locked up like this, she'll just leave again when she's well.'

'And who could blame her?' Anwen shook her head. 'I wish there was something we could do. I don't know what, though.'

'Me neither. Was that all you came for?'

'No. I wanted to discuss an idea with you. And Violet. She's expecting us, if you don't mind waiting a bit 'til you go home.'

Gwen looked at her house. 'No, but I'll just pop in to tell Mam I'll be a bit late.'

She did this, quickly joining Anwen to make the trip to Bryn Road. Violet was ready for them with a cup of tea. They sat at one end of the table, Clarice and Benjy at the other.

'You don't mind if the kiddies eat their supper while we talk, do you?' she said.

'Course not,' said Anwen. 'I left Cadi giving Sara Fach hers. Right greedy thing she is, these days.'

'They all go through that,' said Violet. 'And then there're times when they'll eat hardly anything. Hywel's in the garden, giving us some privacy. Dunno why. Anyway, what is this great thing you have to discuss with us? You seem quite happy about it.'

'You're not—' Gwen started, pointing at Anwen's stomach.

'No! It's quite simple. I've been discussing an idea with Mam and Mamgu, that Idris came up with, about starting a dressmaking business. We could use my mother's front room, and my own, when I get one. The three of us are all good with a needle. Gwen, so are you, and I know Idris mentioned it to you. Even better, you've a good eye for fashion and what goes together.'

'I dunno where I'd fit in,' said Violet. 'I'm 'opeless with a needle. Give me some paints or a pencil, and I'm away, but

274

needlework was never my strong suit at school. It were my sister, Ivy, who were good at it.' Violet looked a little glum.

Gwen remembered Ivy as someone who always endeavoured to outdo everyone at everything – particularly Violet. She was sure it had contributed to her lack of self-confidence.

'I think with a little proper tuition, you could learn to do all right,' said Anwen. 'However, your clothes are the cleanest I've ever seen, and sheets the whitest, despite fighting against the coal dust. I dunno how you do it. And you're a whizz with an iron. You'd be good at washing second-hand clothes and getting them neat and tidy.'

Violet brightened, even smiling a little. 'Thank you for saying so.'

'And you'd be fine at measuring people and showing them what we already had on our second-hand rail. I think starting small with the second-hand stuff, and altering to fit, would probably be wise.'

Gwen leant her elbows on the table. 'How would this work, exactly?'

'Customers would make an appointment with us, like they do with Mrs Bowen,' said Anwen. 'We could all take turns at helping out, looking after each other's children, and so on.'

'Won't Mrs Bowen be put out?' Violet asked.

'That's what I said to Idris, but he said there'd be plenty who'd come to us who wouldn't go to Mrs Bowen's, 'cos they'd think her too posh, like. She is a bit on the pricey side. And I've another idea, about adapting or even making clothes for soldiers who've lost limbs. I got the idea because of Tom and William Griffin, him on Alexandra Street what lost his leg. We could advertise that service far and wide.'

'It sounds like an excellent idea,' Gwen enthused.

'It does,' Violet agreed, 'although this will inhibit me for a while.' She pointed at her stomach.

'That's the beauty of a cooperative: we can all muck in, do as much or little as we can, and get paid accordingly.'

'It's something to seriously consider,' said Gwen. 'I don't see myself working forever at the Big House. I'm not ungrateful, and it's been a good job in many ways, not least because my afternoons aren't too taxing, but it's not something I want to be stuck with forever. Except...' She was going to say she'd miss her afternoons with Tom, walking out somewhere or playing a game, but she knew what it would sound like. Not that she'd done any of that since Elizabeth had returned, so perhaps it was over anyway. She felt a surprising amount of sadness at the prospect.

'Except what?' said Violet.

'That I might have to do my bit in the evening and keep my job, until I could be sure we'd make enough money from it.'

'That's fair enough,' said Anwen. 'Let's go away and think. And we'll need to raise a bit of money to start. We could have a meeting at mine, in a few days, see what Mam and Mamgu come up with. They're both keen on the idea.'

Gwen drank down the last of her tea. 'I'd better get back for my supper. I'll try and come up with something for when we meet again.'

She got up and hugged her two friends, then waved cheerio to the children, before letting herself out the front door. Humming as she almost skipped down the street, she'd already thought of some ideas.

–

Gwen took out the chessboard and box of pieces from the sideboard, laying it on the largest of the three occasional tables in the drawing room, which she'd placed near the window with two chairs from the dining room. It was an attractive gameboard, with its black wood and mother of pearl squares, and inlaid pattern around the edges. She started to put out the chessmen.

She'd been so excited when Mrs Meredith had asked her to 'occupy' her son once again. He should be downstairs soon. Elizabeth was being seen by Dr Roberts this afternoon, so

Gwen reckoned Mrs Meredith was trying to keep the pair of them out of the way. Not that she cared, if it meant she could spend time with him.

Only because we get on so well, she thought. He was sympathetic and seemed to understand things she felt. *Don't forget about his illegitimate child – maybe two.* She clucked at herself. What had that to do with anything? She wasn't getting involved with him.

There was a stir of regret. Maybe in another life, where they were the same class and he hadn't had dalliances and not faced up to the consequence, maybe, just maybe…

She laughed at herself. 'Don't be such an idiot,' she said, just as the door opened, and he came in.

'An idiot about what?'

She thought quickly. 'Oh, um, I put a couple of pieces in the wrong place, and just realised. It's all ready now.'

He walked over to the window. 'It's nice to be able to look over the garden as we play.'

'That's why I put it here.' She waited until he'd sat down, then took her own seat.

'I've missed our games, and our walks. Mother said I didn't need them to occupy me anymore, and that Lizzie would be my companion, but she hasn't really been up to it.' He took a deep breath in and closed his eyes.

'Is your arm hurting? Do you need something for it?'

'Just a twinge. It's fine now.' He blew out a breath through his mouth and relaxed. 'So, what have you been up to, lately?'

As they played, she told him about Anwen's suggestion about the prospective dressmaking business.

'My, that sounds enterprising. But does that mean you'll be leaving?' He slumped a little and knitted his brow.

'Not in the near future. It could be a while before we get it going properly. You're not to tell anyone, mind. I don't want Mrs Bowen finding out about it before we're ready, in case she makes a fuss.'

'Cross my heart and hope to die.' He ran his forefinger in two diagonal lines across his chest.

It was an unfortunate expression, given the war, but she said nothing. They played on, Tom revealing his worries about Elizabeth and how she was being kept poorly by her mother's insistence that she was weak and would take a long time to get better.

'I know she's been very ill, but I don't think it's going to help, Mother keeping her locked up.'

'I can understand your worry. It doesn't seem very healthy. It's better to get a bit of exercise each day and build up your strength. That's what I did after the TNT poisoning. It's not surprising Elizabeth collapsed in the village. She had gone too far for a first time out. It doesn't mean she shouldn't go out at all, though.'

'That's what I told my mother. As did father. And it was her fault Lizzie felt the need to get away so far.'

'I'm not sure blaming people helps. She simply needs to be made aware that Elizabeth should get out for a bit. I know what it feels like to be shut up indoors when you're ill, as I'm sure you do. Couldn't Dr Roberts have a word? He must agree with that.'

'He's not arrived yet, and I'm sure Mother will keep me out of the way in case I say anything. It might be worth having a word with him in the village, though. You are a sensible person, Gwen.'

'No, I'm not that. Just practical.'

They played two games, both of which Tom won, as he had done every other time. During the third game, Gwen got ahead quite quickly, getting excited at the prospect of winning for the first time against such a good player. If only she could keep her nerve. After a few moves, she couldn't believe her luck. Surely not!

'Are you letting me win, or something? 'Cos I don't like winning unless I deserve it.'

'No, I haven't. Why?'

She moved her queen. 'Checkmate, I think you'll find.'

He scratched his head. 'Well I never. I've obviously lost concentration, because I didn't even see that.'

She found herself on her feet, clapping her hands and bouncing with delight. 'I won, I won!'

Tom, catching the mood, also stood. He took her hand in his and they did a little circle dance, giggling. It was the best mood she'd ever seen him in, and it made her heart so glad.

They came to such an abrupt standstill that they both stumbled, still laughing. He took her arm to steady them both.

'Congratulations, Gwen,' he said, planting a kiss on her cheek.

As he pulled away, they froze, looking into each other's eyes. Her heart was thumping in her head. She should step back.

But before she had the chance, he'd lurched forward to kiss her lips. Despite enjoying the initial warmth, she yanked herself away.

'No!'

'I'm sorry, Gwen, I thought you wanted to.'

'I am *not* going to end up like Polly and Jenny.'

'What? What do you mean?'

But his reddening face showed he knew exactly what she meant.

'I know about Polly's baby. And I have my suspicions about Jenny's too, and I am not going to be yet another plaything to be used and disregarded.'

She pinched her mouth in and narrowed her eyes to indicate she was furious, but really she was trying to make herself angry so she didn't cry. For what she really felt was disappointment in him, and in herself for letting them get this friendly, for starting to have feelings for a man who had no regard for women.

'Gwen, it's not what you think.'

'No, it never is!'

With this, she turned on her heel and almost ran to the door, heading out in search of Mrs Meredith. Not to tell her about Tom's indiscretion, oh no, for she knew how that would go. She'd be blamed for leading him on. As she went, she calmed herself.

She found her employer in the kitchen.

'Madam, Mr Tom doesn't wish to play chess any longer, so I've come for new instructions.'

'Oh. I didn't expect him to finish so quickly. In that case, perhaps you'd do a couple of hours in the garden, see what vegetables there are to be picked, or the weeding, or whatever it is needs doing.'

'Yes, madam.' She did a little curtsy and made her way to the back garden, relieved to be out of the house.

—

'Damn, damn, damn!' Tom tapped his head against the glass as he held onto the windowsill.

How could he have been so clumsy? No wonder Gwen had fled the room. Why had he agreed to take the blame for Polly? It was inevitable that people would find out eventually. As for Jenny, that little secret was well and truly out. How had anyone known about that? He'd been right when he'd told his parents that people would assume he was the father of her baby too.

His inclination was to run after Gwen, to explain, but he couldn't cause a fuss now, and who knew, if his mother got involved she might dismiss her, and then he'd be responsible for her losing her job. He saw her go into the garden, towards the vegetable patches. He could go out there now. No, he'd have to bide his time, but not for too long.

—

Tom had walked right past Gwen's house twice the evening before but hadn't had the nerve to knock on her door.

So here he was, the next day, knowing she was in the house, but powerless to go and talk to her without being interrupted or overheard by his family. He wouldn't get a chance to approach her this afternoon, while she was on an errand, as he had another appointment at the psychiatrists in Cardiff.

Bored in his bedroom, he made his way downstairs with a book. Perhaps reading in the garden would prove more inspiring.

Halfway down, he encountered his mother in the hall.

'Tom, I was about to knock on your door. Gweneth is going to pick up my grocery order from Mrs Brace. Is there anything you desire from the village while she's there?'

This was the opportunity he'd been waiting for.

'I was thinking of going in myself, so I'll walk down with her. I'd like to pop into Mrs Davies's and see if she has any sweets. I've had a yearning for some. Perhaps Gweneth could bring them back while I go and look in the bookshop.'

He was making sure he not only had a reason for going, but a reason for doing so at the same time as Gwen.

'Very well, I will inform her, but she is leaving in a moment, so you'd better get dressed properly.'

Back in his bedroom, he struggled to get his waistcoat and jacket on quickly, cursing his single hand, his haste making the task take longer. Finally ready, he went downstairs calmly, finding Gwen at the bottom, waiting for him. She did not look pleased.

She went slightly ahead, holding the gate open until he reached it, then went on ahead once again, taking the path that led to the road into the village.

'Wait,' he called, as he caught her up.

'Did you organise this on purpose, to get me on my own?' she asked, through gritted teeth.

'Yes, but not for the reason you think, Gwen. Don't keep rushing ahead!'

She stopped and waited for him to catch up. 'You've got a nerve, after yesterday.'

'Which is why I want to apologise. And I really do need to explain.'

She set off again. 'What is there to explain?'

'A lot. There's been a massive misunderstanding. About Polly, and Jenny.'

'You didn't deny it yesterday!' Her voice was a low growl, matching that of the pit wheels as they turned on their eternal circuits.

'Because, and this is to go no further, you are correct that both children are connected to my family, but I swear to you that I am not their father.'

She stopped suddenly. 'I don't understand.'

'It's actually...' He took a breath in. 'It's my father who is the children's father.'

'Sorry?' She looked utterly confused.

'My father was responsible. When Anwen saw Polly turn up at the house, clearly with child, and heard me ask her not to tell anyone, she assumed I was responsible. I let her think that, as my father had more to lose if people found out. I was planning on going back to university and had no intention of coming back to the village after my degree, so I thought that would do the least harm. We didn't even know about Jenny's baby until my mother came across the pair of them and noticed how much her little boy looked like me at that age. My father didn't deny it when she confronted him. So you see, little Freddie, and little Herby – and there's the clue – are my brothers, well, half-brothers, not my sons.'

Gwen's eyes were wide. 'Your *brothers*?' She staggered back to lean against the stone wall that ran down next to the pavement. 'I don't know what to say.'

'I can understand how you knew about Polly, but not Jenny, since we didn't know ourselves until recently. Did she tell you?'

'No. She's never said anything except refer to her late husband as the father. But we'd long known she must have been carrying the child before she married, because of when

Freddie was born. When I was cleaning your mother's room, I spotted the photo of you and Elizabeth as children. You were the spitting image of Freddie.'

'We'd better keep walking, as I don't want to get you into trouble for taking a long time,' said Tom.

The two of them set off once more.

'My, what a situation,' she said. 'I can understand now why your mother always seems cross. I'd be more than cross if I found out my husband had done that. I'd be bloody livid. Sorry! I don't normally swear.'

'No, you're quite right. It does give me some sympathy with Mother, though she's always been a bit like that, which is maybe why my father strayed in the first place. Not that I'm defending him. I think what he did was dishonourable. As was my conduct earlier yesterday.'

'You can hardly compare the two,' she said, twisting towards him. 'And if I hadn't thought you'd got Polly and Jenny with child, I wouldn't have reacted in quite the way I did.' She swapped the basket onto the other arm.

'What, you mean, you'd have let me kiss you?'

'I dunno, to be honest. Probably wouldn't have been a good idea, me being the maid, and you *young Mr Meredith*.'

'As if I care about that. Class! Look at my family: my father started his working life as a hewer. We were definitely a working-class family when I was born. My mother, I suppose, would have been considered lower middle class, as her father was a bank clerk. He was good at saving money, a bit of a miser, Mamgu Powell would have said. He managed to afford a nice house and had a bit put away by the time he died, which is where the money for my education came from.'

'Really? Well I never.'

'I've always felt like I had a foot in two camps, as it were, but never really fitted into either. I know Lizzie feels the same... I wanted to kiss you because I really like you, Gwen. More than that. We've got on so well these last few months. You're curious and like to learn things, like I do. I always long to be with you when you're not around.'

By this time they'd reached the bridge. He stopped, as did she, a couple of steps on.

'Your mother put an end to Elizabeth's relationship with Gwilym, so she certainly wouldn't want us walking out, or whatever.'

'Does that mean you'd like to walk out with me? I'm not much of a catch anymore, with my arm.'

'I don't agree. There's plenty you'll be able to do, once you've healed a little more. And I read in a magazine about these artificial limbs they're fitting men with. Made great progress with them, they have.'

'Yes, there's been some talk of me being fitted with one. I don't know how much they can do.'

'You won't unless you try it.'

'So, you do like me?' he said, taking the two steps towards her, looking her in the eyes. Damn it, why was he always so clumsy about things now?

'Yes, Tom. Like you said, more than that.'

'Then, would I be allowed to kiss you?'

She looked around. 'Not here, out in the open. That would be inviting trouble. And I'm working.'

'Later then?'

'Aye, later. Maybe. Best get these chores done now.' She carried on.

He gladly followed, his relief expressing itself in a whistled version of 'It's a Long Way to Tipperary'.

–

Tom spotted Gwen coming down the road towards the bridge, on her way home from work. He'd gone on ahead, telling his mother he was going for a pre-dinner walk. He waited at the entrance of the small bridge, peering up to see when Gwen should appear.

'Pst, Gwen! Down here.'

She spotted him quickly, looking up and down the road to make sure no one was there, before veering off the path and secreting herself with him under the bridge.

'Are you still happy for me to kiss you?' he asked.

'Yes, you can kiss me.'

He bent forward, taking it slowly this time. When their lips met, their bodies also came closer and he placed his arm around her waist. She, in turn, placed her arms on his shoulders.

They kissed for a few seconds, both pulling away and looking out onto the path that ran next to the stream. Happy that there wasn't anyone there, they kissed once again.

'Perhaps we could meet for a walk on Sunday, if you can get away,' he said. 'I'll find some excuse.'

'I've already said I'd take a walk with Anwen and Violet in the afternoon.'

'Could you get away in the evening?' he asked.

'I'll try to think of an excuse and tell you tomorrow if I can.'

'I'm going to suggest that you accompany me to Cardiff next week, to give my mother a week off. But only if you agree.'

'Another trip to Cardiff would be lovely.'

'And tea afterwards?'

'You know I'm not going to say no.'

'Then I'd better let you get back home.'

Peeking out, Tom spotted some old chaps coming down the road from the allotments. He pulled Gwen further under the bridge, putting his finger to his mouth. They took the opportunity to kiss once more, listening as the voices came into earshot. When they'd faded away, he looked out again. The old men were in the distance, as were a couple of other people, walking towards the centre of the village.

'You go first, so it seems like you were having a look at the flowers or something, just in case.' She nodded and went ahead with a, '*Hwyl fawr,*' and a wave.

After a couple of minutes, he emerged back onto the pavement. He saw her go into her house, then turned left to go back home.

He felt relaxed for the first time in a while, a sense of peace filling him. A niggle nudged at the edge of his mind, about his infirmity, and how he wasn't good enough for Gwen, but he tucked it to the back of his brain. Practicalities could wait until he needed to think about them.

Chapter Thirty

Sunday luncheon was excruciatingly quiet. Margaret had cut each piece of her roast lamb, potatoes and vegetables into tiny morsels and was taking a long time to chew each, having lost her appetite. She'd been lucky to get the lamb and had spent much time in the kitchen preparing everything this morning, yet nobody seemed to be hungry.

Herbert, although not visiting his club as often recently, spent a lot of time in the study, doing paperwork. Elizabeth had retreated into herself since the incident in the village nearly two weeks before, spending more time with her head in a book than talking to anyone in the family. Tom, though a little livelier than he had been, often seemed to be staring into space. He was doing it now, fork halfway to his mouth.

What had happened to her idea of the perfect family, of going up in the world? She had dedicated her life to this, yet none of them seemed to appreciate her. She'd forgone many luncheons and teas out since her children had been returned from the war, damaged, but felt like a stranger in her own home.

When they'd all finally finished, she said, 'I have some fresh apricots from our tree which I've stewed. I've made a bit of custard to go with them for dessert. It's not much, but the apricots are tasty enough.'

'Not for me,' said Tom, rising. 'I want to finish my book. Later, I'll take a walk in the village.'

'Perhaps Elizabeth would like to go with you,' said Margaret, not sure it was wise, but wanting to give her daughter a choice, after what Tom and Herbert had said about imprisoning her. At least if she were with her brother, he could be a chaperone.

The look on Tom's face indicated he'd rather be alone, but she'd suggested it now.

'No, thank you,' said Elizabeth. 'Not today. I'm in the middle of a book and would also like to finish it.'

'I'm going to my room,' said Tom.

He left as Elizabeth rose. 'Shall I help clear the plates?'

'No,' said her mother, who'd not let her lift a finger so far, afraid she'd overdo it. 'It's fine.'

'Then may I leave the table?'

'Of course,' said Herbert. 'I'll pick up my papers and get off to the colliery. I've got extra work to do, what with my clerk off with the influenza.'

'I hear there was a death in the village this week,' said Elizabeth. 'One of the overman's wives.'

'Let's not dwell on that,' said Margaret. 'You get on now, and I'll clear this.'

Margaret watched them leave. She retrieved the tray she'd left on the sideboard, and gathered up the crockery and cutlery, taking it through to the large stone sink in the scullery to wash. It was such a shame she couldn't persuade staff to work on a Sunday until lunchtime anymore.

She rinsed the plates, then fetched the hot water from the two kettles she'd boiled just before sitting down to the meal. It should be just right for the washing-up. After adding some shavings of soap and some soda crystals, she agitated the water so they'd dissolve quickly. She scrubbed furiously with the brush, to get the already-dried bits of gravy off.

What had happened to her? She wasn't the kind, carefree girl she'd been when she'd met Herbert. She'd always wanted a better life, to go up in the world, even from a bank clerk's daughter. Although Herbert had only been a hewer when she'd met him, she'd loved him enough to pick him as her partner in life. He'd had plans, and she'd encouraged them.

Was that any different to Elizabeth falling for Gwilym Owen? In her effort to get things right for her family, she seemed to have got them horribly wrong. She'd spun out of control and she had no idea how to get back to the woman she'd been.

It wasn't until her tears dripped into the washing-up water that she realised she was crying. She pinched her eyes shut, the pain of her failure making her body ache.

'I'm going now, I'll—'

Margaret swung round to find Herbert standing in the doorway.

'What on earth's the matter?' He hurried to her side, taking her hand. 'Margaret, what's wrong?'

'Everything! Everything's wrong. And it's my fault. You going off for your dalliances, Elizabeth running away to the war. Probably Tom too, for if I hadn't persuaded him to go to university, he might have had a reserved occupation in the colliery and he wouldn't have lost his arm.'

She sobbed noisily. Herbert placed his arms around her.

'My hands are wet.'

'I'm not worried about that. Shhh now, come on. Lizzie's always had a mind of her own and wanted to make the world better. Tom's always had a love of learning. He was never going to end up in the pit. You only wanted what was best. Yes, maybe you've mollycoddled them a little too much, but I dare say you were only trying to protect them. And you've had a lot to put up with.'

'I know I'm not the nice young woman you married.'

'What happened is my fault,' he said. 'Instead of trying to make things better, I did my own form of running away. I'm so sorry for the way I've hurt you, Margaret. The two of us got so tied up with our responsibilities that we forgot about each other. Perhaps what we need to do is get to know each other again.'

'I would like that,' she sniffed.

'But we should also make it right for Elizabeth and Gwilym Owen. Here.' He took a clean handkerchief from his pocket and handed it to her.

'Thank you.' She patted her nose delicately at first, but realising it wasn't doing the job, gave it a good blow. 'You're right. They're no different to how you and I were. I'm going to go and see him and apologise and ask him to come and see Elizabeth. I'm sure someone said he lives at the end of Edward Street. It's obvious to me now that she rejected Sidney because she still loved Gwilym.'

'That would be a wonderful start. Leave the washing up for now, it doesn't matter. The two of us can do it together, later, like we used to, back in Georgetown. I'll only be a couple of hours at the mine.'

'I will see you later, and hopefully, I'll have mended one thing.'

He hesitated before kissing her head, then left.

—

'Shall we have a walk on the hill when we've sat in the gardens for a bit?' Gwen said to her friends on Sunday as they reached halfway down Edward Street. She felt restless with excitement at the thought of seeing Tom later that afternoon. She only hoped the weather held, even though the warm, August sun shone down on them, for there were clouds on the horizon.

'Oh look, there's Elizabeth's motorcar.' Anwen pointed down Bryn Road as they passed it. They all stopped to watch it coming up.

'It's Mrs Meredith,' said Gwen, her chest tightening. Had she found out about her and Tom and come to have words with her? But the motorcar turned right, towards Anwen's house. Gwen relaxed.

'Probably going to speak to Mam about food for next week or something,' said Anwen, as they carried on.

'Not sure I could manage that walk you were talking about,' said Violet, placing her hand on her bump that looked particularly large, given her small stature. Benjy was holding her other hand, while Clarice skipped ahead. 'I've only another two weeks to go, so I'd better not risk it.'

'Besides, Idris and Hywel are coming to meet us in the park after they've fixed one of the legs on Mam's bed,' said Anwen, pushing Sara Fach in her pushchair, 'so we'd better wait 'til they come down, otherwise they'll wonder where we are.'

'Righty-ho,' said Gwen, who'd normally have felt sad at her own lack of a loved one, but today felt blessed indeed. 'We'll be lucky to get a seat, mind, it being so warm.'

'It's getting a bit cloudy though,' said Violet, whose cumbersome posture had put her in a gloomy mood the last few days. 'And I will need a seat, so someone will have to budge up if they're full.'

'You all right?' Anwen looked concerned. 'I know it must be harder to walk, but you do look a bit pale.'

'Backache, it is. Always get it this end of my time. Been a bit worse today.'

'Are you sure you should be out?' Gwen asked.

'I find a little walk often makes it feel better. And my babbies are never on time. A week and two weeks late, were Clarice and Benjy.'

'What I late for?' said her son, looking up.

'Coming into the world, *cariad*.'

He looked baffled but didn't pursue it.

The women chatted about how Violet had things ready at home for her confinement as they rounded the corner, past the greengrocer's, onto Jubilee Green.

'And I 'ope to goodness that Mrs Murphy isn't attending anyone else when I go into labour,' said Violet, 'for I've had her twice now, and I don't really know the other midwife.'

'There's always old Mrs Kent, at the end of your row,' Gwen joked.

'I wouldn't have her anywhere near me,' said Violet. 'She's not certified.'

'There's some swear by her.'

'I don't care. She—'

'I was just on my way to yours,' a growling voice interrupted them from across the road.

Standing on the pavement next to the gardens was a woman with her hands on her hips and a face full of fury.

It was Delyth Bryce.

–

There was a loud knock on the front door as Gwilym sat at the table with a book.

'Oh, who's that now?' said Rachael, knitting in the armchair. 'Can't we have a bit of peace on a Sunday afternoon?'

'I'll get it,' said Gwilym. 'It's maybe just Idris suggesting a walk.'

'He'd have come the back way.'

He went out to the hall. The rapping had sounded rather official, like the police. Yet the figure, though distorted through the frosted glass, looked feminine. The hair was perhaps a light brown. Elizabeth? He hurried to open it but his breath caught when he saw who it was.

'What's happened?' was his first reaction, afraid that maybe Elizabeth had taken a turn for the worse, not noticing that Mrs Meredith's expression was actually pleasant for a change.

'Oh, so much has happened,' she said in a wistful voice, confounding him entirely. 'Not least of all, I've realised that I cannot run my daughter's life for her, and she must make her own choices. I have come to apologise and invite you to see Elizabeth at the house.'

He couldn't work out whether she was being sarcastic, or maybe he'd not understood her words properly. 'Wh— what?'

'I know this must come as a surprise, but I'm trying to make amends.'

He looked for signs of the usual haughtiness, but there were none. Her expression was indeed one of hopefulness, her eyes unblinking as she awaited an answer.

'Of course,' she added, 'I'm assuming you'd still like to see Elizabeth?'

'Yes, yes, I would.'

'I can give you a lift now, if you are ready.'

'No, I need – I need a few minutes. I'll walk over, if it's all the same.' He wanted to tidy himself up, put some newer clothes on.

'Whatever suits you best.' She smiled now, not a condescending grin, or a mirthless smirk, but one that was optimistic. 'Right.' She seemed unsure what to do. 'Yes, I'll see you soon then.'

She walked back to the motorcar. After closing the door, he rushed back to the kitchen.

'Who was it then, *bach*?' said his grandfather, already sitting in the armchair with a newspaper.

'Mrs Meredith.'

'What on earth did she want?' said Rachael.

'She wants me to visit Elizabeth, now.'

'You'd better go then, *bach*.'

'Yes. Yes.' He rushed upstairs to get changed, not quite able to take in what had just happened.

–

Delyth was dressed stylishly, in a mid-blue calf-length skirt with a smart, matching jacket and an embroidered blouse. There was a straw hat sitting on her neatly pinned hair. Only the voice, and the sneering expression, gave away the unpleasant and untidy shrew she'd been.

Gwen and her friends came to a standstill. Anwen tucked the pushchair in behind her.

'Clarice, come here!' Violet called, as the little girl skipped on down. She hurried back, to be held close by her mother's arm.

'I've come for my daughter!' Delyth barked.

'We've adopted her,' said Anwen, 'so you've no right to her.'

'I bloody well have! I gave birth to her.'

Benjy burst into tears, while Clarice said, 'Is that lady a witch, Mam?'

A small crowd gathered at a distance, with some people in the gardens coming to the fence.

'Witch? I'll give you bloody witch. She's the one who spirited my baby away.' Delyth pointed at Anwen.

Gwen had suffered as much of this woman as she could bear. 'You abandoned her! She could have died of hunger, for all you cared. It was only Mrs Williams finding her and getting the police involved that saved Sara Fach.'

'Sara Fach! Stoopid, that were, naming her after her own sister. And that's rubbish, that is, that I abandoned her. Only went for a walk while she were asleep, and when I returned, she were gone.'

'You never returned, you liar,' said Anwen. 'You took all your things with you.'

Gwen noticed a young lad running off from the crowd, down and round the bottom corner. She hoped he'd been sent to fetch Sergeant Harries before this got out of hand. But what could Delyth do, against the three of them? Nevertheless, Gwen stood in front of Anwen.

'I've been hearing all about how you've told lies to people about me,' said Delyth. 'Oh yes, I've had someone in the village more than happy to pass on bits of information, for a tidy sum. I can afford it now, see.' She ran the tips of her fingers down the expensive fabric of her outfit. 'Done well, I have. I'll be able to do better for her than you will. And she's called Rhian.'

'It doesn't matter,' said Anwen, leaning past Gwen. 'She's legally mine and Idris's, and we love her and *you* can't have her.'

'She's bloody mine, now give her back!'

Delyth started to stride across the road. Gwen walked backwards, pushing Anwen, Violet and the children back to protect them. If the woman came any closer, she'd give her a good hiding, if she had to.

—

Margaret's relief spilled over into tears, as she got into the motorcar and drove back down Edward Street. At last, she'd done something her family would appreciate. She'd show them what a kind and thoughtful mother she could be. It was the start of a new Margaret.

She wiped her face with the back of the hand, unable to retrieve her handkerchief from the handbag as she drove, but still the tears came. How glad she'd be to get home, to tell Elizabeth the good news. In her effort to still her tears, she missed the turning for Bryn Road. Never mind, she'd turn down Jubilee Green and go round that way instead.

As she took the corner, she had an urgent need to sneeze. Her vision blurry with tears, she swung around the bend, to find herself confronted with the astonished eyes of a young woman, before she heard screams and a sickening thud.

Margaret pulled the handbrake sharply, dazed. What had just happened?

She got out of the motorcar, looking behind it to see a woman lying limp on the road. People were streaming from all directions. Her maid, Gweneth, was kneeling next to the prostrate form.

Oh good Lord, had she run someone over?

On the pavement, there was a small shriek of distress from a dark-haired woman with two small children, who Margaret recognised as a friend of Anwen's.

'My waters have broken' she sobbed.

Chapter Thirty-One

Hearing Violet's plaintive cry, Gwen didn't know whether to stay where she was or see to her friend. The sight before her made her sick to her stomach. There was blood spattered on the road too. A woman knelt down beside the body. It was Sister Grey, in normal clothes, so off duty. She felt Delyth's neck.

'She's gone, I'm afraid. Nothing we can do.' Sister Grey stood up. 'You there, could you fetch Dr Roberts,' she said to someone close by.

'My Brian's already gone,' said a voice.

'And my son's gone for Harries the police,' said another.

'Then go and fetch Mrs Murphy on Walter Street and tell her – where do you live, – Mrs Llewellyn, isn't it?'

'She lives at four Bryn Road,' said Gwen.

'Tell her to get to Mrs Llewellyn at that address.'

The messenger ran off to do the deed.

'We'll take her home,' said Anwen, 'Won't we, Gwen?'

'Yes, of course.' Gwen looked to where Mrs Meredith was standing in the middle of the road, staring down at the body with a haunted look.

'I – I didn't see her there,' said Margaret. 'Just came out, she did.'

'It's all right, Mrs Meredith,' said Sister Grey. 'I saw what happened. Now let me check you over.'

'I – I'm fine.'

'All the same.'

'Hywel, I want Hywel,' said Violet, trying not to cry. 'Who'll look after the kiddies?'

Gwen spotted Idris and Gwilym's brothers, running down to see what had happened. 'Hey, Jenkin. Go and fetch Hywel from your brother's house and tell him to come here. The babby's on its way.'

'Whaat! Come on, mun.' He grabbed Evan and they raced off.

'Would you please keep a respectful distance,' said Sister Grey, to those trying to take a closer look. 'Ah, Mr James, thank you.'

The greengrocer stepped past Gwen, who was walking Violet slowly to the corner. In his arms was an old blanket. The Sister took it and placed it over Delyth's body.

'Oh, what a time, what a time for this to happen,' said Violet. 'And in front of... ooh.'

Anwen got the children to hold onto the pushchair.

'Mam, you all right?' Clarice asked, her little voice breaking up. 'Is that shouty lady all right?'

'I wan' go hoooome,' Benjy said on a long moan.

Both Violet and her children were crying. Sara Fach caught the mood and started crying too. Then Anwen started.

Delyth was the little girl's mother, after all, thought Gwen, tearing up. For all her faults, what a terrible story to have to tell the child when she got older. She looked back once more, spying Sergeant Harries arriving.

'Have you any pains?' Gwen whispered to Violet.

'Just, just the back, l – like before.'

They hadn't gone far when she heard footsteps and the sergeant's voice behind calling, 'Mrs Hughes, Miss Austin!' and then saw Hywel running towards them, shouting, 'Violet!'

Sergeant Harries caught them up. 'I'm told Miss Bryce was arguing with you ladies. A few questions, if you please.'

'Can't you see we need to get Violet home?' said Gwen, rounding on him. 'She's about to give birth!'

'Ah, well, yes, I'm sorry,' he said, going red. 'I'll catch up with you later.' He ran back the other way.

Hywel reached them, breathing heavily. 'Come on, let's get you home,' he said, scooping Violet up in his arms. 'You all right with the kiddies, Anwen?'

'Yes, Uncle Hywel. I'll take them home and we'll hold onto them until we hear from you. Mrs Murphy will hopefully be at yours by the time you get back.'

'Thank you so much.' He walked ahead of them, Violet resting her head on his shoulder.

'Perhaps I should go back to the accident,' said Gwen to Anwen. 'I'll come back to yours after, to give you a hand with the kiddies.'

'All right. I'll get this lot out of it and settled.'

Gwen turned round and went back to Jubilee Green. Mrs Meredith was still standing where she'd left her, the colour drained from her face. Sister Grey stood next to her as Sergeant Harries took notes. He had Delyth's handbag hanging off his wrist. It was an absurd sight that was almost funny. Except it wasn't.

There were still a lot of people milling around. Up the hill, Mr Meredith was striding towards the scene, a look of horror on his face.

'I've been told my wife's run someone over,' he said, nearing the group.

'It was an accident,' said Margaret, her voice flat. 'She just ran into the road.'

'That's right,' Gwen confirmed. 'Delyth had been shouting at Anwen, saying she wanted her daughter back. She ran into the road as Mrs Meredith's car came round the corner.'

'It was hard to stop,' said Margaret, 'going downhill.'

'There'll have to be an enquiry,' said Harries. 'But everyone so far seems to be in agreement. I wonder if she'd been here thieving. I found these when I was looking for an address.' He opened the bag to reveal a pile of one-pound notes.

It triggered a memory for Gwen. 'Anwen told me, before her father was arrested, that he had some one-pound notes

298

too. She thought later, when the thieving and racketeering was exposed, that they must have come from selling stuff on. And Delyth was his fancy woman.'

'We'll have to look into that, of course,' said Harries.

'In the meantime, you should get your wife home,' Sister Grey instructed Mr Meredith. 'She seems unscathed but be sure to contact Dr Roberts if she has any pain.'

He nodded and assisted her to the car.

'Do you need any help, sir?' Gwen asked him.

'No thank you, Gweneth. We'll see you tomorrow.'

'Very well, sir.'

As they drove away, Harries said, 'Thank you for your help, Miss Austin. I will have to take proper statements from you and the other two ladies. If you'd let me know when Mrs Llewellyn has had her baby and is ready to see me, I'd be grateful.'

Two young men came up the hill with a stretcher. Someone must have been down to fetch them from the hospital.

'Hasn't Doctor Roberts arrived yet?' Gwen asked.

'No,' said the Sister. 'I've just been told he's having to deal with a couple of new influenza cases. Now, let's get this poor unfortunate down to the mortuary.'

Gwen walked back to Edward Street, to Anwen's house, not wanting to see them lift the body and carry it away. She doubted Tom would turn up later this afternoon. He'd need to be with his mother, and as disappointed as she was, she needed to be with her friends.

–

'Lizzie, there's someone here to see you,' said Tom, coming up past the flower beds to where she was sitting in a deckchair, reading.

'Is it Anwen?' she said, putting her bookmark in place and closing the book. She had been hoping she might call by.

'No, it's Gwilym. I've shown him into the drawing room.'

Her delight in the prospect was immediately tempered by caution. 'But if Mama sees him here…'

'It was Mother who went to fetch him, apparently. Said she was sorry and that he should come and see you and make amends.'

She pushed herself out of the deckchair. 'How… strange.'

'I agree. Would he lie about it?'

'Absolutely not, but it is so out of character for Mama. I'll come in and see him in the drawing room.'

'I'll be in my room if you need me. Are you going to make amends with him?'

'I have no idea what's going to happen,' she said. There was a nugget of hope in her heart, but after all that had happened – with her running off and only leaving a letter, then becoming engaged to Sidney – she could maybe only hope for some kind of closure.

'Good luck.'

She took a few breaths for courage, then strode with confidence to the drawing room.

'Gwilym. It's lovely to see you.' She kept three paces away, not knowing if an embrace would be welcome.

'And I'm glad to see you looking so much better. Did you know your mother was coming to see me? Your brother seemed surprised.'

'I'd no idea. What exactly did she say?'

'Something about so much happening and not running your life for you. And then she invited me over. She offered me a lift, but I needed time to think, so I walked.'

'So, she's still in the village?'

'I suppose so, otherwise she'd have arrived before me.'

Maybe she was giving them some time, Elizabeth thought. If there was anything to give them time for.

'Elizabeth, how are you now?' He had the look of someone talking to an invalid. How tired she was of that.

'So much better for seeing you. I feel so silly for fainting in the village. I'd walked too far for a first trip out.'

'That pleased I was to see you, but really worried when you collapsed. I asked Gwen to keep me informed about how you were doing. Not to pry though, or tell me anything personal, like.'

'And I asked Gwen about you, at least, at first. I didn't know if you'd want me in your life again.' That was as far as she'd go, admitting her feelings, until she could be sure she would not make a fool of herself.

'And I thought you were gone forever when I heard of your engagement. Did you love him?' The last sentence was said quietly.

'No.' She shook her head vigorously. 'I thought, with you unreachable, and with life being so precious, that… To be honest, I'm not sure why I ever thought it a good idea. I suppose I respected him and thought it would grow into love. I got to know Sidney better when he ended up at my casualty clearing station, injured. Without his mother there, I could see he was a decent man, who cared about things. I thought that if I couldn't have you, he'd make a good husband. But when he came to see me here, I knew straightaway I could never love him, not the way I… Anyway, I told him just that.'

'How'd he take it?'

'Very well. He said, after the war, I was to contact him if I'd changed my mind.'

'Do you think you will?'

'No… I am sorry, Gwilym, I haven't invited you to sit down.'

'I'm fine. I've missed you, Elizabeth.'

'And I you, Gwilym.'

They both stood awkwardly, he examining the carpet, she the chair just past him.

Finally, she couldn't stand it any longer. She closed the gap between them, holding out her arms, which he gladly went to. Soon they were in a tight, passionate embrace of longing, and their lips met. Now Elizabeth really did feel that she'd come home.

She led him to the Chesterfield and they sat close to each other. They clasped hands, and, unable to take their eyes off each other, spoke of their time apart. Around twenty minutes passed before there was a tentative knock on the door.

'Maybe that's my mother,' said Elizabeth. 'Come in!'

Tom entered. 'Sorry to disturb you, but was Mother going on anywhere? Only she's not back yet.'

'She gave me the impression she was coming straight back, since she offered me a lift,' said Gwilym.

Tom leant away from the door for a moment. 'Ah, that sounds like her and Father now.'

He went back to the hall, leaving the door ajar, but he was soon back.

'I'm not sure what's happened, but she's in a state of distress. Something about someone being knocked over.'

Elizabeth rose and rushed out to the hall. 'Whatever's the matter?'

'I can't talk about it,' said her mother, going up the stairs in tears.

'She knocked somebody over in the village. Some woman called Delyth Bryce.'

'The mother of Sara Fach?' said Elizabeth.

Gwilym was close behind. 'Is she all right?'

'No, she's dead, I'm afraid.'

'Oh!' Elizabeth's hand flew to her mouth. 'How on earth—'

'She just ran out on the road as your mother took the corner in the motorcar. She couldn't stop it in time. Anyway, I'd better go and make sure she's all right,' said Herbert.

'I'll come back another time,' said Gwilym. 'Your mother needs you now.'

'Thank you. Maybe we could meet tomorrow, after you've finished work. I can walk to the gardens easily now and I could meet you there, say, three-thirty?' And they wouldn't have to hide.

'Yes, all right. Take care.' Gwilym kissed her cheek and left.

After he'd gone, Tom, who'd been looking away to give them some privacy, said, 'Our mother tried to do good, and something really bad happened. It doesn't seem fair.'

'No, it doesn't. I'll make some tea, you fetch the whisky. Mama will need a little for the shock.'

As would she.

Chapter Thirty-Two

'I'd have thought she'd have given birth by now,' said Gwen, checking the clock on Anwen's wall. 'Her waters went at, what, around half past two? It's gone five now.'

'Babies don't normally come that quick, even after the waters going, and even though it's her third,' said Enid, sitting in the armchair, sewing, as was Cadi, who nodded in agreement.

'Uncle Hywel said he'd come the moment there was anything to tell us,' said Anwen.

'I hope he comes soon,' said Clarice, sitting with Benjy at one end of the table with an old jigsaw puzzle Enid had found in her cupboard.

'Me too,' echoed Benjy. 'I excited to see new babby.'

'Aw, bless him,' said Gwen, feeling his enthusiasm, though sensing it was subdued after what they'd witnessed earlier. What a day for a new life to appear.

Both children had been quiet since they'd been brought back. They'd been told simply that the 'hurt lady' had been taken to hospital.

If there was no news in the next hour, Gwen decided she'd say she was popping home for a bit. She ought to see if Tom turned up, even if it was unlikely. She wouldn't stop long if he did.

They heard male voices from the scullery, where Idris was fixing the washer on the tap.

Anwen stood up. 'That could be him.'

They all tramped out to the kitchen.

'Uncle Hywel, has it come?'

'Yes,' he said, beaming. 'And it's a healthy boy. Gethin Ioan.'

'After both your fathers!' said Anwen.

'That's right. Violet's asked me to fetch you, as she'd like you two to see the babby first.'

The children came running out of the kitchen.

'We've got a brother?' said Clarice, dancing on the spot.

'Yes, another brother for you, and a new one for Benjy.' Hywel picked the pair up, one in each arm, and carried them out.

'Come on, then.' Anwen took Gwen's arm and propelled her out of the back door, obviously keen to see the new arrival too.

–

Gwen made it to the small woods near the stream, not far from the bridge, just before six o'clock. She leant against a tree, her mind wandering. Checking her wristwatch after a while, she saw that at least fifteen minutes had passed. She'd have to assume he wasn't coming.

–

There had been a restrained atmosphere all week at McKenzie House. Hardly anyone had spoken, even Gwen and Enid had communicated in muted tones in the kitchen and scullery. Mrs Meredith had taken to her bed and, with the tables turned, Elizabeth was now looking after her.

Tom had apologised to Gwen for not turning up at their appointment, then had briefly explained why his mother was on Edward Street. Few other words had been exchanged, least of all about when they might meet again. Was that it, Gwen wondered? Had the tragedy made him realise their situation was hopeless?

It wasn't until Friday afternoon that Tom caught her alone, cleaning the dining room.

'I am sorry, it must seem like I've been ignoring you all week.'

'I'm sure you've been busy with your mother,' she said, purposefully sounding unemotional.

'Not really, since she's been shut away most of the time. Somehow, it seemed respectful, in light of what had occurred, not to meet or speak of our feelings. But it hasn't made me any less keen on you.'

The smile he gave her melted any fears she'd had of being slighted.

'I'm glad to hear it.'

'My mother's asked me to tell you that you can go early. I think she'd like us to have the house to ourselves as she's been particularly down today.'

'I am sorry to hear that. Perhaps she needs something from the doctor, to calm her. It wasn't her fault, you know. I don't think anyone could have stopped quickly enough.'

'Sergeant Harries came around yesterday evening. Apparently, someone who witnessed the accident has come forward to say she was driving too quickly. So they've come up with a charge of reckless driving.'

'I wouldn't have said so.' Though had she been aware of the motorcar until it had hit Delyth? Not really, as she'd been concentrating on protecting her friend.

'Let's hope a jury thinks so too.'

She wondered if she'd be called as a witness.

'Would you be able to meet me this Sunday? Maybe earlier than usual, say, four o'clock?' he suggested.

'I don't see why not. The same place?'

'We can start there. It would be nice to take a walk, maybe along the stream and up into the hills.'

'I'd enjoy that.'

'Oh, and, I hope you don't mind, but I'd like to tell Elizabeth about our relationship.'

The fact he wanted to tell someone as close as his sister pleased her no end. 'Of course. If anyone will understand, she will.'

'Thank you. You get off now, and we'll see you tomorrow.'

She took the cleaning caddy back to the kitchen, where Enid was still cooking.

'You going now, then? Miss Elizabeth told me I could go, but I said I'd get things ready so they could just put them in to cook.'

'I'll see you tomorrow, Mrs Rhys.'

A strange sensation came over Gwen as she left. She felt the disconnection between, on the one hand, taking orders from young Mr Meredith while, on the other, walking out with him. It was like she was on the edge of two realms, but Tom's side was beyond a thick glass barrier: she could see in, even touch parts of it through small windows, but couldn't enter. She wondered whether that was how Elizabeth had felt too. Or perhaps Gwilym. Even now they had reconciled, she couldn't see Margaret Meredith accepting her as a partner for Tom.

On the way home, she headed towards Anwen's house, hoping she had a few minutes to spare. She needed to talk to someone.

Anwen was in the garden, picking some runner beans off the tall plants, when Gwen reached her gate.

'Ah, just the person I want to see,' said Anwen. 'I've got some news.' She put her bowl down.

'Ditto. But you first.' She entered the garden, still trying to summon the courage to tell her tale.

'I wrote to Delyth's family, as Sergeant Harries found out their address in Treharris. I got a reply today, from her mother, Blodwen Bryce. She'd already had the police round, telling her what happened. She wrote to me that there was some big falling-out four year back, but she didn't say what. She had no idea about the babby and wasn't interested.'

'So at least you won't have her trying to claim a legal right.'

'No. And her attitude confirms to me that Sara Fach will have a better life with us than she could ever have had with them,' said Anwen.

'So are the police any closer to knowing where all the money came from? Could your father have given it to her to look after?'

'If they do, they haven't told me. I'm still wondering about this informant. Esther Williams is still the most likely suspect, having been her landlady while she were here.'

This made Gwen feel awkward. 'If I have a chance, I'll try to find out.'

'So, what was your news?'

Should she say it didn't matter? Or it was that Margaret was being charged? No, she couldn't reveal that confidence. 'I'm, well – now, you've got to promise you won't tell anyone, not even Idris.'

'That sounds serious. I promise.'

'I'm walking out with Tom. We have feelings for each other.'

'Is that wise? He is a one for sparking inappropriate relationships, and then look what happens.'

'But that's just it,' said Gwen, coming closer to hold onto Anwen's wrists. 'And again, you *must* keep this to yourself. Tom isn't the father of either baby. It's Mr Meredith.'

'*Either* baby?'

Gwen had forgotten that Anwen didn't know about both and reddened at her stupidity. 'Oh dear, yes. I'm afraid he's also the father of Jenny's baby.'

Anwen took a step back. 'Mr Meredith?'

'Please, don't tell anyone.'

'Then why didn't Tom contradict me when I accused him of being the father of Polly's baby?'

'To protect his father. He felt he had less to lose.'

'Goodness.' Anwen stared ahead, her eyes wide. 'Well, I have a great deal more respect for Tom now than I did. How noble of him.'

Idris wandered out at this point, holding a newspaper. 'Hello Gwen! I've just come to tell Anwen what I've read in the paper.'

'Some good news, I hope,' said Gwen.

'I'm afraid not. They've discovered it wasn't only the czar of Russia who was shot, but his whole family, the daughters and young prince as well. I know the czar was a dictator and an oppressor, but to kill his whole family...' He shook his head mournfully.

'That is terrible,' Gwen agreed, taking a few moments before saying, 'I'll leave you to it and see you at chapel on Sunday.' She went back to the path and walked along the backs of the houses.

Terrible. And she couldn't help but think of Delyth Bryce, an awful woman, a bully and a manipulator, but she didn't deserve that end either. Would a jury conclude that Mrs Meredith had been at fault? Not a murder, but some kind of manslaughter?

She wouldn't say any of that to Tom, of course, and hopefully it wouldn't come to that.

–

Elizabeth had looked forward to seeing Gwilym even more today, weighed down as she was with worry about her mother. It had been a week now, and still Mama had barely set foot out of her room. She'd even offered to drive her somewhere for afternoon tea, such as it was these days, but her mother had announced that it was unlikely she'd ever get in the motorcar again.

Elizabeth was waiting for Gwilym by the front gate, relieved when she saw him appear up the path from the road. She went down to meet him, taking his arm as they walked back up, relating the current state of her mother.

'It must be hard for all of you,' he said. 'Though I can understand how knocking someone over and killing them would play on your mind. It must be terrible to think you're responsible.'

'And the trouble is, I wonder if she might be,' said Elizabeth, voicing the thought she'd dared not tell anyone else. 'She was very emotional that day, what with her and father starting to put things right between themselves, and then taking the decision to come and see you. Maybe she wasn't concentrating.'

'From what I've heard, Delyth Bryce was in a right state, shouting and screaming, and ran out into the road as the motorcar came round. I've never driven a motorcar, obviously, but I've ridden bicycles,' said Gwilym. 'It's a sharp bend and you can't see anything until you get round.'

'Somebody told Sergeant Harries she was going too fast.'

'And most other people told him she wasn't. I reckon someone has an axe to grind, but they're outnumbered.'

'Unless the court thinks everyone else is covering for her because she's the manager's wife.' Elizabeth stopped to undo the gate. 'Come on, the kettle's on the range and I've even managed to scrape together some ingredients for a few bakestones.'

'Haven't had any of those in a while.'

'We must keep a couple for Tom.'

'Where is he today?'

It wasn't her secret to tell, that Tom was meeting Gwen, not yet. He'd only told her about the relationship that morning, and she was still trying to take it in. What a strange situation, their parallel romances that crossed barriers.

'He's gone out for a walk.' She took his hand and led him through the hall to the kitchen. 'Let's take our tea outside since it's such a lovely day. I've got the table ready.'

'I like a picnic,' he said.

Out in the garden, he perused the vegetable patches before sitting down. 'They're doing well,' he said. 'Not that I'd expect anything else from you.'

'It's Gwen we've got to thank for that. She was given the job of maintaining it. I've not been able to do much until recently. I would like to start a market garden though, after the war.'

He looked surprised. 'I thought a while back, while we still had the big allotments, that I'd like to do that too. But, I dunno… Mining's all I know, really. I'm not a businessman.'

'You can learn that. It's green fingers that are important.'

'Aye, maybe.'

'Would you mind me starting a business, after we married?'

His eyes stretched in alarm. 'After we what?'

Now was not the time to be faint-hearted. 'Where is this all leading, if not to marriage, Gwilym? We've wasted so much time already.'

He chuckled. 'Oh, aye, but I guess I always thought it'd be me doing the asking.'

'And I'm sure my mother would be horrified, but I'm a modern woman who can't always wait for someone else to step forward. Do you mind that?' It wouldn't be to every man's taste, though surely he knew her well enough by now.

'It's one of the many things I love about you, Elizabeth. I still need to ask your father for permission, though.'

'Of course, but I don't think you'll have any problems there. So, it only remains to decide when.'

'I don't think that's the only thing. There's where to live, for a start.'

'One thing at a time. I was thinking next year. Spring. I'm hopeful that the war will have finished by then. I feel that's where it's heading. If not, then that's just the way it will be.'

'My, you have it all worked out.' He lifted his cup for a sip, but she could see he was smiling.

'I assume also that my mother's inevitable court case will be over by then.'

'There is that. All you've said makes sense to me. Spring it is, then.'

She leant towards Gwilym to seal it with a kiss. He met her halfway.

Providing there was nothing else to get in the way. She banished the pessimistic thought, determined to find some calm before returning to the storm that was her mother's situation.

'It makes a change to walk by the stream, instead of up in the hills,' said Gwen, hiking with Tom.

'And we have the trees to hide away in, should we want to steal a kiss.' He let go of her hand and placed his arm around her shoulder.

'Not that there seems to be anyone else here today.'

'And what would we do if we met someone?'

She'd considered this. 'Pretend we'd come across each other, while out walking separately?'

'That's what I'd plump for. Oh, I do wish we could be honest and show the world how we feel. I'd love to go to my parents now and say, "Look, this is the woman I love." If they've accepted Gwilym, it's no different.'

She stopped dead, forcing him to do the same. 'You do love me, then?'

'Of course I do.' He pulled her to him with his good arm and planted a peck on her lips.

'You've never actually said so.'

'Neither have you. But I'd say I had now, wouldn't you?'

'Not exactly,' she teased.

'Gweneth Austin, I – love – you!' he announced.

'Shhh,' she said, elated but worried someone would hear.

'I don't want to shush.'

'You don't want it getting back to your parents, or mine, come to that, before we've had a chance to tell them.'

'It's your turn now.'

Although he'd said the words, she still had that ever-present fear of being made a fool of. What if he said, *I don't really*, or claimed she wasn't a *lady*?

For goodness' sake, this is Tom, not that horrible Ralph Tallis.

'I love you,' she said.

'See, that wasn't so hard, was it?' He pulled her to him and kissed her properly.

They carried on, along the stream as it trickled merrily along its course. A blackbird was singing a happy melody in a tree somewhere.

'I have some good news,' he told her. 'I'm going to Cardiff to have an artificial limb fitted.'

'That's wonderful,' she said, skipping backwards to face him.

'I hope it will be. There'll be a lot of adjustment. And, while I'm trying to sort out what I'm going to do with my life, Father's asked me to take up a clerk's job at the colliery. Sadly, the chap whose job it was died of the Spanish 'Flu. I wouldn't say that was exactly good news, given the circumstances, but it's an opportunity.'

'That must be the man on Owain Street whose funeral it was yesterday. How terrible. But I'm glad you're taking the job, for I know you said that kind of occupation would bore you.'

'Beggars can't be choosers. By the way, I've told Lizzie about our relationship. She's very happy for us.'

'It's really strange, after us both walking out with Ralph Tallis, that Elizabeth and I should have a similar situation. And not only that, both of us also became ill through the jobs we did for the war. She tried to make friends with me, back when we went to the picture house together to see *Battle of the Somme*, but, because she's higher class, I didn't give the friendship a chance. I wonder, if we'd become closer, whether Ralph would have been able to fool us so easily.'

'Probably not. I, for one, am glad that he didn't have serious designs on you, for that would have been my loss.'

'And Gwilym's loss if he'd been serious about Elizabeth.'

'Then he's lost out twice over. More fool him, I say.'

Yes, more fool him. She could forget him and how small he'd made her feel. Tom had shown her that she was worth loving, and that was all she needed.

'I think,' said Tom, 'that now my mother has accepted Gwilym, it will soon be time to tell my parents – and yours – about us.'

Gwen felt a bubble of excitement form in her stomach, though it was tempered by caution. 'Won't that make my working there awkward? I can't afford to lose this job, not yet.' Did that make her sound selfish? If Tom wanted to tell their parents, that sounded serious. Did that mean…?

'And Gwilym works for my father – in a way, though I know they both work for the coal company,' said Tom. 'When I start the clerk's job at the mine next week, I'll be earning, so we'll be fine.' He sounded more optimistic than he had done in a long while.

'Be fine for what?' she said, hopeful, but not wanting to assume anything, despite his declaration of love.

'Oh, my dear,' he said. 'Do I have to spell it out?' He laughed. 'They say faint heart never won fair lady, so…' He twisted around and knelt on one knee, taking hold of her hand. 'Gweneth Austin, will you marry me?'

She hadn't expected to laugh when somebody finally asked for her hand in marriage, but it was the pure joy coursing through her that caused it, and once she started, she couldn't stop. In between each bout of laughter, she managed, 'Of course… I will… Tom.'

He stood back up, laughing too. He grabbed her waist with his good arm and swung her awkwardly around, which made them both laugh even more.

When he had put her down and they'd both recovered, she said, 'It's wonderful to hear you so positive about your job, assuming we'll be fine without my wage, but I do like working. And, I suppose Anwen, Violet and I could get going with the sewing business.'

'Yes, you could, of course. What about we leave it a week before telling our parents, so it doesn't come on top of the Lizzie and Gwilym situation, and the accident, and we'll tell them next Sunday.'

She thought for a while. A week. It was a scary prospect, but if it meant not having to hide her relationship with Tom… 'Yes, next Sunday it is.'

Margaret awoke to the dim light of early morning with a start. The lingering recollection of a dream about a woman standing at the bottom of her bed, her body bloodied, hurling accusations at her about dangerous driving, hung around in her mind.

Sweat poured down her body, causing her to fling back the covers. Herbert had returned to the bedroom, as a comfort in her time of need. And he was, but she didn't want to wake him and trouble him with this. He had been awoken too many times when she'd called out already. At least she must have been silent this time.

She made her way to the door, feeling around the familiar furniture. Slowly, her eyes adjusted to the gloom. She padded along the landing carefully, then took the stairs quietly, while holding the rail. She didn't want to alert anyone to her nocturnal restlessness and disturb them. Her poor family: they had suffered enough already.

In the kitchen, she switched on the light, grateful for the ready electricity available to them in the mining village. She sat at the table, wondering whether to make herself a cup of tea. No, she couldn't be bothered.

What a ridiculous creature she'd been the last few years, trying to control the lives of her family members. No wonder Herbert had found comfort in other women's arms. Both Tom and Elizabeth had run away to the war, had run away from her. And if she hadn't been so horrible about Gwilym, and ended up having to make amends, she'd never have been in the motorcar, going around the corner at the moment that the Delyth woman had been crossing the road. It didn't matter that she'd been harassing Anwen, or that she was some floozy who may well have been involved with the racketeering, she was a living human being.

It was her fault the woman was dead, through her arrogance. She was a stupid, *stupid* person. Tears poured down her face.

Outside, the birds had started their morning chorus. She'd always loved the sound of it, but now its cheerfulness brought nothing but sorrow. She didn't deserve being treated to things she loved. And what of the trial? The letter for the trial date had come yesterday. Eighth November, 1918. Her fate would be decided in a little over two months. How humiliating that would be, sitting in the dock, like a common criminal. If they found her guilty, she could go to prison. How would that affect Herbert's job, or any further prospects? How would her children hold their heads up? Nobody would want her on their committees. And she'd never be able to return to the village again. The humiliation, oh, the humiliation.

She must have nodded off at the kitchen table, for she awoke from yet another dream, one of herself in the dock at court, the judge pointing an accusing finger at her. Except it wasn't a judge, it was Delyth Bryce again.

There was some whisky in the dining room sideboard. It might afford her some oblivion for a while. As she stood, another idea occurred to her. She dragged herself towards the scullery. There'd be something even better in there.

Opening the cupboard with the cleaning items and rifling through, she came across a bottle of oxalic acid. The maids used it to lift stains from wood and for removing rust. Hadn't she read somewhere recently, in the newspaper, of a woman who'd used this?

She returned to the kitchen to fetch a glass.

Chapter Thirty-Three

Gwen left her house slightly earlier than normal, wanting to walk slowly up to McKenzie House and enjoy the beautiful morning.

Despite dawdling, she still managed to get to the house a little earlier than she'd expected, checking her wristwatch to find it was still ten minutes to six. She took the wristwatch off, placing it in her handbag, then changed into the maid's uniform, the one she used only for cleaning, which wasn't as smart as the one she put on in the afternoon.

Her first task was always to scrub the grates. She went to the kitchen to fetch the kettle and a pan to fill up from the scullery tap.

Humming to herself as she opened the door, she stopped dead when she saw Mrs Meredith there, slumped over the table. There was a glass next to her, with the remains of a clear liquid. Oh dear, she must have come down in the night for a drink and fallen asleep. She would hate being discovered in her nightgown by a maid, but how could Gwen get on with her work unless she woke her up?

By a maid. How was she ever going to accept Gwen as a suitable match for Tom, on whom so many hopes had been placed? Just because she'd accepted Elizabeth's choice, it didn't mean she'd feel the same about Tom's.

'Mrs Meredith? Madam?' She spoke softly at first, hoping to rouse her, but she didn't stir. She tried again, only louder. 'Mrs Meredith!'

Nothing. She'd have to shake her. Her employer wouldn't appreciate it, but what else could she do? She joggled her lower arm. Still nothing.

It was then that she noticed the blue bottle on the chair next to Mrs Meredith. Perhaps she'd had indigestion? She picked it up, her jaw dropping at the label. Oxalic acid. She'd used it only yesterday to rub down the front gate. Surely this had nothing to do with the glass? She lifted it from the table to smell the contents. There was a slight whiff of something unpleasant; it certainly wasn't water.

'Oh Lord, oh no! Mrs Meredith, Mrs Meredith!' She shook her shoulder more forcefully now. 'Wake up!'

The clock in the hall struck six as Enid came through the kitchen door. 'My, you're early, *cariad*, I – oh, good heavens, what's happened?'

'Mrs Rhys, would you ring Dr Roberts? I think Mrs Meredith might have taken something.'

'I – I've never used a telephone before.'

'You look after her then, and I'll go.'

Enid nodded and Gwen left. She'd used the phone before to call tradesmen on Mrs Meredith's behalf a couple of times. She also knew that the doctor's number was Rhymney 11. She only hoped he wasn't out on some other emergency.

–

'Mrs Meredith, can you hear me?' said Dr Roberts, as Margaret let out a long groan. 'Can you tell us what happened? Did you swallow the oxalic acid?'

'Can't go – to prison...'

'Do you have any pain?'

'Stomach – hurts.'

He opened her mouth to look inside, causing Margaret to let out a whining moan.

'Mrs Rhys, is there milk in the house?' he asked.

'I believe there's still some in the bucket outside.'

'Then please fetch a glass quickly.'

Enid ran off to the scullery.

'Can I do anything?' said Gwen.

'Fetch a blanket, please.'

She rushed to the hall and up the stairs, to the linen cupboard on the landing. About to head back down with a thick woollen blanket, she was halted by Mr Meredith as he came out of the main bedroom.

'Gweneth, is my wife up already?'

'Sir, she's in the kitchen, the doctor's here.'

'Why on earth is the—'

Gwen didn't wait for him to finish, instead sprinting back down to fulfil her orders. Mr Meredith followed her, reaching the kitchen just after she did.

'What the devil…? *O Duw*, what's happened to her?' He went to his wife's side, hunkering down to look at her. 'Margaret?'

'Move away, Mr Meredith.' Dr Roberts put the glass of milk to her lips. 'Please drink this.'

'Gweneth, what happened?' said Herbert, pushing his greying black hair back roughly and holding it there.

'I think, sir, that she might have drunk some oxalic acid.'

'Why? Did she mistake it for something?'

Gwen looked round at Enid, whose hand went to her mouth.

'She said she couldn't go to prison,' Gwen told him.

'Oh, sweet Lord.' He placed his head in his hands.

After shaking her head and refusing at first to do what the doctor asked, Margaret finally accepted the milk, taking small sips.

'Aren't you admitting her to the hospital?' said Herbert. 'Shall I phone to tell them to expect her?'

'Help Mrs Meredith with this,' the doctor instructed Enid, who came and took his place.

Although Dr Roberts took Herbert to one side, Gwen was able to hear what was said.

'The thing is, sir, this is likely an attempted suicide.'

Gwen immediately understood what he was getting at, though Mr Meredith seemed to take a little longer to understand.

'If the police get wind of it,' said the doctor, 'she would be charged and might spend a month or two in gaol. With the other case also coming up...'

'I understand,' said Herbert, his face pale. 'But can you treat her at home properly?'

'I believe so. According to what Miss Austin told me about how much was in the bottle yesterday, and how much is there now, I would say she's taken a fairly small amount. She will need constant watching, to make sure there are no side effects, and, well...'

'To make sure she doesn't try it again?'

The doctor simply nodded.

A cheery 'Good morning' was heard, followed by, 'What's everyone doing in here?' as Elizabeth strode into the kitchen, her long hair still down. 'Dr Roberts?'

'I'll explain,' said Herbert, turning his daughter around.

Elizabeth caught sight of Margaret. 'Mama? What's wrong with her?'

'Let the doctor get on,' her father insisted, pulling her away to the hall.

Margaret had now finished the milk. Her pallor bordered on grey. 'Couldn't even do a good job of killing myself,' her gravelly voice groaned. She clutched her stomach. 'Oh, oh no...'

She stood abruptly, knocking the chair over as she moved away from the table, in time to be sick on the floor.

'Some more milk, if there is any, Mrs Rhys,' said the doctor, leading Margaret back to the chair. 'And if you'd be as kind as to clear this up, Miss Austin.'

'Of course, sir. Will she be all right?'

When he didn't reply, she went to find the kettle and pan, the ones she'd wanted for boiling the water when she'd first arrived. Other people being sick always made her feel nauseous too. She'd have to hold her breath and get on with it. At least she'd never been depressed enough to want to end her life.

–

Margaret was eventually settled in bed, 'stable', as Dr Roberts put it, with instructions to the family to ring him immediately should she take a turn for the worse. Gwen wondered at the wisdom of not taking her to hospital, though she appreciated the reasons.

She was getting ready to serve breakfast in the dining room, with Enid dishing up the last egg, when Tom came into the kitchen.

'Lizzie says she's not hungry. She's sitting with our mother instead. There's no need to take mine to the dining room, I'll have it here. Father has already gone to work. He'll be back for lunch.'

'What would you like me to do with the spare food?' said Enid, looking a little irked at the prospect of wastage.

'Please do help yourselves, the two of you. And have a cup of tea and sit with me.' He pointed at the tea set, ready on the tray.

Enid didn't seem sure but followed Gwen's lead.

When they were seated, Tom said, 'We really are very appreciative of your quick actions this morning in summoning Dr Roberts, Gwen. He didn't seem to think she'd taken enough of the poison, but all the same, you may have reduced the harm it would have done. And thank you for your help too, Mrs Rhys.'

'I feel sorry to the heart of me that she felt bad enough to do that,' said Enid. 'Begging your pardon, sir.'

'No, I appreciate your sentiment, Mrs Rhys. Clearly she has taken the motorcar accident much more to heart than we'd even realised.'

'It doesn't seem right that they'd lock someone up who was already feeling desperate enough to end their life,' said Gwen.

'I'm sure we can rely on your discretion,' Tom said. 'We wouldn't want people knowing about—'

'Of course,' the women said, more or less together.

They sat in silence after that, until Enid, finishing the meagre bacon rasher and half a piece of bread she'd given herself, said, 'I'll start the washing-up.' She took the plate and two pans she'd used to the scullery.

'Gwen, I think maybe we'll have to delay telling our parents about us. Perhaps until after the court case.'

She was disappointed, but what else could they do? 'When are you likely to find out when that is?'

'The letter came yesterday. It's eighth November. I wonder if that's what prompted, you know.'

She made sure Enid wasn't about to come back before stroking his hand. 'Maybe it was. And of course we should wait. Now would not be the right time.'

'Thank you for being so understanding.'

What else could she be? She smiled to reassure him, then ate up the rest of the breakfast quickly.

'I'd better get on,' she said, standing. 'The house won't clean itself.'

He took her hand and caressed it. 'I'll speak to you later.'

Chapter Thirty-Four

Gwen was wandering home from work slowly one evening, watching the mist getting a little denser as she reached the dip in the path over the bridge. Although it was only the last day of August, autumn was already on its way, and the temperature had dropped the last few days.

It had been ten days since Gwen and Tom had decided to delay telling their parents about their relationship. In that period, they had not had much opportunity to spend time together. They had only met briefly outside the house on Sunday and one evening in the week. Tom had attended the psychiatrist in Cardiff alone, the two Fridays since the incident. It was an intolerable situation, but what could she do?

She was always glad now to leave the Big House, with the gloom hanging over it. Mrs Meredith had not left the bedroom since that fateful morning. It was as if she'd given up. It had been made known in the village that she had suffered a slight fall and had sprained her leg. Elizabeth had served her meals and cleaned her room, so Gwen hadn't seen her at all. Elizabeth had also taken over giving Gwen tasks, which didn't include entertaining Tom.

As she came out of the thicker mist and approached her house, she noticed Esther Williams lurking close by. Not again. She wondered what message had come via Mrs Tudur this time, as there had been a few, via dead relatives who were 'looking after' Daniel. They were never specific, only that he was 'alone' and 'frightened' with people he didn't know. Were they supposed to conclude from that information that he'd been captured by the enemy?

'Mrs Williams, how are you?'

The woman came hurtling towards her in a state of high excitement. 'What a day! Such a lucky day. Look, look!'

She thrust a letter towards Gwen as they walked along. Gwen took it and started reading, but Esther told her what was in it all the same.

'He's alive! Mrs Tudur was right. He was found by the French, injured. He lost his memory and ended up in a French hospital. Quite badly cut up, he was, when a bomb went off, my poor boy, but he got stitched up they say, so that's all healed now. The shock of it left him for months without memories. But things are slowly coming back, and now they're sending him to a hospital in Brighton. Oh, happy day! I wish I could afford the fare to go and visit him, but quite a way that is, I believe.'

'That's wonderful news indeed, Mrs Williams.' And a lucky chance for Mrs Tudur, thought Gwen. She hoped Esther wouldn't start relying too much on the woman after this.

The letter was removed from Gwen's hands before she'd had a chance to finish it for herself. 'And now, you'll be able to marry!'

'The thing is, Mrs Wi—'

'He won't be back straight away, of course. But that gives you time to think about what you're going to wear and so on. You have such good taste in clothes. I'm sure Mrs Bowen would have something lovely she could adapt, like she did for Anwen Rhys.'

'I think we're going a little too quickly,' said Gwen.

They'd reached Gwen's front door; she wondered how quickly she'd be able to escape and get inside the house.

'Of course not. We'll have to find out when he's coming home, for you could get a license. And then we need to…' She carried on with plans that were never going to come to fruition.

She remembered something Anwen had said about Delyth Bryce's informer a while back. Now might be as good a time as any to broach the question.

'Mrs Williams, I've been meaning to ask you, did Delyth Bryce get in contact with you at all, after she left? We've been wondering how she found out about Anwen adopting Sara Fach.'

Esther's mouth gaped open. 'Why would you think I'd tell that woman anything? Kept myself to myself, I have, recently. I helped on the big allotments, when they were still going. Been quiet, I have.'

Maybe Anwen had got it wrong after all. 'Please don't take offence, but Delyth was your lodger. I just thought maybe she'd been in touch and you'd perhaps said something innocently that led her back.'

'No, I most certainly didn't. Hurt, I am, that you'd think so. I know I had a reputation for being a gossip in the past, but I've stopped that now. I suppose it's better that you're open with me than think it and not say it, if we're to have a good relationship as mother-in-law and—'

Gwen's front door opened, and Ruth Austin stood there. 'I wondered where you'd got to. Evening, Mrs Williams.'

'I was just telling Gwen the wonderful news—'

'That Daniel's alive after all,' Gwen finished. 'I'll tell Mam all about it indoors. I'll let you get along, Mrs Williams, as it's chilly out here and the mist looks to be getting thicker.'

'Of course. I'll let you know any further news. And you can make plans!'

Esther scuttled away and had soon disappeared into the mist.

'What was all that about?' said Ruth.

Gwen breathed out a massive sigh. 'I think she has me lined up as a possible mate for her Daniel, that's all.'

In the kitchen, Gwen greeted her father, who was sitting in one of the armchairs by the range with a *Cambria Daily Leader* spread wide. Gwen sat on the other armchair, rubbing her hands together to get warm.

'I wouldn't want Esther as a mother-in-law for you, that's true enough,' said Ruth, 'But…'

'But what, Mam?'

Albert lowered the newspaper. 'What's all this then?' asked Albert.

'Mrs Williams has heard that Daniel is actually alive.' Gwen told him about the letter.

'What's that got to do with Esther being your mother-in-law? Is there something you haven't told us?'

'I did tell you that Mrs Williams had the wrong idea. But what were you going to say, Mam?'

'Just that, Esther might be a *character*, for want of a better word, but Daniel was always a nice boy. You know, you could do worse.'

'Mam!'

'Is he interested in you, then?' said Albert. 'I thought you was just friends.'

'We are!'

'Your mother's not wrong, though. A job at a bank, he's got, could have prospects. He could likely give you a better life than one of the miners here.'

'Oh Da! That's not a reason to marry someone.'

'It looks like he'll be back soon, either way, along with the rest of them.' He held up the newspaper once more. 'Good news in here, very good news. And our boys in the Welsh brigades have a lot to do with it.'

'What's happening then?' Gwen leant forward with interest, hoping the optimism was justified this time, not just another report to boost morale at home.

'The brigades have moved forward miles and miles, and captured loads of places, it says here. They've taken thousands of prisoners. And they've recaptured Mametz Wood!'

Where Violet's first husband died, thought Gwen. And a dozen other men from the village.

'And they've recaptured a pile of other places.'

'And no doubt lost some of our own men along the way,' said Ruth.

'It says here that the casualties have been light on our side.'

'Well I do hope you're right,' said Gwen. 'For I long for Henry to come home.'

'As do I,' Ruth said on a long sigh. 'As for Esther, I'd make darn sure she didn't dominate your life. And since Daniel worked in Tredegar, you could get a place there.'

'Not back to this! Don't be ridiculous.'

'No need to shout,' said her mother. 'Now make yourself useful and pop the kettle on.'

It was tempting to holler, *I'm going to marry Tom, and he's an even better prospect!*

Was he, though, with his arm missing? She picked up the kettle and took it to the scullery to fill. It didn't matter whether he was or not; that was who she loved.

But a small voice niggled at the back of her mind, whispering, *He's put off telling his family.* Only because of his mother's situation. What if it was an excuse? Yes, Elizabeth and Gwilym had got together, but Elizabeth had always been a simpler soul, one who'd had no airs and graces. Tom had always been cockier in his younger days. What if he turned out like his father, using his position to take other women? After all, she'd never have guessed it of Mr Meredith, to look at him.

She was concentrating on these thoughts so much, she hadn't realised the kettle had filled up until the water spurted out and all over her waist area. She jumped back.

'Oh!'

That would teach her to have such silly thoughts. Tom would tell his parents about them when the time was right. She was sure he would.

Chapter Thirty-Five

Elizabeth was grateful for Anwen's company at the court in Tredegar today, to have someone else there, other than her father and Tom, even though she'd been called as a witness. Gwen was here also, for the same reason, as were Sister Grey, Mr James the grocer and a few other witnesses to Delyth Bryce's accident. Sergeant Harries was sitting down the front.

Had it really been two years since she'd accompanied Anwen to court in Monmouth, when her father was on trial? So much had happened since then. Yet the last two months had passed exceedingly slowly, their lives put on hold – hers and Gwilym's, Tom's and Gwen's. Even Anwen had been unsettled, wanting to bring to a close this terrible episode with Sara Fach's mother. She looked pale today, and out of sorts. Elizabeth hoped she wasn't feeling guilty about a part of her life causing this havoc. It all stemmed back to her father really, Madog Rhys. He had such a lot to answer for.

In the dock her mother sat motionless, looking down at her lap. She'd dressed in dark brown, a small, neat hat picked out to match, to show that she was sombre and sorry, as she'd put it, not wanting to look frivolous in any way. Elizabeth looked around the courtroom, at those from Dorcalon who'd been there on the day of the accident. Which of them had claimed to witness her mother going too fast?

There was a commotion as the door opened once more, and an older woman, maybe in her fifties, bumbled in, moaning and wailing about her poor daughter and how justice should be served.

'Who's that?' Elizabeth whispered to Anwen, next to her.

'From what she's saying, I've a nasty feeling it's Delyth's mother, Blodwen Bryce.'

'I thought she'd disowned her daughter.'

'That's what she said in her letter. Oh goodness, look who's with her.'

It was Rose Pritchard, helping her to her seat. Gwen turned to Anwen. 'You don't think she was the one keeping Delyth informed, do you?'

'Of course she was,' Elizabeth replied. 'And the one who's come to speak against my mother's defence.'

Light dawned on the faces of the other two women, but there was no time to explore the idea before the command 'All stand' was given.

She didn't remember Rose being there that day, but the butcher's, above which she lived, was only a few doors down from where the accident had happened.

The judge and solicitors entered the courtroom. The charge was read out.

'You have been summoned for driving at a speed dangerous to the public through the village of Dorcalon on Sunday the eleventh of August, 1918, which resulted in the death of Delyth Bryce.'

'She killed my daughter, and I want recompense,' called the woman who'd entered with Rose.

The judge banged his gavel, announcing, 'One more outburst, and you will be removed.'

Rose pulled Mrs Bryce down and whispered in her ear.

Tom looked at his sister, narrowing his eyes in query. Elizabeth shrugged.

The court clerk added, 'There are also damages being sought by Mrs Blodwen Bryce, who was being kept largely by her daughter's wages.'

'The nasty, grasping little liar,' Anwen muttered.

Margaret pleaded not guilty to dangerous driving and was asked to give her account of the event by the prosecuting lawyer. She told the story as her children had tutored. Elizabeth took Tom's hand and he curled his fingers around hers. They hadn't coached their mother because they'd believed her to be in the wrong, but because she'd been so emotional in the retelling of it to them, they were afraid she'd make herself look guilty.

'You say you were going at a speed slow enough to take the corner,' the prosecuting lawyer started, 'that you were driving safely. Yet you've made no mention of a horn being sounded in warning. Would that not have been wise when taking a sharp bend?'

'I don't think one has to,' said Margaret. 'And I wasn't going fast.'

'You say that, but there is a report that you took the bend far too quickly, that you were startled by seeing someone in the road and you had no time to stop.'

'No, that's not the case,' said Margaret. 'Most people will tell you I was going slowly.'

'People whose jobs are in the colliery, who rely on your husband for a job? People who can be intimidated?'

'No, of course not! I wouldn't do such a thing. And Mr James the grocer isn't—'

'You wouldn't threaten people with loss of a job?'

'I haven't the power to dismiss people from the colliery,' said Margaret, more confident again now.

'Then why were you heard, at the end of December 1917, saying to a Mr Hywel Llewellyn, and I quote, "Don't incite him to ignore me, I'll have you both sacked."? It is alleged you were referring to a Mr—' he checked his papers, 'Gwilym Owen. Did you say this?'

'Who on earth told you that?'

'Answer the question, Mrs Meredith,' said the judge. 'Did you threaten to get Mr Llewellyn and Mr Owen sacked?'

Elizabeth knew this had been the case, as Gwilym had told her of this exchange recently. But where on earth would the solicitor have got this information? She looked into the crowd, at Rose. Hadn't Gwilym said they'd been on Jubilee Green, by the shops? She could have easily overheard from the butcher's.

'I don't think that's exactly what I said. It was just an, an idle threat, that's all, to keep him away from my daughter.'

'Not the first threat you've made, by all accounts. You threatened to take money from the wages of your cook, Rose Pritchard, when you dismissed her for a crime that you never reported and which couldn't be proved.'

'That was an entirely private matter. I didn't wish to bother the police with it.'

'Maybe because it wasn't true? And you're well known for bullying your daughter, which is what *you* were accused of by Mr Owen.'

The defence lawyer stood up. 'I object, my Lord: this has nothing to do with the case in hand.'

'Sustained.'

'I'm just trying to demonstrate the defendant's intimidating behaviour, my Lord. I have no more questions for the present.'

Elizabeth didn't relish relating this to Gwilym, who would feel guilty at his words being used against her mother. Perhaps she shouldn't tell him, yet she didn't want to keep secrets from him.

The defence lawyer asked Margaret a few questions, giving her the opportunity to relate the accident once more as the fault of Delyth Bryce, not as a consequence of her driving. Despite this, when he'd finished and she was allowed to walk away from the stand, she was slouched, like a woman defeated.

Anwen was called as a witness first, maintaining that Margaret hadn't been speeding, and that Delyth had jumped into the road in a fit of rage, as the motorcar came around the corner. The other witnesses called did likewise, none being persuaded otherwise by the prosecuting lawyer.

'We'll take a break for luncheon at this juncture,' the judge announced. 'We will resume at two o'clock.'

As people left the courtroom, Anwen said, 'I won't be a moment,' and went down to catch Margaret's lawyer before he disappeared.

Herbert and Tom left with the others, but Elizabeth waited for her friend. She saw Anwen take an envelope from her handbag and hand it to the lawyer, who nodded and said a few words before they parted company.

'What was that all about?' said Elizabeth, when she returned.

'Just giving that letter I received from Blodwen Bryce to the lawyer. It's a good job I thought to bring it,' said Anwen, before rushing out of the door.

—

When they returned to the court at two o'clock, Rose was the first witness called. She looked smug, a superficial smile plastered on her face. She performed a little wave for Mrs Bryce.

'Miss Pritchard,' said the prosecuting lawyer. 'Can you tell us what happened on the afternoon of Sunday the eleventh of August?'

'Well, see, I'd just come out of our shop – the butcher's shop, you know, on Jubilee Green, what we own, see – and I saw Delyth Bryce there, asking for her baby back, which was reasonable. Anwen Rhys did steal it, see, from Esther William's house, behind Delyth's back, and did claim to the authorities that she'd abandoned it, which she hadn't. So upset was Delyth, poor love.' Rose pulled her mouth into a frown. 'Crossing the road, she were, as there were no traffic there, see, and then Mrs Meredith's motorcar came hurtling round the corner, going much too fast, like she always do. Maniac, she is. She'd never have been able to stop in time. Poor Delyth didn't stand a chance.'

'And Mrs Blodwen Bryce, I believe, is widowed and infirm, and relied on her daughter for money.'

'That's right.'

'Thank you. No more questions.'

Elizabeth sat forward as the defence lawyer stood, sending a small prayer to the Almighty.

'Miss Pritchard, how come you're the only one out of all the witnesses who claims that Mrs Meredith was driving too fast?'

'Because she's the pit manager's wife, and she can get people sacked, like was said earlier. Right mean, she is. She sacked me for something I didn't do.'

'Really? Isn't it the case, though, that stolen items were found in your home last year, and you spent a month in gaol?'

'Someone put them there.'

'Objection, my Lord,' said the prosecuting lawyer. 'This has nothing to do with the current case.'

'I'm simply establishing that Miss Pritchard may not be the most reliable, or honest, of witnesses.'

'Carry on,' said the judge.

'Is it true that you'd been communicating with Miss Bryce, who had been paying you for information about her daughter, who she had abandoned and was consequently adopted by Mr and Mrs Hughes?'

'I – No. It's not true.' Rose stuck her bottom lip out like a sullen child.

'And are you, maybe, hoping to share some of the compensation that Mrs Bryce is hoping to obtain?'

'Course not.'

'For you've been heard to say on a number of occasions, that you'd get your own back on people?'

'No.'

'And isn't Mrs Meredith one of those people you'd like to get revenge on?'

'No!'

'Do not shout in my court,' said the judge.

'I put it to you, Miss Pritchard, that the events of August eleventh are just as the other witnesses have described, and that your account is different because it's a lie, an opportunity, as seen by you, to sully the name of someone you want to ruin.'

'That's not true! I am telling the truth. She can't bribe me, see, Mrs Meredith, 'cos I don't work in the mine, and neither does my father.'

'I have no more questions, my Lord.'

'In that case, we move onto the last witness. Call Sergeant Rhodri Harries.'

Elizabeth became nervous. It was one person's word against a few, yes, but what if the judge believed her mother had threatened the witnesses? What did the sergeant have to add when he wasn't even there? He wasn't known for his invest-igative skills, and she wasn't aware of them bringing in any detectives.

The prosecuting lawyer had no questions for Harries, so the defence lawyer stood. 'Sergeant, you didn't witness the accident on eleventh August.'

'No sir, but I took the witness statements, most of them on the day. The only person who came forward later was Rose Pritchard. She said she was afraid to come forward before, in case Mrs Meredith was able to pull strings and get rid of her father from the butcher's.'

This was bad, thought Elizabeth. She put her arm through Tom's whole one and leant against it. Their father's face was emotionless.

'And do you think that was the case?'

'In my opinion, no, sir. I talked to witnesses who said they remember Miss Pritchard standing outside the butcher's, a few doors down. I went and stood there myself, and there wasn't the best of views.'

'I see.'

Elizabeth sat upright. Harries had actually had doubts and done something about it off his own bat? That made a change.

'Furthermore, in Miss Bryce's bag, I found a collection of one-pound notes, twenty in all.'

There was a gasp from the spectators.

'Talking to the police in the surrounding areas, I eventually found that the serial numbers on the notes followed or were similar to notes recovered from a felon arrested in Merthyr Tydfil a few months back, who'd made money selling stolen goods to profiteers. I'm afraid that a similar numbered one-pound note was spent in the confectioner's in Dorcalon.'

'Where is this going?' said the judge.

'We're getting there, my Lord,' said the lawyer. 'Carry on, Sergeant.'

'Mrs Davies, the shop owner, mentioned it to me only a couple of weeks ago, after she heard that pound notes were found in Miss Bryce's bag. Unusual, it is, for anyone to pay with a note round here. It transpired that it was Miss Pritchard here who'd given it to her. She assumed at the time she'd acquired it from her father's butcher's. I asked Stanley Pritchard about it, and he had no knowledge of it. He came to see me a few days ago, said he'd been searching in her room for money that had gone missing from his own shop, and he found a few letters – from Delyth Bryce.'

'He did what?' Rose screamed, jumping up from her seat at the front.

A court official rushed over and made her sit back down.

'And what do these letters reveal?'

'That Rose Pritchard was indeed passing on information about Delyth's abandoned daughter, Rhian, as she called her. But it was obvious they were talking about Sara Fach Hughes.'

A number of voices started muttering. Elizabeth looked at Anwen, whose face was scrunched up in anger. 'How dare she!' she hissed.

The judge banged the gavel several times. 'Silence in court! Carry on.'

'My Lord,' said the defending lawyer, 'It seems clear to me that, given the number of witnesses who claim that Mrs Meredith was going at a reasonable speed, and given that Rose Pritchard was too far away to be a reliable witness, and had an interest in blackening her ex-employer's name, that the speeding claim is untrue. Therefore I recommend that this case be dismissed. Furthermore, despite Mrs Bryce's claim that she was supported by her daughter, I have acquired a letter that states that Mrs Bryce cut her daughter out of her life four years ago, and they have not seen each other in that time.'

'May I see it?' said the judge.

The lawyer handed it over. The judge read through, frowning. After he'd finished he said, 'So she can't have been supporting her mother.'

Elizabeth looked towards Blodwen, whose mouth was pinched in as she glared at Anwen.

'No,' the lawyer confirmed. 'I have no more questions.'

The prosecuting lawyer stood. 'I have no further questions, my Lord.'

'In which case,' said the judge, 'I declare there to be insufficient evidence to prove any kind of negligence, so there is no case to answer. And, either way, there are no grounds for compensation. Court dismissed.'

Elizabeth looked over at her mother, whose relief was obvious. It was the most relaxed she'd seen her in weeks.

'You can't do that!' Blodwen Bryce balled, but the judge stood, ignoring her.

'Thank God that's over,' said Herbert.

'Is it, though?' said Elizabeth, wondering what their ex-cook might do next to get her own back.

'Look, what's happening there?' said Anwen, pointing towards Rose.

Sergeant Harries was going over to her, along with the two constables who'd been sitting behind Margaret in the dock. Tom started to speak, but Elizabeth hushed him.

'Rose Pritchard, we're arresting you on suspicion of receiving stolen goods.'

'I've not stole nothing. I was given that money.' She tried to sidestep them.

'Which was obtained by selling stolen goods,' said Harries.

'But I didn't—' She struggled as they handcuffed her, trying to bite the older constable, but soon they had her confined.

'Let's face it, Miss Pritchard, it's not the first time, or the second, is it? Take her away, boys.'

At the back of the courtroom, Blodwen Bryce was also being questioned by a couple of policemen.

When Elizabeth's attention drew away from the scene, she realised her father had gone down to meet her mother. She and Tom waited for them to return.

'We'll leave you to it,' said Anwen. 'There's a motorbus due in ten minutes, so we'll go and catch it.'

'Of course,' said Elizabeth, 'and thank you, both of you.'

'Thank you, Anwen – and you, Gwen,' said Tom, smiling.

Gwen smiled back before following Anwen out. The other witnesses had already left.

Tom put his arm around Elizabeth. 'Come on, let's get our mother home. I think we have cause for celebration, at last.'

'Are you going to tell them now, about Gwen?'

'On Sunday. Let's get this over first.'

'I'm so pleased you've found someone, Tom. What with a possible end to the war soon, this could be the start of a new phase of hope for us all.'

'I do hope you're right, Lizzie.'

–

Today was the day. Gwen sat at the table in her kitchen, with her back to the wall, watching her mam, da and mamgu as they drank their post-dinner cups of tea. She felt slightly sick as her stomach rolled. This should be a happy day, but how would they take it, especially as she'd kept it to herself all this time? Surely they'd understand her reasons. She didn't have much time, so she'd better make this quick.

'I suppose it's back to normal at the Big House, tomorrow,' said Mamgu Bertha. 'No more worry about a looming court case. It must have been strained these last coupla months.'

'It will certainly be a relief,' said Gwen.

How she wished she could tell them exactly what it had been like: Mrs Meredith in the house all of the time, mostly in her bedroom; Elizabeth in charge; she and Tom trying to act normally. In most ways, she hoped things did go back to normal, and yet, Elizabeth had been a much easier person to work for. And would she even keep her post after today? It was a good job she'd made a start on the sewing, doing bits and pieces for people of an evening. She'd had a look at some of her older clothes, working out how to update them and maybe sell them on.

'I, um, have something to tell you all,' she started.

'You're not giving this job up already, are you?' said Ruth. 'You've not got the sewing business up and running yet.'

'No, it's not that, Mam. Though it's possible I will have to give the job up. It's just, there's a young man I've been walking out with. He wants to come over and speak to you later.'

'You kept that quiet, *fach*! Is there something wrong with him?' said Albert.

Gwen thought about Tom's arm, but that wasn't what her father meant. 'No, Da, in fact he's very respectable and, well—'

There was a loud rapping at the front door.

'Oh who's that, now? Just as you're telling us something important,' said Ruth.

'I'll go,' said Albert, making for the door.

'Who is this young man?' asked Bertha.

'I'll wait until Da gets back.'

When he returned, she wasn't sure whether he was pleased or puzzled about something. 'Well, there's a mystery solved. Come in, lad.' He leant out of the door and gestured someone in.

He'd come already? They'd agreed on half past two and it was only quarter past. She wasn't ready.

Through the door came a figure, but it was one in uniform. He removed his cap and shoved it under his arm.

'Hello Gwen, Bet you're surprised to see me. Come to claim my girl, I have.'

It was Daniel Williams.

Chapter Thirty-Six

'So, what is this important news you have to tell us?' said Margaret, pouring the post-luncheon coffee in the drawing room. 'It's all very mysterious.'

Tom couldn't believe the change in his mother since the court case two days ago. After walking like an old woman weighed down with years of trouble for the last couple of months, she was upright once more. Yet she hadn't gone back to her old self, the sniping, controlling, always gloomy personality she'd become in recent years. It was like someone had dressed her in a youthful cloak of hope and possibility.

'If it's to do with the artificial limb, we already know about that,' said Herbert.

Tom looked at his sister, who knew what was coming. She smiled and gave a nod of encouragement.

'You see, I've met someone with whom I want to spend my life.'

'But you've not been anywhere,' said his mother, looking concerned. 'Oh, in Cardiff, when you've been going on your own? Well, who is she?' Margaret leant forward. He could tell she was trying to smile but was worried about what was coming.

'No, not someone in Cardiff. It's Gwen.'

'Gwen? You mean our maid, Gweneth?'

'Only our maid for the time being. She's starting a clothing business.' He hoped this might help his mother see that she was enterprising.

'I'm very happy for you, son,' said Herbert. 'She seems like a very nice girl. Lizzie, you don't seem surprised.'

'No, Papa, I confess I already knew.'

Margaret still hadn't offered any kind of opinion. She just said, 'Mmmm,' and stood to straighten her skirt. On sitting, she said, 'She reminds me of myself at that age, full of life and confidence. I hope she never loses it. After all, I married a working-class man, even though I was middle class, well, lower middle class, I suppose, and that worked out all right.' She took the hand of Herbert, sitting next to her, offering him an affectionate smile.

'Is that it?' said Tom.

Margaret looked back at him. 'What else did you expect? I'm tired of fighting everyone. It's time for some peace in my life. And to be honest, it's just a relief that you and Elizabeth are to be settled down. I thought it would never happen. You've got a job now, and I'm sure you could apply for all sorts of very good desk jobs with your education, especially after the new limb is fitted. So, have you asked her parents for her hand?'

'Not yet. I said I'd go over this afternoon.'

'No time like the present, lad,' said Herbert.

'But it's only ten past two and I said – oh well, I suppose it's better to get it over with. Then maybe Gwen and I could take a walk while it's still sunny.'

'But you must bring her back here for us to congratulate her,' said Margaret. 'It would be better out of work hours.'

'Very well!' He jumped up. 'Wish me luck.'

–

Daniel seemed to be enjoying relating his account of being shot and left for dead, then being recovered by the French, concussed and unable to remember anything.

This was terrible, that he'd just turned up, thought Gwen, standing like a statue as he related the story. Why hadn't he written to tell her he was coming back, if he intended to keep up with the friendship? And why had he referred to her as his 'girl'? When he hadn't communicated after news of his discovery, she'd thought it a convenient opportunity to cease their connection, even though Esther had given her an address.

'I'm sorry I didn't write,' he said. 'My memory was still patchy until recently, and then Mam said how much you'd missed me and I remembered the letters, which must still be in my knapsack with the brigade. Hopefully it'll find its way back to me eventually. Don't suppose I'll be going back to the war now, since it looks likely to come to an end soon.'

Had his returning memory played tricks on him about their relationship?

'You've certainly been through a lot,' said Gwen. 'But the thing is—'

There was another knock at the door. She checked the clock. It still wasn't half past two.

'Who is that, now?' said Bertha, all the while knitting as she listened to the unfolding events.

'I'll go again,' said Albert, heaving himself up once more.

Daniel carried on, telling them about his train journey from Brighton to Dorcalon, his excitement building. Gwen wondered what was taking so long at the front door.

Daniel's, 'So, as I said,' clashed with Gwen's, 'The thing is,' and neither managed to finish before Albert led Tom into the room.

'What's *he* doing here?' said Daniel.

'I think there might be some kind of misunderstanding somewhere,' said Albert. 'Since Mr Tom has just asked for your hand in marriage, Gwen?'

'He what?' said Daniel. 'He can bugger off. Gwen's my girl. Been pining after me, she has. Mam told me. Didn't know if I had a hope with her, but there you go. So, Mr *Meredith*, you've had a wasted journey. As if you could provide for her now, anyway.' He indicated the arm.

Enough was enough. Gwen went to Tom, putting her arm purposefully around his stump. 'I'm sorry, Daniel, but it is you who's had the wasted journey. I have never said anything to your mam about *pining* for you. Tried to tell her we were simply friends, I did. She had completely the wrong idea, but I stopped contradicting her because I thought, well, that it didn't matter.'

'Because you thought I was dead?'

'Well, yes. I'm sorry if she gave you the wrong idea, or if I inadvertently did so by anything I said, or didn't say, but I was trying to keep her spirits up. I thought you realised I was just writing as a friend.'

'Well, yes, I suppose I did, until she told me otherwise.' He looked away and his feet shifted awkwardly. 'I guess I'm not wanted here, then. I hope you'll be very happy with Mr La-di-da.'

He slapped the cap back on his head and marched to the door, as if on parade.

'I'm sorry, Daniel.' He was in the hall before her last word was completely out. 'Oh dear.'

'It's not your fault,' said Tom.

Albert ran out after him, but the front door must have shut before he reached him, as her father was soon back.

'Well, Gwen *cariad*, you are popular today,' said Bertha.

'Mam, Da and Mamgu, let me introduce Tom, who, well, I hope is my fiancé. Da?'

'It's all right, I give you my permission. Despite what I said before, it's that relieved I am, that you're not betrothed to Esther William's son, though the lad hisself seems all right.'

'Yes, he's all right, but not a patch on Tom here.' She snuggled up to him.

'So, what does your mam make of this, then?' said Ruth.

'Both my parents are absolutely fine about it.'

'They are?' said Gwen, surprised. She had expected at least some objection from Mrs Meredith.

'Yes, she is. She's changed a lot since the car accident.'

'Well sit down, *bach*,' said Ruth. 'I'll get you a nice cuppa tea and you two can tell us your plans.'

Chapter Thirty-Seven

Gwen dusted the hall, singing to herself. She couldn't believe that her and Tom's relationship was not only out in the open but accepted by all the parents. She'd spoken with Mrs Meredith that morning, and they'd agreed she should continue working there until a new maid could be found. Gwen was sure her future mother-in-law didn't think it 'seemly' for her to be the maid, and maybe she was right. She'd worried about losing the wage before. Now it seemed like an opportunity to get the sewing business going with her friends.

The phone in the study rang. Should she answer it? As she considered this, Elizabeth ran from the kitchen to do so. She was back in a minute, her face alight.

'Gwen! My father has just had a phone call at work from a friend who has another friend who works in the government, to say that the armistice was signed this morning. The war is over!'

The two of them joined hands and danced around, cheering.

Margaret appeared from the drawing room. 'What on earth is going on?'

'Mama, Father's just rung to say the armistice has been signed. It's over!'

Margaret clutched her chest. 'Oh my goodness, at last.' Tears came to her eyes and soon she was sobbing.

Elizabeth embraced her. 'You should be happy! The war's finished.'

'That's why – I'm crying. I never thought we'd see the day.' She sniffed and took a handkerchief from her pocket to delicately blow her nose. 'Now, why don't you go off to the village and tell people the good news. I dare say Herbert will get word to the miners on the shift, but many in the village won't know yet. I'll tell Tom.'

'Come on, Gwen,' said Elizabeth. 'Get your proper clothes on and let's go down. We could tell Anwen and Violet as well, while we're there. And our other news.'

'If that's all right,' said Gwen, looking at Mrs Meredith for confirmation.

'Of course, I meant both of you. Off you go now.'

Gwen lost no time running to the scullery to change, calling as she went, 'Mrs Rhys, it's all over!'

–

Gwen and Elizabeth had told everyone they'd come across as they went into the village, then made a point of going into all the shops to tell people there. They decided to head to Anwen's next, arriving as she was coming out of the door.

'Hello you two,' she said, pulling the pushchair onto the street. 'I'm just taking this down to Violet for Gethin. Sara Fach refuses to sit in it anymore. So independent, she's become.'

'I suppose she is nearly two now,' said Gwen. 'We'll come with you, as we've come to tell you both that the armistice has been signed.'

'So it's over? Oh, happy day! I must go and tell Mamgu before we go.' She disappeared back into the house for a minute or so. 'She's that pleased, she's singing a song about it to Sara Fach,' she said, as she came back.

Arriving at Violet's, they all knocked impatiently.

'What on earth?' said Violet as she came to the door, cuddling the baby.

'The war's over!' Anwen shouted, as Violet's next-door neighbour, Mrs White, left the house.

'Is it?' she called up.

'Yes. The armistice has been signed.'

'I'll just go and tell the Prowses,' she said, running past them. 'In fact, I think I'll knock all the neighbours up.'

'Good idea,' said Elizabeth.

'You going to let us in?' said Gwen. 'I've got some other news.'

'Of course. Bring the pushchair in the hall for now.'

In the kitchen, sitting down, Violet said, 'Come on then, what's your news, Gwen?'

'I'm betrothed!'

Violet looked at Anwen. 'Who to?'

'Tom.'

'Tom? Tom Meredith?' She looked at Elizabeth, as if for confirmation.

'Yes, that's the one!' Gwen said, chuckling.

'Well, I never!' said Violet. 'I didn't even know you were walking out. Did you two know?' She looked at Anwen and Elizabeth.

'Tom did tell me a couple of months back,' said Elizabeth.

'I've only known for a little while,' Anwen confessed.

'Sorry,' said Gwen. 'I needed to make sure nothing was going to go wrong again, that's all. And, it was a little… difficult.'

'She means, with my mother,' said Elizabeth. 'But fortunately, she's had a huge change of heart, and, having accepted my engagement to Gwilym, well, she could hardly refuse Tom his true love.'

'That's lovely news.' Violet stood to hug Gwen.

'Thank you, it's such a relief to be able to tell people.'

'I have some news as well,' said Anwen. 'Idris and I, we're expecting an addition to our family, next June.'

There was more hugging.

'I thought you seemed a little out of sorts at the court,' said Elizabeth.

'Yes, a touch of morning sickness, except it's all day. But it's happened, at last. It's like the babby was waiting for the end of the war, for a more hopeful future. And I dare say that there'll be a few more babbies in the next coupla years.' She looked from Elizabeth to Gwen. 'And maybe another for you too,' she said to Violet.

'It is quiet with Benjy at school now, but then, we'll have our business to keep us busy.'

'Of course, your sewing business. How is all that going?' said Elizabeth.

'Let's settle down with a nice cup of tea,' said Anwen. 'And we'll tell you all about it.'

Epilogue

Peace Day, Saturday 19ᵗʰ July 1919

'Are we all ready then?' said Anwen, impatient to be out of the house. She held the baby, not quite a month old, in her arms, while Idris, already on the pavement, held Sara Fach's hand as she twirled him round in her effort to skip.

'We've barely got back from the service and parade this morning, and it's back to the chapel we're going again,' said Cadi, bustling out of the kitchen. 'I dunno why they had to get married on Peace Day.'

'They didn't know that when they arranged it,' said Enid, following her out. She looked up at the sky. 'At least the weather's cheered up for them, and there's a bit of sun.'

The family made their way to Bryn Street. Halfway down they met Violet coming out of number four, with Clarice and Benjy. Hywel was close behind, with eleven-month-old Gethin, giggling as his da joggled him.

'How's little Hope today?' said Violet, peeping over the blanket the baby was wrapped in.

'Asleep, for the moment.'

'Aw, bless her.'

They headed off towards the Ainon Baptist chapel, in an even longer line now. As they walked past the gardens, more joined the throng, mainly people Anwen had known most of her life. Passing the other side of Jubilee Green, Anwen spied Esther Williams, standing outside her house, looking down at the passers-by, her arms crossed.

348

'She doesn't look happy,' said Violet, nudging Anwen.

'No. She hasn't forgiven Gwen for misleading Daniel, as she put it.'

'Some things never change,' said Idris.

Across the road, the demobilised Dorcalon soldiers of the 114th Brigade of the 38th (Welsh) Division marched as if on parade, towards the chapel. Their uniforms had been replaced by suits. Henry wasn't among them, no doubt already at the chapel. The men had been home four months now. It was as if nothing had happened, yet Anwen could tell by their eyes, when she spoke to them in the street or at the chapel, that the war had changed them.

But hadn't the war changed them all? She looked back to that outing to Barry Island, the day before war had been declared, in August 1914. Life had been so different for her, for Violet, for Gwen, and for Elizabeth. None of them could even have guessed at the changes that the war would have brought.

At the chapel, she was surprised to see Polly Coombes in a back pew, with her sister-in-law, Mabel. She wondered if the Merediths had spotted her, and what they thought of it. There were a lot of well-wishers here, so possibly they'd not seen her, but were they likely to make a fuss if they had?

Anwen's family took seats on the left-hand pews, behind Gwen's family, the children bustling and chatting. The Merediths were seated in the middle pews, while the Owens were on the right-hand side. Gwilym and Tom were at the front, with Henry standing next to Tom, having agreed to be his best man.

'I'd better go and do my duty,' said Idris, who was Gwilym's best man.

'When pretty brides come, Mam?' said Sara Fach, cuddling up to Anwen.

'They won't be long, *cariad*.'

Soon the music struck up and everyone turned to look.

Gwen walked down the left aisle, while Elizabeth took the right one, their fathers beside them. Elizabeth's long-sleeved silk dress crossed over at the front and had a short organza skirt over a longer silk one. Her veil was waist-length and covered much of her head. Gwen's dress was looser, with ivory embroidered lace netting over a silk satin slip. Her veil was shorter. Both dresses were calf-length. The frocks had been a joint effort between Anwen, Gwen, Enid and Cadi. Violet had contributed with her skilful ironing.

Sara Fach knelt up on the chair and let out a long, quiet, 'Ooooh.'

The baby stirred, her eyes fluttering open as she tried to focus on her mother. The name Hope had been Anwen's suggestion, but Idris had readily agreed.

Hope was what she had for this little babby, and for all of them in Dorcalon, now there was peace.

A letter from Francesca

Once again, I've been touched by the messages of support and the lovely reviews I've received from readers for my first two *Valleys* books.

My characters in Dorcalon have come a long way since the first book, *Heartbreak in the Valleys*, their lives changed by war and circumstances at home. This time, I wanted to tell Gwen's story, but I found Elizabeth putting her hand up eagerly to say, 'Mine too!', and so started their parallel tales. Since their clashing lives in *War in the Valleys*, I suppose it was inevitable that their paths would cross again.

I've always liked Elizabeth but felt a little sorry for her. She was a kind and selfless person, yet stuck between two worlds, looked down on a little by one, and mistrusted by the other. Would she ever really fit in either world? Gwen had a similar problem: she was getting used to being able to afford fancy things with her good wages from the munitions factory, but this situation was likely to come to an end when the men returned home. What would she do then?

This period of time was one of huge change for women, and it's likely the war had a great deal to do with persuading those in power that women were capable of making an equally valid contribution to the country. They worked in the factories where men had been called up, including the dangerous munitions factories. They became police officers, bus conductresses and drivers, train porters and carriage cleaners. Women went into the war zones as part of the Women's Army Auxiliary Corp (WAAC) as cooks, clerks and driver mechanics, among other jobs. Those in the Women's Royal Air Force (WRAF) became mechanics, drivers and clerks. Then there were the regular nurses and the VADs, along with some female doctors, many of whom worked on the war fronts. And this is just touching the surface.

A lot of these jobs disappeared for women after the war, but it was the slow start of a more equal world for women.

It was a time of upheaval and fear for my characters, a time of not knowing what their ultimate fate would be. But it was also a time of possibility for Elizabeth, Gwen, Violet and Anwen – when they weren't being held back by various members of their family and acquaintances!

If you'd like to discuss the novel with me, or discover more about it, I'd love to chat to you on social media here:

Facebook: www.facebook.com/FrancescaCapaldiAuthor/
Twitter: @FCapaldiBurgess
Blog: www.writemindswriteplace.wordpress.com/

Thank you for taking the time to read my book, and if you're interested in finding out what happened next in Dorcalon post war, the fourth *Valleys* book will be published in a few months' time.

Best wishes,
Francesca xx

Acknowledgments

A big thank you, once more, to Keshini Naidoo and Lindsey Mooney at Hera Books for giving me the opportunity to tell more stories in the *Valleys* series. And also a thank you to Jennie Ayres, whose editing skills have been invaluable.

I'm grateful, as always, to my friends and fellow writers for their ongoing support and encouragement. Meeting up, in person or on Zoom, and having a good chat about life and writing, has certainly kept me going.

Thank you also to all the friends on various online writing groups and organisations, especially the Romantic Novelists' Association.